THE
CALIFORNIA
I LOVE

THE
CALIFORNIA
I LOVE

LEO CARRILLO

PRENTICE-HALL, ENGLEWOOD CLIFFS, N.J.

Decorations by Don Perceval

Library of Congress Catalog Number 61-15167

First printing........October, 1961
Second printing......January, 1962
Third printing.......January, 1962

Printed in the United States of America

11261-T

DEDICATED TO

my beloved wife Edith, my daughter Antoinette,
and my brothers and sisters
who have urged me to lift the curtain of time
on idyllic fiestas and the fandangos of long ago
in our splendid, joyous land of song and gaiety
so that we might hear through the ages the
tambourines, castanets, guitars, violins, flutes and horns
creating an immortal symphony of contentment
in my California.

Amigos

Here I stand with my sombrero in my hand. I want to tell you of my gratitude and sincere appreciation for the warm understanding and kind help I have had from a man who knows the love I have for my California. It was he who entered into my thoughts and memory and helped me to uncover again the treasury of tales I am telling you here (which my forebears forbade me ever to repeat).

This fine person is Mr. Ed Ainsworth, eminent columnist of the *Los Angeles Times*. Though a Texan born, he has made California his home and written many books about the West. As my collaborator he helped me arrange my material, balance it and pace it. For this sympathetic guidance I can only say—

Gracias, Mi Querido Amigo!

Leo Carrillo

CONTENTS

PRIMERA PARTE DEL LIBRO

The Splendid Era

SEGUNDA PARTE DEL LIBRO

Spirit of the Land

TERCERA PARTE DEL LIBRO

"The World's a Stage"

CUARTA PARTE DEL LIBRO

Reincarnation of the Caballero

THE
CALIFORNIA
I LOVE

PRIMERA
PARTE DEL LIBRO

☙

THE SPLENDID ERA

LEO CARRILLO

☙

INTRODUCTION

If you read my little verses, of my breezes from the West
Don't look for masterpieces, they wouldn't stand the test.
I'm not a long-haired poet, know little of technique,
I only write the things I feel—and I know whereof I speak.

BECAUSE

I have an affliction it lingers and lingers,
A sort of an itching that comes in my fingers.
It has its beginning somewhere in the brain,
Thought upon thought—just an endless chain.
It seeks its way out again and again
And finally reaches the point of my pen.
It's the want of expression that comes to all men,
The do for the doing that satisfies then.
So whatever I write and whatever you read,
I am the one who planted the seed.
So should there be praise—or perhaps contradiction—
Remember it came from that awful affliction.

THE FOOTPRINTS OF THE PADRES

In the footprints of the padres, before the gringo came,
In the days of the old missions, in the days of Spanish fame,
When those dear old Spanish families ruled the Golden State—
What a different California at that very early date.
The blackeyed señorita and the caballero too,
And the sun baked old adobe were never known to you.
Where are those good old families of the early yesterday?
Listen, mi amigo, to what I've got to say:
There were the Picos and Carrillos with their many leagues of land,
And their ranchos filled with cattle which they hardly had to brand.
Domingues, De La Guerras, Sepulvedas and others,
And they lived here side by side with the peacefulness of brothers.
They trusted one another much different then than now,
And they did a lot of thinking to avoid most any row.
Then you came, amigo mio, and you saw the lands we had,
And you wrote back to your mother and your mother told your dad.
And when they read your letters of the beauties of our state,
They packed the many things they had and shipped them wagon freight.
Then you crowded all around us, inch by inch you hemmed us in,
Till we'd scarcely room to breathe in—it really seemed a sin.
Then you took away our ranchos that were given us by Spain,
And you took our señoritas—see, the answer is quite plain:
Now the children of the daughter whose grandad's blood was Latin
Are scattered from Point Loma clear back to Manhattan.
It's just a simple story from your amigo in the West—
I couldn't help a telling you—just to get it off my chest.
                    Damne Yanquis!

CHAPTER I

GENESIS OF A CABALLERO

Crumbling walls of sun-baked clay
Telling tales of yesterday....

THE adobe is my birthstone.

What else could it have been in the little mud-brick pueblo of Los Angeles on the day of my birth when there was celebration and much merriment and dancing at the Plaza? It is true that I have no recollection of the occasion except from hearsay, but reliable witnesses have told me what happened.

The adobe? Perhaps gringos would question why I speak of it as a birthstone at all. They might say it is just a dirt brick.

To me, the adobe is more than that. It is the good earth upon which the questing steps of men and women have trod for so many centuries seeking something fine from life. With this good earth is mixed the water upon which all mankind has depended for existence since life was created. And upon this earth and water the sun has cast its radiant beams to unite the mixture so that the resultant adobe is the happy fusion of nature's finest elements.

Even the making of the adobes is a symbolic act. The water and earth are mixed under the bare feet of man himself. Man treads with vigor and purpose upon the adobe to which straw has been added for strength. Man, who always is noblest when he works, thus furnishes his labor to what God has given him, and from the honest toil the adobe emerges ready to be placed in large forms for drying in the sun.

When they are baked by nature's own heat they are used for the building of homes. We are surrounded then in our dwellings by the elements of earth and water fused by the divine actinic rays of the sun. The adobe bricks become the witnesses of our lives. These adobe walls mellow with age. They share in the love of our young people, the birth of our children, the death of our old.

They enclose us comfortingly. They are our shelter from cold and heat. They enfold us like a mother's arms.

Of course, it might be said that more elegant birthstones could be chosen. The scintillating diamond is credited with indications of wealth and power. The star sapphire is linked with good fortune and even with the Star of Bethlehem. The ruby is associated with strange deeds and spells cast upon those born within its sphere.

Yet the adobe possesses qualities which none of these can match.

País, agua, sol.

Earth, water, sun.

To those of us of Spanish blood whose veins carry the red fire pumped from the hot fountains of medieval Castile, the very simplicity of the words sanctifies them. They are elemental. We are elemental.

País means more than soil or earth, far more than the Spanish word "tierra," which is merely mundane. It means something spiritual; that as a man's feet touch his native ground there is a mystic bond between him and the dust from which he was moulded. And wherever Spanish blood goes, this idea goes with it.

So in California del Norte, granddaughter of imperial Spain, born of the union of Conquistadores with the new land on the Pacific shore, the inheritance was very strong.

It is true, too, that on the day of which I speak El Pueblo de Nuestra Señora la Reina de Los Angeles de Porciuncula—which we have cruelly abbreviated to "Los Angeles"—was animated in all the area of the Plaza with another fervor typically Spanish. It was having a fiesta.

The sun came up with strength that morning, shining down as if in warm benediction upon the adobes it had helped to create. Almost all the houses were built of this adobe. A relatively few modern, baked-brick business buildings stood proudly among the modest adobes. A notable one was the elegant three-story Pico House, a fine hotel which stood just across the roadway to the southwest of the Plaza on the exact site where my great-uncle, the notable military leader, José Antonio Carrillo once had his home.

My family—my father and mother and their four children—lived in what was known as the Bell Block, a long row of adobe dwellings, mostly one-story, running along the east side of Los Angeles Street from Aliso to First. Part of the Bell Block was two-story, with a wide verandah.

Silence had descended upon all the Plaza region just before dawn.

Then scarlet streaks stabbed the sky above the gentle hills to the east, and a warm breeze caressed the large leaves of the young rubber trees planted in a large circle around the Plaza.

A young man's voice, accompanied by the gentle strumming of a guitar, was heard in the strains of *Las Mañanitas—The Little Mornings*—as he serenaded beneath the window of his loved one.

In contrast to this tender scene, three drunks lay on the parched grass of the Plaza snoring gently as the first wandering sunbeams came creeping into the pueblo. The sun shone on the flat roofs of the little adobe houses, all of them covered with brea or tar from the tar pits to the west. Somewhere a cow bawled for the milker and roosters crowed vociferously to welcome the new dawn. The innumerable half-wild dogs of the Plaza area roused from their torpor long enough to scratch for fleas. The sun was hot even at this early hour. It was going to be a typical August day.

The tinkling of water could be heard where the Zanjero, the keeper of the community's water supply, walked along the Zanja, or Mother Ditch, from which the poor people still scooped their drinking water in these days.

The Zanjero was a very important man in the community; he received more salary than the alcalde or the councilmen because his duties were considered the most important of any. Now he was checking the Zanja to see that everything was all right for the people who soon would be coming with their buckets and jars for water for their homes.

It was the sixth day of August.

A good reason existed for the selection of this particular date for the fiesta. Times had been hard in the pueblo and many had gone to bed suffering the pangs of hunger. Masa, the ground corn for tortillas, was difficult to obtain. Some simply did not have the few centavos necessary to buy the daily supply.

But everyone had joined in the desire for a fiesta. It was decided not to hold it on August fourth, which was St. Dominic Day, but on the sixth, which was the observance of the Day of Transfiguration. St. Dominic was a dour, self-denying saint who did not look with favor upon merry-making, music and eating. It would have been inappropriate to have it on his day. But the

Day of Transfiguration was one of extreme holiness in the church and thus a religious note could be added to the celebration. So the fiesta committee had chosen the sixth and the people had joyously begun their preparations.

The señoritas had been busy washing and ironing their best—the bright colored flaring skirts, and the white blouses with the tight bodices, ornamented with crimson, green and gold embroidery, and had been gloating over their treasures such as the high Spanish combs and the black earrings—the aretes—which they planned to wear during the fiesta and the dancing.

The young cabelleros likewise had been making preparations. Their saddles with the silver ornamentation were polished bright. Their horses had been groomed until they shone with great brilliance. Even the bridles and stirrups had been oiled and polished so that they too were at their peak.

Now as the sun crept higher, casting long shadows from the adobe homes, the whole pueblo seemed to begin to awaken at once. The smells of sausage, fresh roasted peppers and tortillas floated from the windows. From the homes came the sound of tortillas being slapped with the bare hands.

In many homes, too, blown egg shells were being filled with confetti so as to form the cascarónes for breaking on the heads of the merrymakers in traditional Spanish style.

All during the morning the pace of the preparations grew more frenzied. By the time the sun peered straight down on the pueblo, casting no shadows at all, the gathering of the townspeople and country dwellers from miles around was in full swing.

The all-pervading and unmistakable odor of fresh horse manure grew more intense as the mounted visitors arrived and engulfed the whole Plaza region.

One group of guitarreros having been up all night playing in one of the cantinas, came in tipsy parade down Los Angeles Street, too tired to sound another note, one portly musician dragging his bull fiddle behind him.

Just as the guitarreros were going by in the dust of the street, a young woman far along in pregnancy came out on the verandah of the second-story of the old adobe Bell Block. She walked slowly and carefully and a faint smile appeared on her lips as she watched the weaving figures below.

One of the musicians, carrying his guitar under his arm, looked up and saw the young woman and waved his hand and bowed. She waved in return.

"It is a pity that the Señora Carrillo's husband is so far away at this time," the guitar player said to one of his companions who was carefully carrying a violin.

From the verandah Señora Carrillo could see preparations for the fiesta going on all up and down the street. Down toward the Plaza there was great activity around the kiosco, or bandstand. Seats were being arranged for the officials and the dueñas who would oversee the evening's festivities. Tables were being set up for the feast.

Señora Carrillo gazed wistfully at the scene wishing she might be taking a more active part. She tried to picture where her husband might be on his business trip to Magdalena in Sonora for a group of mining men in Los Angeles. Desperately she wished he would return, because she knew the hour of her delivery was near.

A stately white-haired woman in her late fifties came on the verandah and said, "Oh, there you are, Franciscita. Have the boys been looking after you all right?"

"Oh yes," responded Señora Carrillo. "Carlos has been sleeping in the sala every night in case I needed him and Juan has been staying with me all day."

"How do you feel?" inquired Tía Chona.

"He is a most active little rascal. He kicks me all the time and I don't think it will be long now until he is born."

"Be careful of the stairs," warned Tía Chona, "and send one of the children for me when your time comes. I have told Dr. Salazar you may need him today or tomorrow."

"I hope so. I am wearied by this heat."

A horseman clattered by kicking up clouds of dust in the street and Señora Carrillo involuntarily looked quickly at him as she did at every passerby in the vain hope it might be her husband. She knew he could not possibly be home for another month.

The rest of the day dragged slowly by for Señora Carrillo, after she went inside again and tried vainly to nap in the hot upstairs bedroom. She wished for the cool of the evening so that she could sit on the verandah in comfort and watch the fiesta.

The sun by now was beating down with such ferocity that an observer could readily tell why the roofs of the little adobe buildings were flat—the brea was liquifying so that it might have run off the roofs if there had been any slope. The smell of the hot tar made Señora Carrillo feel a little sick.

Then suddenly the first great wrenching labor pain struck her. She gritted her teeth and then bit her lip to keep from screaming.

"Eulogio!" she called as soon she could speak.

A boy about ten with strikingly intelligent dark eyes and a thatch of black hair came running into the room.

"Call your cousin Juan, please!"

Frightened by the look on his mother's face, Eulogio ran hastily downstairs to summon his cousin Juan Alvardo who was on the sidewalk talking to a group of boys about the fiesta.

"Quick, mother wants you!" exclaimed Eulogio.

Juan ran upstairs. After one look at Señora Carrillo he knew it was time to go for the doctor and to send for Tía Chona.

"I'll be right back!" he promised in a frightened voice. And he too ran down the stairs and towards the office of Dr. Salazar, who spent most of his weary life responding to calls like this.

Within 15 minutes Dr. Salazar, in his long black frock coat and carrying his battered instrument case, arrived on horseback at the stairway just as Tía Chona also came up puffing and red-faced.

Dr. Salazar, besides his long coat, had on striped trousers, fine but well-worn boots, and a white shirt and black tie.

His goatee and moustache were white. His careworn eyes looked out at the world with compassion. His spendid, long-fingered hands were stained with iodine and tobacco.

"Is this to be her sixth child on the sixth of August?" asked Dr. Salazar quizzically. "I've lost count."

"No, her fifth," said Señora Chona Alvarado.

Dr. Salazar put down his instrument case in the bedroom, took off his coat, and gave Tía Chona some instructions which both knew were superfluous; Tía Chona had been through this as often as the doctor.

"Now, Francisca, this isn't going to take long," said Dr. Salazar soothingly to Señora Carrillo.

She nodded between the agonizing pains.

"My own fiesta!" she gasped, and Dr. Salazar smiled at her spirit. . . .

A few hours later, after the old adobe walls had witnessed once again the miracle of birth, it was momentarily quiet in the room.

The old doctor mopped his brow and gave some final low-voiced instructions to Tía Chona.

My mother lay very still in the bed. From her pale lips came the slightest murmur of a crooned cradle song, *La Golondrina*.

Dr. Salazar looked at her in surprise.

"She does well, our little bird," he said to Tía Chona.

He approached the bed.

"What is it you wish to name your son?" he asked gently.

My mother roused and spoke clearly, a mouthful of liquid Castilian syllables:

"Leopoldo Antonio Carrillo."

The doctor wrote it down in his little book, nodding in approval: "Leopoldo—'Bold for the People'—an old name, and a good one."

He shut the little book, put it in the side pocket of his long coat.

Just then, from outside the window, came a burst of joyous music. The fiesta parade was going by. The gay voices of señoritas and caballeros, raised in song, floated up to the room. Guitars and violins joined in the mirthful melody, a horn led a sunburst of sound.

"Por Dios!" exclaimed Tía Chona. "Look at the baby! He is keeping time to the music!"

"Impossible," said the good doctor, as he moved towards the door with a final glance at my mother. He walked wearily down the steps, as the music receded in the distance.

As he mounted his horse and turned into the roadway, Dr. Salazar was too tired to notice that he had become, as it were, the last unit in the fiesta procession. He rode along, hardly aware of the deepening twilight or of his surroundings, or that the merrymaking marchers were just ahead of him. In his pocket he carried my name. He was my proxy in the fiesta.

It was the only time I was too young to ride in the parade myself.

CHAPTER 2

THE SPREADING FAMILY TREE

I was suckled on the essence of California lore and cut my teeth on golden legends of the West.

In my family, I never needed the Arabian Nights. We had our own. It was compounded of the mighty saga of priests, leather-jacket soldiers, grizzly bear hunters, vaqueros on horses swift as the wind, ropers who flung a reata with the precision of rifle fire, grandees of the rancheros, and dancing girls with castanets who sang the siren song of California to the tune of a Spanish guitar in a jasmine-scented patio.

And even as a small child I remember being everybody's cousin.

We Carrillos would have made great international spies, if that had been our destiny. We certainly infiltrated California. When José Raimundo Carrillo, my great-great-grandfather and the companion of Father Junípero Serra, trudged the bloody, weary 1000 miles from Loreto up the jagged backbone of Baja California to help found the new colony of "Alta California" in 1769, he mulched a family tree that has spread its branches along El Camino Real and all its byways.

From my earliest days I was taught to respect the family name. This was in no spirit of contempt or disdain for others. It was simply a cherished Spanish tradition of self-respect. If you did not honor your own name and live up to its legacy and responsibilities, how could you expect others to honor and respect you?

The name is pronounced "Cay-reel-yo," with a liquid Castilian double "l." It is not pronounced "Care-reeyo" with the "y" for double "l" as in Mexico. The Mexican adaptation of Spanish is a beautiful variation in itself, but we of Castilian lineage prefer the original liquid sound for the double "l." It is part of our heritage.

In my journeyings in Spain I have traced the Carrillos with the two "r" and two "l" spelling back to the year 1260 which really is more than two hundred years beyond the date, 1492, recognized as the one in which modern Spain was unified. That latter date, the same as the discovery by Columbus, marked the capture by King Ferdinand and Queen Isabella of the Alhambra in Granada, last stronghold of the Moors who had held Spain in bondage for 700 years.

We were known as "the Carrillos of Albornoz," and I have one document dating back hundreds of years showing the family crest.

Of course, I was unaware of Spanish history or the significance of crests when I was a child running around in the dust of the Los Angeles Plaza. I just knew I had a hell of a lot of cousins. It was pretty confusing at times.

A whole scad of new family connections would visit us and we—that is my parents and older brothers and sisters—would trade a bewildering mass of genealogical information and come up with the exact blood relationships of all of the newcomers. Part of the time it was a bore to me because usually I didn't even care to remember the names of my fifth cousins twice removed. Occasionally, though, some real exciting new relatives would appear; boys who were good bird-nest robbers or rabbit-trap makers, and then I was glad I was a Carrillo and kin to so many families.

On the table in our sala, or living room, was a thick calf-bound book next to the Holy Bible. It was Volume II of Hubert Howe Bancroft's famous *History of California.*

I can well remember the awe I felt when, before I could read, it was pointed out to me that in the back of this beautiful book, in "The Pioneer Register," there were four solid pages of material in small type dealing with the Carrillo family in California.

The book had recently come out and was among the treasures of my family. My father used to read some passages of it to us when we were still small. I remember that Bancroft said in regard to my great-great-grandfather, José Raimundo, that "he may be regarded as the founder of the Carrillo family which must be considered in several respects the leading one in California by reason of the number and prominence of its members and of connections by marriage of so many of the best families."

More exciting was Bancroft's appraisal of my great-uncle José Antonio Carrillo, the splendid lawyer and military leader, when he said "no Californian could drink so much brandy as he with so little effect." I think he had a hollow leg. He was described as a gambler and, to quote Bancroft, "of loose habits." This meant little to us children at the time although later I heard great-uncle José Antonio quoted as having said, "I like blondes and I don't care a damn how they got that way."

Great-uncle José Antonio married two sisters successively, first Estafana Pico and then her sister Jacinto Pico, both of whom were sisters of Pio Pico. This explained the close relationship our family always felt with Pio Pico, who was the last Governor of California under Mexican rule, and his brother Andrés, the great cavalry leader who defeated the Americans under General Stephen W. Kearny at the Battle of San Pasqual in San Diego County during the Mexican War.

Always I lived amid legends. They were my welcome companions. They formed my finest heritage.

One of my early companions was another barefooted kid who was part Basque. He came from way out the other side of the Los Angeles River in a region known as Boyle Heights. We used to say, kidding him about being a Basque, that we Carrillos had been baptized with holy water but that he had been baptized with sheep dip. Sometimes he would throw rocks at us for this remark.

Later he and I became life-long companions. We rode in more parades together than there are hairs in a horse's mane. His name is Eugene W. (Gene) Biscailuz. He was in the Sheriff's Department of Los Angeles during some of its most exciting days and later was sheriff for more than a quarter of a century. He made history which will live forever.

Family history, in a way, was a strange thing in our home. We were violently and demonstratively American by birth and inclination, yet the example of our immediate forbears in California was always held up before us. We had no vestige of ancestor worship, yet we were taught to be proud of the accomplishments of those whose name we bore and to try to live up to the great example which they had set in the history of California.

It always seemed to me that the living presences of my grandfather, great-grandfather, and great-great-grandfather, were with us in our home at all times. It is true that my grandfather was still alive when I was a young man and I was able to see him in the flesh. But his father, and his father's father in turn, also were so real to me that I found myself participating, as it were, in their adventures even though they had been dead for many years.

My great-great-grandfather, José Raimundo, was one of the leather-jacket soldiers who accompanied Father Serra and Captain Gaspar de Portola to California, arriving at the site of San Diego on July 1, 1769. He was a native of Loreto, the great pearlfishing port on the Gulf of California from which Father Serra started his long journey overland to Alta California. We learned that his father's name was Hilario Carrillo, but we knew little else of him. José Raimundo Carrillo was married to Tomasa Ignacia Lugo by Father Serra himself in 1781.

This was the same Father Serra who never caused the spilling of a drop of blood of any heathen at any mission where he personally was the spiritual ruler. He used no weapon. He won the battle with a crucifix.

In the marriage document of José Raimundo and Tomasa Ignacia it was particularly specified that José Raimundo was "the legitimate son of Hilario Carrillo." I really don't get it. So far as I know, none of my ancestors was a bachelor.

From the union of José Raimundo and Tomasa Ignacia came two men whose names rank high in the political and military annals of California.

One of these was Carlos Antonio de Jesús Carrillo, my own great-grandfather who became Governor of California and was one of the most notable figures in the period just before the American occupation. My great-uncle was José Antonio Ezequiel Carrillo, the great lawyer and cavalryman who actually made it possible for his brother Carlos Antonio to become Governor. He was the Jim Farley of his era. My grandfather, Pedro C. Carrillo, who became a judge in Los Angeles, was the son of Governor Carlos Antonio. My own father Juan José Carrillo was educated at Holy Cross in Worcester, Massachusetts and possessed a splendid education which he demonstrated in all the various occupations he pursued in Los Angeles and Santa Monica. He was successively a bookkeeper, a railroad worker, a waterworks superintendent, then a livery stable owner, judge and first mayor of Santa Monica.

The names and dates of my ancestors in themselves never meant much to me even as a child; I was more interested in their adventures and exploits.

We reveled in this atmosphere of stories and legends. Every day there was reference to some exploit of José Raimundo, José Antonio, Carlos Antonio, and others of the Carrillo family.

One of my favorites was the story told of my great-uncle José Antonio who had led a small party of cavalry against the American invaders who were seeking to march up from San Pedro and capture Los Angeles during the Mexican War in the 1840's. José Antonio devised a remarkable scheme, during the engagement, known as the Battle of Dominguez. This occurred near the Dominguez Ranch in the area of what is now Compton.

The Americans in quite large numbers were marching on foot toward Los Angeles from their ships. The Californianos, with just a handful of cavalry, were supposed to stop them. José Antonio devised a plan. He had his cavalry-men attach pieces of brush, old cowhides, and all sorts of heavy objects to their reatas. These were dragged across a dusty spot ahead of the oncoming American force. Then the horsemen dashed in and out of this dust cloud so that they appeared as a tremendous force of cavalry. The Americans were completely confused as to the numbers of the Californianos. Actually there were only fifty in the contingent under the command of José Antonio.

Then, in the battle which ensued, the Californianos resorted to another trick. The Americans, already dismayed at the apparent size of the opposing force, met another obstacle. The Californianos had brought into action an old four-pounder cannon which had previously been buried in the garden of Inocencia Reyes to keep Commodore Robert Stockton from capturing it in a former march on Los Angeles. The cannon was mounted on a creaky old wagon and a skittish gray mule was hitched up to drag it into battle. Some reports say the mule broke loose at the first shot and was never seen again.

My great uncle José Antonio ordered his men to attach reatas to this gun. There were only eight cannon balls left and a group of Californianos was appointed to penetrate beyond the American lines and to pick up any dead cannon balls and bring them back quickly so they could be fired again. When the battle of Dominguez Ranch began, the Californianos were woefully outgunned. They were equipped only with old muskets, pistols, and lances while the American troops had the latest weapons. But the old four-pounder turned the tide. Good powder was short but there was enough for a few firings and a little homemade powder which had been manufactured in San Gabriel was put to use. Each time the gun was fired the men on horses quickly would pull the cannon back with the reatas so that the advancing Americans had no chance to capture it. By the time the powder had been used up and the cannon balls had been retrieved from behind the lines and brought back for use again, the Californianos had triumphed. Six Americans had been killed and the rest were so discouraged that they turned and retreated to their vessels in San Pedro.

The Americans, numbering several hundred, were under the command of Captain Mervine of the *Savannah* and Captain Archibald Gillespie from the *Vandalia*.

The American dead were buried on the little island in San Pedro Bay and this forever after was known as Isla de Los Muertos—Dead Man's Island—until it was cleared away many years later for the enlargement of Los Angeles Harbor.

The maneuver of the outnumbered Californiano cavalry at the Battle of Dominguez was an important landmark in military history. It marked one of the first known uses of the "smoke screen."

This same remarkable José Antonio Carrillo was the one who signed the Treaty of Cahuenga with Lt. Col. John C. Frémont, early in January, 1847, ending the Mexican War in California.

Then, only a little more than two years later, José Antonio was held in such high esteem under the new American regime, that he was selected as one of the delegates to the Constitutional Convention at Colton Hall in Monterey in September and October of 1849. He rode his horse all the way from Los Angeles to Monterey. This convention framed the remarkably fine California Constitution under which California was admitted to the Union the next year, and the name of José Antonio Carrillo appears on the framed document in Colton Hall.

Governor Carlos Antonio Carrillo was cast in a somewhat different mold. He was less positive in his actions than Don José. It is true that he attained distinction, serving as administrator of the Pious Funds and the Mission Lands during the secularization of the California Missions.

But some doubt exists whether Gov. Carlos Antonio was the equal of his mighty brother in military prowess. The story is told that in one of the innumerable "wars" which characterized the spasmodic Mexican rule during and 1820's and 1830's Carlos Antonio was the leader of troops marching against rivals from the north. The two "armies" met in what is now Cahuenga Pass—actually pronounced "Cow-Winga" Pass from an old Indian word.

Carlos Antonio summoned his troops with a mighty flourish of drums and trumpets and when they were lined up before him he delivered an inspiring speech:

"Camaradas, hermanos, amigos! We are here ready to die for our great cause. Prepare for battle! We will fight to the death! However, Camaradas, I advise that if the pressure of the enemy becomes intolerable, you retreat. And having a bad leg, I will start now!"

The battle of Cahunega Pass then raged for three days with cannon shot and much name calling. At the end of three days one mule had been mortally wounded. So everybody got together and had a barbecue.

Stories of events like these permeated the whole atmosphere in which my brothers and sisters and I lived. They were woven into the fabric of California life like the pattern on a fiesta shawl.

It was difficult sometimes to separate the present from the past. Spirits seemed to dwell with us as well as living people. Great deeds formed part of our daily conversation. Legends were interwoven in our daily lives. We played games which utilized the feats of our ancestors and our kinsmen.

We celebrated the Fourth of July with fervor but we clung to the old Castilian customs at Christmas and on religious holidays. Ours was truly a fusion of two civilizations. We were twins in our cultural heritage.

I lean on no dead kin, but the stories I tell are not mine alone. They are filled with the spirits of those who have gone before.

Now it is my joyous duty to transmit them to those who come after.

Follow me, amigos, along El Camino Real!

CHAPTER 3

VENTURE INTO THE UNKNOWN

Most vivid of all the memories out of the deep twilight of my childhood is the first night I spent away from my own bed. Until that evening the sanctuary of bed was taken for granted. I went there each evening as the shadows drew a welcoming coverlet over the flat-roofed pueblo and our adobe home. It was as natural and primitive a rite as if I had been some little prehistoric child, tired of playing with my spearheads and carved dinosaurs, going into the warm firelight of my cave to sleep on wolf furs.

But now I was shaken. I had gone visiting. My whole environment, for this night at least, was different and terrifying. I had ventured into the great world. As I lay rigid in the strange bed a new element was added to life. It was fear. The consciousness of enemies lurking in the darkness came to me.

Then I heard a strangely comforting sound. It was a gentle, hardly audible buzzing; like a muted lullaby. I knew it wasn't human singing, but it made me feel as if I had a tiny friend looking after me there in the terrifying dark.

"Hello," I whispered.

The little buzzer, I fancied, whispered back, "H - e - l - l - o, bzz - bzz."

I had never encountered a mosquito before.

We carried on quite a conversation.

My tenseness did not depart entirely, yet the idea of a small, invisible companion helped me.

Sleep finally conquered my tired body although a vague uneasiness persisted, born of the consciousness of being in a strange bed. Even what I supposed to be the comforting song of the mosquito was unable to lull me completely. Actually I received an even ruder shock when I awoke in the morning.

The enemy had attacked under cover of darkness.

The damn treacherous mosquito had bit me. Our friendly conversation hadn't meant a thing.

This was the first time such a thing ever happened. The swelling red welts on my face and arms made a far greater impression that the pain they caused. They taught me that never again could I have complete trust and security in my small realm.

The incident made such a lasting impression on me that later, in my vaudeville days, I used a mosquito sequence. I transplanted the mosquito, of course, from my bedroom on the old rancho and made the locale a delicatessen store. Then with appropriate noises I indicated the descent of the mosquito, first towards some sugar and then as the climax its hasty retreat from an encounter with limburger cheese.

So, after all, some good came out of my childish adventure although at the time I was disillusioned with the world.

The mosquito, incidentally, identified the locale of my visit. It was on a ranch near Ballona—pronounced Buy-ona—Creek close to the Pacific Ocean in a region which since has become known as Culver City.

The creek was lined with willows, the branches leaning so far over that their lacy leaves caused little ripples and eddies. The sun sparkled on the water as it meandered towards the ocean. In the shallows under the willows I could see pollywogs and whole schools of minnows which excited me as much as if they had been great game fish in the Pacific.

All my life I have been a fisherman. Maybe it was beneath the willows on Ballona Creek that I first became intrigued with fishing.

It is certainly true that one of my triumphs took place the morning after my encounter with the marauding mosquito. The aunt whom we were visiting evidently noticed my unhappiness because she daubed my welts with one of the poultice home remedies then so popular and effective, and sent me forth to "see the place." It was an old California ranch which seemed to belong in its setting near the lazy stream.

I wandered beneath the fruit trees, heavy with their summer's yield, and came to the willows and the creek.

At this time I must have been about five years old. I certainly had never been fishing. But the sight of the minnows stirred my inventive talents, in the same mysterious fashion that every boy who first feels the overpowering yearning to battle the finny creatures of the depths is affected. I knew I needed a fish hook but there was no place to get one.

So I resorted to the "tackle" of every kid who lacks conventional hooks and lines. I borrowed a straight pin and bent it and tied it to an ordinary piece of twine. Next I found a good damp spot in my aunt's garden and dug up some worms—gusanos, we used to call them in Spanish.

Worm on my improvised hook, I stole to the water's edge. Something intuitive told me not to try to fish in the extremely shallow water for fear of driving the quarry away with the splash. Instead, I tied a small irregular pebble to the string near the pin and dropped it out a little way from the bank; maybe 14 inches in depth, anyway.

Then a wonderful thing happened. I felt a tug on the line, a tiny twitching. My nerves jumped, my senses all came alive. I pulled on the string with the pin. And there, miracle of miracles, on the end of the line was a fish. It must have been all of 2 inches long but to me it looked as great and fearsome as a gigantic shark.

Tremblingly I tossed it up on the bank and grabbed it with my bare hands as it fell off the hook and started flopping back towards the water.

Yelling with excitement I ran towards the old adobe home where we were visiting and showed my prize to all members of the household.

The fish was too small to eat but not too small to remember. It was my first fishing triumph. . . .

Strangest thing of all, though, was this. Many years later, after I had appeared in successes on the New York stage, I came to Hollywood under contract to Metro-Goldwyn-Mayer Studios at $3,500 a week.

On the day of my arrival I was assigned to a beautiful dressing room on the great MGM lot in Culver City.

I went into my dressing room and looked out the window, noting the Baldwin Hills, the distant sweep of the Santa Monica Mountains, the vista toward the sea, the vast expanse of the film lot itself.

Suddenly I realized that this location was not new to me. It was familiar indeed. Just outside there beyond the window where I now stood as a $3,500-a-week actor, I saw the exact spot where, beneath the willows so many years before, I had caught my first minnow. I had come home.

CHAPTER 4

BLOOD AND DOMINOES

Around the old Plaza in Los Angeles the most distinctive sound I can remember was the soft slap of Chinese slippers along the wooden sidewalks, in the brick streets, or through the dust.

This sound went on night and day because the Cantonese never seemed to get much sleep.

A persistent sound, too, was that of the Chinese theater—the Hia Hee. The performance would go on until the early hours of the morning with gongs, firecrackers, screams and hideous minor key sounds that were supposed to be music.

The tongs and joss houses surrounded the Plaza and invaded the areas which formerly had been occupied by the Mexicans and early California settlers.

Often I would tour the Plaza area in a vehicle which had been created for me out of a soap box and some hand-carved wooden wheels. On this I would go into Chinatown and mingle with its inhabitants.

Smells and sounds still come to me out of the past with all the freshness of yesterday. This was only a few decades after the so-called Great Chinese Massacre in Los Angeles when many Orientals were killed by a mob at the Plaza. It was by far the worst example of mass violence in the history of the city.

My father was Chief of Police at this time. It was a nasty job.

So many killings took place and so few people were willing to be witnesses to bring anyone to justice. This was long before I was born but I remember my father telling us about the difficulties he encountered. He tried to enforce the law but there was very little cooperation from the Chinese, Indians, and even some of the Californians who frequented the Plaza area where most of the violence took place.

Father used to scare us half out of our wits by his eye-witness accounts of the massacre when we were old enough to hear about it. His part in it was an important one but the mob spirit was so great that the few law officers were completely overwhelmed and unable to cope with the various groups running wild throughout the whole area.

By freakish chance, the horrible incident grew out of a kidnapping among the Chinese themselves. Most of the tongs lived near Calle de los Negros and despite their enmity some of the rival groups were actually next-door neighbors. A young and beautiful Chinese girl was abducted at night, and vanished completely. The tong from which she had been stolen was so aroused that it sent a message to its members in San Francisco to come down and help seek revenge.

The steamer *California* actually did bring down a load of villainous-looking Chinese heavily padded where they were carrying the knives and hatchets favored in their private wars. They were expert at hiding these hatchets by innocently folding their arms with their hands inside the wide sleeves, so they could lash out with their weapons instantly.

Hostilities flared with such violence that many of the battling Chinese were arrested and taken before Justice William H. Gray.

Father went to capture one of the ring leaders. All the law officers knew about the hatchets and the other weapons which the Chinese used so father was especially cautious as he went down one of the long dark halls in a house close to the Plaza.

At the far end he found a locked door. He made a lunge and knocked in the door but still could see no one.

Then, on a hunch, he yanked up the filthy mattress on an old iron bed. There underneath was a Chinese who sprang up and lashed out with a two-foot-long knife trying to cut off father's head. Father made a big swipe with the heavy stick he carried and paralyzed the Chinese's arm. The knife clattered to the floor and father got his boot on it before the frenzied Oriental could pick it up again. Then he dragged the Chinese off to jail.

The judge lectured the prisoners in English and released them on bail because it was difficult for most of the American officers to distinguish one Chinese from another, making identification of the guilty ones difficult.

Everything was quiet the next morning and in the early part of the afternoon. My father, the police and the judge began to hope the trouble was over. Suddenly, though, at 5 p.m. the tong war broke out again and blood began to flow in the Calle de los Negros area.

Police officers and a number of citizens rushed to the trouble zone but the Chinese, instead of running away, barricaded themselves and refused to submit to arrest, as if they felt it was their privilege to fight among themselves as they had for centuries. Officer Jesús Bilderrain called on the hidden Orientals to surrender. He moved toward the adobe building where they were hidden. Shots resounded and Officer Bilderrain fell with bullets in his shoulder and wrists. His fifteen-year-old brother also suffered a wound in the right leg, and lay writhing in the street.

It was then that the event which set off the massacre took place. Robert Thompson, a citizen rushed forward to try to rescue Jesús Bilderrain. A frenzied Chinese with a revolver in each hand rushed forward and killed Thompson as he bent to assist the wounded officer.

At the same time a volley came from behind the iron shutters of the adobe and a number of onlookers were wounded.

This set off a chain reaction.

Angered Americans poured into the Plaza area from all directions as word of Thompson's death swept through the town. From the start it was a mob without a leader. The screaming, cursing men were armed with rifles, pistols, and knives. From the stores along Commercial Street and North Main Street ropes were seized for the obvious underlying purpose of the mob.

Just as the crowd reached its peak in size, about 1,000 men, a Chinese suddenly ran out of the barricaded adobe and tried to escape across Los Angeles Street. He waved a razor-sharp hatchet as he dashed toward the Los Angeles River. A man named Romo Sortorel outran the Chinese and captured him in a flying tackle although Sortorel's hands were cut as the Chinese fought him with the hatchet. Emil Harris, a city detective, rushed up and momentarily rescued the Chinese.

However, the crowd by now had caught up and began a blood-thirsty chant: "Hang him! Hang him!"

Detective Harris managed to get as far as Temple and New High Streets, about three blocks, with the yelling crowd surrounding him as he tried to protect the Chinese.

At this time there was a large corral at the corner, with high gates made of heavy uprights and a large cross piece. The crowd spotted this and immediately recognized the framework as suitable for a gallows.

The unfortunate Chinese was dragged toward the gate and a rope with a hastily-tied knot was put around his neck. He was lifted up and dropped from the makeshift gallows, but the rope broke. The crowd which had been silent for a moment as the hanging was attempted broke out again into yells and oaths. Immediately the victim, who was almost unconscious, was hoisted again and this time choked to death.

While this was happening the bars in the United States Hotel and in all the other places on Main Street were being emptied as new members joined the mob or tried to stop it.

My father said that just after the first hanging Sheriff James F. Burns, a small man who had been a school teacher before becoming a lawman, arrived on horseback, and immediately began to try to form a posse to arrest the ringleaders of the mob. He raised his arms above his head and called for emergency deputies. The crowd was so excited that not a single man came forward to join him and my father. Then the Sheriff called out:

"I order you to disperse!"

Nobody moved.

Just then a messenger arrived with word that a new gallows had been set up near Goller's Wagon Shop at Los Angeles and Commercial Streets. Immediately the men who had been listening to the Sheriff started for the new scene of activity.

It was here that the frenzied crowd showed diabolical ingenuity. Two big wagons had been stood on end and a huge timber placed across them. Chinese were being hanged from this in quick succssion. As soon as the quivering body quieted and the victim had been pronounced dead, the corpse was taken down and another unfortunate prisoner strung up in his place.

In the midst of all this, with the bloodthirsty crowd screaming, some freak incidents were taking place. A. J. King, one of Los Angeles' leading citizens, was eating supper when some children rushed by calling out that the Chinese were killing white people. King jumped up and grabbed his rifle and two revolvers but he was in such a hurry trying to hold all of the weapons that one of the revolvers went off and shot the tip off his finger. He had to go to the doctor instead of the hanging.

In another place State Senator Cameron E. Thom, a fiery Virginian who bore the title of Captain and had been City Attorney and District Attorney of Los Angeles at the same time, tried to back up Sheriff Burns. He got up on top of a box while the Sheriff climbed on a barrel to see whether they could gain the attention of a portion of the mob.

The Sheriff was so aroused that he waved his arms and stamped his foot and suddenly fell through the top of the barrel and was momentarily out of sight. As soon as the Sheriff had been rescued he, Thom, Judge R. M. Widney, James Goldsworthy, H. C. Austin and my father rushed after a new bunch of rioters who were carrying a Chinese up Commercial Street toward Main where stood the gate which had already been used once. In the face of the whole mob, the few men with the Sheriff seized the Chinese and took him to jail.

"I thought for a minute the mob might string us up too," father said.

All this time the hangings were going on swiftly from the wagon. Father related that the bodies were piled up like cordwood as they were taken down.

Many of the people in town became so worried about their Chinese cooks and house servants that they hid them in basements and closets and locked all the outside doors against the mob. Some of these poor Chinese cowering in their hiding places could hear the screaming crowd outside because residences were then scattered all through the so-called business district which was clustered within a few blocks of the Plaza.

For many hours the mob went up and down the street after it had hanged the last Chinese it could find. When the Sheriff, his aides, and father finally took the grim census of the dead it totaled twenty-two.

Coroner Joseph Kurtz called together a jury and a verdict was given in just nine words:

"Death through strangulation by persons unknown to the jury."

Father was sickened by it all. The thought of the useless slaughter haunted him the rest of his life, although he had tried his best to stop it.

He always said, "Only one man deserved to hang—the other twenty-one were the bonus of mob madness."

CHAPTER 5

RIDING THE DRAGON

NONE of the horrors of the massacre penetrated my childish mind at the time I rode my home-made wagon around the Plaza to visit my Cantonese friends. I suppose my mother and father must have felt I was perfectly safe because they never gave any indication of worry. But undoubtedly I was associating during the daytime with tong members who were perfectly willing to take the life of another Chinese when darkness came and the "wars" began.

It was perfectly natural for me to pick up the sing-song, sibilant language of the Cantonese and I would find myself at home switching from Spanish to Chinese to English without any conscious effort.

The first Chinese I learned was simple: "Holama, siloko." ("Hello, little boy.")

"Huye naia?" ("Where are you going?")

And my answer would be "Fon du quoy." ("Home.")

Before I learned my abc's I was counting in Chinese, "yit, gay, sam, seay, um, luk, tet, pot, geu, ship." After that I learned "one, two, three," and "uno, dos, tres" in the languages which really should have been more natural to me. I suppose the fact that the Chinese always were using an abacus and continually haggling over the prices of vegetables and rice, caused me to pick up numbers quicker than I would have otherwise.

By the time I was old enough to toddle around Chinatown, a generation had elapsed, and the Chinese I knew apparently were unaffected by memories of the massacre. They continued their traditional life which they had transplanted from their home country into this foreign and seemingly incongruous area.

Out of the little shops or tongs would come the rattle of dominoes. These figured in many kinds of games.

In those days the Chinese did not take coffee breaks, they took gambling breaks. If they had a few moments away from their jobs they would rush over to risk what little money they had on a domino game or some other form of gambling which stirred their ancient blood.

At this time I must have been all of three years old but perhaps for this very reason the impressions were that much more vivid.

Our Chinese servant, Ah Yoiu, used to pull me in my funny little wagon as we headed for the Plaza and the domino and fan tan games. Ah Yoiu, I believe, was my first Chinese baby sitter although he didn't really sit, he just rolled me along, then did his sitting at the domino tables. Often, when I was tired and he was gambling, I would be lulled to sleep by the weird sound of the flageolet, that venerable fipple-flute instrument so favored among the wood winds by the Chinese, which had been imported from their homeland, and by the Chinese gongs and wood blocks pounded together.

The coolies still wore their queues and it was never thought proper to have a haircut. A man would have been considered an unusual specimen if he went down the street without his long hair hanging down in the back. It was his great joy and one of his most prideful possessions.

The Chinese with their truck gardens were the lifesavers of the primitive agricultural areas surrounding Los Angeles. They were natural salesmen for this kind of produce.

In their wide Oriental hats made of woven bamboo like baskets, the coolies would go around the Plaza region with big baskets of vegetables on bamboo poles. Their shrill cries could be heard for long distances as they went from house to house crying in their pidgin English:

"Weg-tee-bool—welly cheap!"

These peaceful vegetable peddlers seemed to be transformed by some magic into a different breed at night. It was then that the tongs, cliques, clans, or clubs into which the Chinese were divided really came into operation.

They belonged to the See Yups, the Sam Yups, the Oleon Tong, and the Hip Sing Tong.

Tong wars were a common thing in those days and human life among the

Cantonese was very cheap. Quite often a friend of mine who had been peddling vegetables one day would be found lying dead the next morning in a gutter, the victim of a tong fight. Nobody seemed particularly concerned about the deceased in these instances.

This was hard for us to understand because, in their relations with the other nationalities who lived around the Plaza, the Chinese were extremely friendly and constant in their friendship. If you were a friend of one of them it was not for a week or a month or a year, it was for life.

They were absolutely honest, and once the word of a Chinese had been given to a white friend you could depend on it forever, no matter what pressures arose.

They made the most wonderful servants imaginable. The Chinese cooks in particular became so much a part of the homes in which they served that it was almost impossible to imagine getting along without them. Their loyalties were without bounds. They would do anything for their "folks."

I suppose, looking back on it now, that I must have associated daily with the opium smokers, opium peddlers, and murderers. They were all such charming people that no suspicion ever entered my mind that they were capable of doing anything wrong.

I used to wonder about some of the old Chinese men. They would lie down on boards covered with a sheet in the back of the shops. Before them was a lamp with an open flame. In their hands they held opium pipes about a foot and a half long, with stems an inch in diameter, and a bowl the size of a doorknob with a small hole in it.

The opium came in jars like thick syrup.

The old men would roll one end of a yen hulk, like a big hat pin, in the opium jar until there was a little ball of opium about the size of a pea on the end of the pin. They would roll this around and around to solidify it, hold it over the open flame, and then inhale the fumes through the pipe.

Soon they would go into happy oblivion.

I suppose they were actually out riding some Chinese version of Cloud 9, chasing dragons, and otherwise enjoying themselves in the dreams brought on by the opium. To me they merely appeared as venerable old gentlemen who, on occasion when they were in their right minds, said the customary "Holama, Siloko" to me with as much friendliness as anybody else.

It was a lucky thing for me, I guess, that I was too small to say to any of my friends, "Loan me your pipe."

I might have been out there riding the dragon, too.

CHAPTER 6

THE DAYS OF THE LIONS

WE kids never knew how poor we were. Our parents had to do all the worrying. Life went on for those of us who were still in childhood as if money and hard times were something in a fairy story, far away. We ate what was given to us, played in the streets along the Zanja, went around the Plaza talking to the Chinese, the Indians, and the Californiano loafers who were there and we were totally unaware there was a depression throughout the land.

But the fact that father became temporarily crippled when a hand truck at the depot ran over his foot was something we could all understand. It was in our own family; we saw our father suffering. We saw our mother's worry. While this affected us, we were still too young to face the real perils of life which confronted our parents. It was difficult for them to know where food was coming from one day to the next to feed all the children.

There were six of us by now, Elisa, Ygnacio, Atala, Eulogio, Diana, and me.

One day we knew great things were happening. Mother began packing all of our belongings, including the pans, dishes, and clothing. Father's foot was better by now although he still limped, but he was busy packing too, taking particular care to see that his books and papers were put away properly for the long journey we were to take.

We all knew, in general, that we were going to a place by the sea and in fact we had visited near there occasionally but now we were actually going to make a tremendous move of 18 miles to a place called Santa Monica. Our Tía Arcadia de Baker lived there in a fine house. Moving to Santa Monica by the sea!

It sounded very exciting to us although we were not familiar with the sea and we wondered just how it would be to live close to it.

At last the great day came for the actual move. We went down to the old Southern Pacific Railroad station at Alameda and Commercial Streets and got on a train. It was the first time that all of us had been on a train together. The coaches fascinated us and we leaned out of the windows with great interest as we waited for the small engine to start. At last there was a mighty blast on the whistle and we moved slowly along Alameda Street, grinding over the rough track until we came to what is now 33rd Street in Los Angeles where we turned west. Way out there in the country on a place called Grand Avenue, although it was strictly a country lane, there was a little station, the first one, where we stopped ceremoniously, although nobody got on or got off.

The idea of traveling 18 miles at all was rather overwhelming for we had been accustomed to staying close to the Plaza in Los Angeles. Next we came to a station called Ciénega, then on to The Palms; finally, amid great excitement on our part, we arrived at the old depot in a sort of depression in the ground at Ocean Avenue in Santa Monica. The conductor called out "Santa Monica!" in a loud voice although it seemed a little unnecessary as there was no place else for the train to go except to run into the ocean.

Mother and father busied themselves getting off the suitcases, sacks, blankets, and all the other paraphernalia which they had carried with them. We piled off the train and ran as fast as we could to the top of the bluff to look out over the sea. Below us the breakers were hurling themselves in great crashing masses onto the shore, sending white spray high into the air and causing a thunderous noise. We were all so startled at the immensity of this gigantic thing called the sea and the loneliness of the immense horizon at which we looked that we all began to cry at once. Mother and father came to us and tried to comfort us. She told us that we would learn to love the sea because it was a place where we could go bathing and where we would have a great deal of fun on the beach. For the moment we were too terrified to be much reassured. We were happy to go with our parents to a little house on the rear of a lot back of Rapp's Saloon and beer garden. This was on the south side of Second Street between Utah and Oregon Avenues, which would now be Broadway and Santa Monica Boulevard, one of the great bustling centers in the modern city.

The house was so small it seemed impossible that we all could squeeze into it, yet we managed somehow. As I was the smallest I was put in a room with my brothers Eulogio and Ygnacio. Mother made a hammock for me out of an old brown blanket which she strung up on two ropes. I was still so shocked at the sight of the sea and so nervous at the idea of the waves crashing into the house and killing us all that mother had to stop her unpacking and come into the room and rock my little hammock while she sang *La Golondrina*. This old song, which had been my cradle song, eventually soothed me and I dropped off to sleep. But my brothers punched me during the night because I was having nightmares about the ocean and kept waking up and hollering that I was drowning. Eulogio told me in the morning that it was one of the worst nights he ever spent trying to calm me down.

When the bright sun came up in the morning all of the horrible fancies of the night faded away and a spirit of exploration entered into all of us. We started out to see Santa Monica.

First thing of all we went to visit two cave dwellers. I guess you could call them cave dwellers because that is what it amounted to. Two Indians, one of them enormously fat, were going to help father in his new work as a fisherman.

One was called Guatamote. He was almost blind, and sometimes was led by a little "seeing eye" boy. The other was Paisano Gordo, the fat one. They lived in the barrancos or caves in the bluff between Pacific and Strand. In later years I helped to create, as a member of the California Beaches and Parks Commission, the present State Beach Park on this site. But that morning as we tagged along with father to meet his new helpers we were not thinking about beach parks or anything except the stimulating prospect of seeing two cave men.

The dwellings in which Guatamote and Paisano Gordo lived certainly came up to expectations. The caves were covered over with old pieces of driftwood, tin, and even seaweed so that the men had to crawl into a small entrance as if they were going into an Eskimo igloo.

Old Guatamote came crawling out of the cave and squinted at father as he tried to see him with his blurry, old eyes. Paisano Gordo stood and bowed, his huge stomach quaking with some sort of inner mirth which we never quite could understand because he was always on the verge of starvation. They were two of the dirtiest humans we kids had ever seen and their presence was noticeable even though we were several feet away and there was plenty of fresh air. But their gentle souls made up for their bodily deficiencies. They talked with father about the prospects of fishing and before long we were all out on the old Bernard Wharf which ran 1600 feet out from Strand Street and was used for unloading freight from the little vessels which came in to Santa Monica.

That day we began a new existence. All of us fished for a living. We sat on the wharf and dangled our lines into the blue water of the Pacific, soon becoming accustomed to the gentle roll of the swells as they passed underneath the pier and then dashed themselves upon the beach. It all became exhilarating, a lark and lots of fun after our first fears had dissipated.

The little minnow which I had caught in Ballona Creek seemed like a mere pygmy after I snagged my first sea bass on the pier at Santa Monica. I battled the creature which seemed as large as a whale to me and I think I've had few prouder moments than when I landed it with the aid of my father. The minnow and then a sea bass! They started me on a love of fishing which has stayed with me ever since. But at that particular time we were not fishing just for fun. We were fishing for food and for a little money because the surplus fish were packed and sold to cafes and restaurants and even to an occasional tourist who didn't want to catch his own.

Those first few months we ate little but fish and tortillas. Mother managed to obtain enough corn for the masa and we also got some hog fat in which to fry our fish. I suppose some people might have tired of such a diet but we were having so much fun during the hours that we were not fishing that we cared little what we had to eat just as long as it was filling.

Father worked harder at this time than anyone I have ever seen. He had a friend, old Juan Valenzuela, who owned a rickety team and a plow. In the mornings they would plow up a big furrow along each side of the Bernard Wharf and all of us would dig out the clams. Guatamote, Paisano Gordo, Valenzuela, father, and the older boys would carry the clams up to the house. Then they would sort and box them. These, plus any fish which we had caught during the day, would be taken to the depot which was just off Railroad Avenue, now the great Colorado Boulevard, and shipped to Los Angeles. It was a long way from the beach to our house and another great distance to the railroad station when you were carrying heavy boxes of clams or fish, but father kept at it day and night, sometimes packing until midnight after we kids were sleeping soundly.

All around us lay adventure. One of the big events was a trip to the "Tears of Santa Monica," the pools which Father Crespi had discovered and which now formed the water supply of the little town. It was father's job to see that the moss and algae were cleaned off the surface of the water so that when it ran through the mains from about where Sawtelle is now to Santa Monica, it would be clean and pure.

In this great expanse of meadows and ciénagas where the alfilaria grass and the other wild grasses grew knee high to the thousands of grazing sheep and cattle only one tiny human habitation was visible. This was the little adobe house of Ike Johnson who was Tía Arcadia's ranch overseer.

By now father owned a buckboard with the rear seat reversed so that it faced outward. My brothers and I sat there with our guns and as we traveled over the plains we shot English plover and curlews which seemed to nest around what is now Mount Olive. Coyotes and jack rabbits abounded. We hunted quail in the arroyos where Hollywood Boulevard now stretches its magic miles. The plover and the quail let us vary our fish diet now that we had money enough for ammunition and knew where to hunt this game.

Most exciting of all for me were the mountain lion hunts. The smell of the fresh blood and the entrails thrown out by the slaughter houses attracted the lions in great numbers to the canyon where my house now stands. We had friends there in that area, Lico Peña and the Marquez boys. We also learned to hunt with dogs that the Peña and Marquez youngsters provided. We would start the hunt near the slaughter houses and then follow the dogs as they chased the lion over toward Mount Olive. Quite often the lion would take refuge in a sycamore tree, with the dogs clamoring at the base, the boys yelling and everybody wondering whether he was going to get his head clawed off.

My brothers were the most venturesome of all. They were splendid with a reata and if the lion was close enough to the ground to be reached at all they would try to lasso him. If they succeeded in getting the loop over his neck they would drag him down and the pack of dogs then would close in and there would be a tremendous fight. Many of the dogs were mangled and came home bleeding and torn or were left dead at the scene, but it was so exciting that in the heat of the fray we forgot our own fear and clustered around cheering the dogs as they fought with the lion.

Other times if the lions were too high in the tree or if we saw they were going to escape we would shoot them with rifles. The people of the area were glad to get rid of the creatures because the mountain lions occasionally would attack small children.

Lions, fish, quail, plover, dogs, horses, coyotes, swimming, lassos, branding, fiestas!

The mountains and the sea were mine.

I was a different kind of Huckleberry Finn; a California variety.

CHAPTER 7

BRAVE PURSUIT

Tío Alfredo was the most inoffensive looking man I ever saw. His mustaches drooped and his kindly brown eyes looked out at the world with a benevolent expression. His feet were small and his hands rather stubby. He never seemed to get angry about anything. We called him Tío Alfredo or Uncle Al interchangeably for we spoke both Spanish and English in our home and sometimes blended the two.

My first recollection of Tío Alfredo is when excavations were being made for our new home in Santa Monica. Father had torn down the old two-story board-and-batten house into which we had moved after our lean days when he and the Indians were fishing and clam digging for a living. Now he was building a much nicer one. Uncle Al was down in a hole in his shirt sleeves digging away with the Indians, making a común. Grandfather Carrillo, the Judge, stood on the edge of the hole immaculately dressed and with his fine beaver hat on his head, and scolded Tío Alfredo and the Indians without any apparent cause. For some perverse reason we kids got rambunctious, too, and began to tease Uncle Al. Father, who was working nearby, put down his hammer and came over to us.

"Don't ever do that again," he said sternly. "Your Uncle Al doesn't deserve that kind of talk; you must respect your elders. And he is a brave man."

That ended the incident for the moment and even Grandfather who had heard the dressing down we got walked away as if he were in deep thought.

Uncle Al had just returned from some place called Arizona but the name meant nothing to us.

Father said nothing further about the incident at supper time and we thought he had forgotten the whole matter. But when Tío Alfredo went out for the evening Father asked us kids to come with him onto the porch. He sat in a big leather chair and stared out toward the ocean for a few minutes.

"My children," he said gravely at last in precise Castilian, as my brother and sisters and I waited apprehensively, "we all are inclined to judge by outward appearances. That is wrong. You should learn it early. Just because your Tío Alfredo chooses to be kind and help us by digging a hole for the común does not mean he is a peon or deserving of your scorn or disrespect. That is merely his way of assisting us. He is Don Alfredo Emilio Carrillo, a gentleman, a graduate of the great college, Holy Cross in Massachusetts, as I am, and he has fine courage. He is muy hombre! Muy valiente! Let me tell you a story."

Once more he paused to let his words sink in.

Then he related an incident which concerned the time when he himself was Chief of Police in Los Angeles. In Southern California, at that time, two of the most feared and notorious bandits who ever lived in this region were terrorizing people everywhere. They were known as Red Jack and "Killer" Hensley, Wells Fargo Express robbers. Murders, highway and train robbery, rape and every sort of crime had been committed by the two. Finally they were being sought by so many sheriffs that they fled across the Colorado River into Arizona.

At this time Uncle Al was helping father occasionally and he had come favorably to the attention of the United States authorities in Los Angeles. They called him in one day and asked him if he would like to be a Deputy United States Marshal and go after Red Jack and Killer Hensley.

In his mild manner, Tío Alfredo said, "Sure."

His instructions were simple and to the point, "Bring them back dead or alive." Tío Alfredo nodded and got on his horse and headed for Arizona, leading a pack horse. This was just about the time the Texas-Pacific Railroad, now the Southern Pacific Railroad, was ready to be put into operation, but Uncle Al didn't want to fool around with any trains. His old horse was the same plodding and steady sort as himself, and they made a good pair.

It was a task in those days just to reach the Colorado River because of the fearful desert which had to be crossed and the scarcity of water. Uncle Al took his time, planned his trip well, traveled at night to avoid the heat. With almost uncanny instinct he found the water holes and finally rode into Yuma. Here he found out the direction in which the desperados had ridden. The next morning he started out, heading eastward along the Gila River into the parched desert country which extended all the way over to Tucson and Tombstone.

Tío Alfredo was intimately familiar with Arizona. He knew the water-holes, the long dry marshes, the sites of Indian camps. From this knowledge he was able to guess quite accurately the trail the killers would be taking if they were headed for El Paso and the wide open spaces of Texas, via the southern route, as reported.

His journey was not as haphazard as it might have appeared. All along the way he kept his trained eyes open for signs of the fugitives. Beyond Yuma, from these signs, he became convinced he was correct in believing he was following along only a few days or hours behind Red Jack and "Killer" Hensley.

Day after day he rode through this terrifying country, plodding up long dry washes where it seemed impossible that any water had ever fallen. Flinty rocks cut the hooves of his horse and the great barbs of the cactus seemed to reach out to ensnare both him and his mount. The giant sahuaro cactus, which seemed to grow only on the eastward side of the Colorado River, surrounded him in some places like great forests. Even the mountains were different from those in California. They tore jagged holes in the intense blue sky with their knife blade silhouettes. The tallest peaks seeming to pierce heaven itself.

It was so dry that on some days Tío Alfredo rarely saw a bird or rabbit. The Organ Range of mountains shimmered on the horizon.

All of us kids were sitting on the edge of our chairs as father got to this part of the story. We waited in suspense for him to continue. This story was our "TV."

He told of Uncle Al going along the Gila by Indian sign paintings on big rocks, of seeing huge Indian dwellings made of adobe and of suffering thirst when he could not find any water hole. Finally he passed Tucson and went into the rough country between there and Tombstone.

At this time General Nelson Appleton Miles, the great Indian fighter who had already defeated the Cheyennes, Comanches and Nez Percés and had chased the Sioux and Sitting Bull and other chiefs into retreat, was on the trail of Geronimo, the fierce Apache leader who knew every hideout in Arizona and Northern Mexico. All the Apaches were on the war path and Uncle Al, in addition to his worries about water, was constantly on the alert for any lurking Apaches.

His fears were well founded. One day as he rode into a little arroyo, after cautiously examining all the surrounding country, he suddenly heard a war whoop and three braves rode into the other end of the arroyo, firing as they came.

Tío Alfredo calmly picked off one of the Indians with his 45-60 rifle—I now have that rifle on the wall of my den—then wounded a second who was knocked from his horse but at that very moment was struck in the leg himself by a rifle bullet. He and the remaining Indian rode forward at a gallop towards each other, firing as fast as they could. One of Tío Alfredo's bullets struck the Indian in the hand and the gun was knocked from his grasp but the Indian reached over his shoulder into his quiver and pulled out an arrow quickly fitting it to his bow. He let fly with this arrow just as Uncle Al shot him in the head with a pistol bullet. The arrow came straight into Uncle Al's right side below the shoulder.

The third Indian was trying to get up off the ground and Uncle Al used one of the two remaining bullets in his revolver to kill him.

Uncle Al got down off his horse, made a little mud with some water out of his canteen and plugged up the bullet hole in his leg as best he could. The arrow had gone clean through the skin of his side but had glanced off his ribs and, while he was bleeding badly, he thought this would let up in a little while.

After he had examined his wounds and decided he was able to go on, he remounted and headed towards Tombstone. The fight had occurred in the middle of the afternoon and it was getting dark as Uncle Al rode along. He felt weak and feverish but the mud had helped to stop the flow of blood from his leg and the wound in his side also had coated over, so he was sure he was not going to hemorrhage to death.

He decided to go as far as he could that night and get help in Tombstone.

As he rode along he now was doubly cautious. Suddenly his horse indicated that it smelled something ahead. Uncle Al stopped and peered into the darkness. Down in a little hollow beside some greasewood he saw a small fire.

Of course he had already reloaded his rifle and pistol and was ready for any encounter, but he was not anxious for another fight with Indians at this moment. He was as silent as a cougar as he crept forward towards the fire dragging his bad leg. When he got close he was astounded to see that here before him were the two men he had been trailing for miles. He recognized them easily because he had met them once in Los Angeles. Red Jack and Killer Hensley were squatted over the fire, and Uncle could smell the delicious fragrance of coffee.

Without hesitating, Tío Alfredo called out, "Surrender, I've got the drop on you." Quick as a flash Hensley jumped up and shot toward the sound of the voice. Uncle Al fired back and Hensley dropped. Red Jack in this interval had leaped out of the glare of the firelight and began to pump bullets toward Uncle Al. Uncle Al shot carefully again and Red Jack also fell. Cautiously Uncle Al approached and checked the two men. He found that both were dead.

Their sightless, open eyes stared up between the grotesque arms of a giant sahuaro cactus, just as the tip of the moon appeared over the eastern hills, casting a ghastly light upon the corpses.

Tío Alfredo lifted both bodies across the pack horse and tied them on. After that he calmly went over and drank the coffee of the dead killers and then headed into the night once more.

As dawn was breaking he rode wearily into Tombstone. He was bloody, unshaven, and dirty. He ached in every joint and his fever was so high that he could scarcely see. But he made his way to the U.S. Marshal's office.

There, apologetically, and in his mild voice he made a request, "Señor Marshal, will you do me a great favor? Please take care of these bad men. I have a very long way to go back home and I am afraid they will spoil."

The Marshal was named Wyatt Earp!

We kids never again teased Tío Alfredo Emilio Carrillo, Deputy United States Marshal.

CHAPTER 8

THE SAD LEGACY OF TIÓ ANDRÉS

It was always fiesta at the old adobe casa of Tío Andrés Machado.

I well remember my early visits to this wonderful, peaceful, romantic ranch, a carry-over of the greater days of early California. In my ears still rings the crackling rhythm of castanets and when I close my eyes I can see the lovely Spanish fandangos, those animated dances—the jota! the jarabe!—in keeping with the spirit of the music: Guitars! Violins!

Although we called him "Tío Andrés," he actually was my great-uncle instead of plain uncle. But what is a mere generation or two to a Spanish Californian? Parientes is the word, "kinfolks."

This Andrés Machado was a descendant and heir of the great Machado family which had put its imprint on all the vast territory from Aguaje de la Centinela to La Bahía de Santa Monica.

The sprawling adobe house, built around a patio in traditional style, was the scene of my first night away from home already mentioned, and nearby was gurgling Ballona Creek where my triumph in minnow fishing occurred. Through the patio ran the zanja to supply water for the house. It was a spot calculated to be dear to me. Still, over and above that, it did form in gaiety and ease of living the bridge between the pastoral age of California and the modern onset of noise and bustle which we have labeled progress. Everyone who went there sensed this.

The mornings and evenings were best. As the sun came up and the wisps of fog retreated through the thick leaves of the nogales—the walnuts—and pears, peaches, apricots and apple trees, smoke began to rise from the kitchen chimney and delicious smells stole through the house. Tortillas de harina— flour tortillas—those thin unleavened heavenly circles made from softened ground wheat were baking upon the hot griddle. Slices of ham flavored from the thick smoke of mesquite wood in the smokehouse were broiling beside them. Duck eggs were adding their aroma as they bubbled in the hog fat. Frying all over again—their very name gave the recipe, "frijoles refritos"— were the soft mashed pink beans so delicately flavored with cheese and bacon drippings; and sometimes slices of cheese, frijoles con queso.

Coffee in the big black coffee pot steaming in the huge open hearth added its fragrance to the symphony of delectable smells.

Outside, the sound of brooms with their soft swishes upon the mellow red tiles of the patio porch and the pathways between the geranium and the lemon verbenas formed a lullaby for the late sleepers. The banty chickens raced eagerly for unwary worms who had failed to heed the warning of oncoming dawn to return to their underground homes. Peacocks—the Pavo Real (the king's special dish)—screamed in the orchard, and aggrieved roosters, answering the challenge, crowed back as loudly as they could.

Tía Gracia and Felicita, the daughter of the house, presided in the kitchen. The earthen floor of this cocina shone with the patina of old ivory from decades of sprinkling and light sweeping.

Directing the chopping of wood and the feeding of the horses, cows and fowls were the sons Manuel, Alcala and Agustín.

Tío Andrés himself supervised everything with a benevolent but watchful eye, but always with partiality for the horses, which were of San David and Ecco stock.

"Lift that right front pastern of the brown mare," he would say to the muchacho caballerango in the half light of the warm barn. "She was a little cojo (lame) yesterday."

Or, "The pinto foal did not suck well last night. Give him a small physic."

By now the sun would have risen high enough to peep into the patio, and it was time for breakfast. Felicita would go to the triangle of iron hanging from the covered porch and strike it with the metal bar, sending its message to every corner of the hacienda, to the fields, to the orchards, to the pastures.

So began the day.

The evenings, in their way, were even better than the mornings.

As the sun went down over the Pacific, a little mist rose from the creek beneath the willows, and mourning doves came cooing to rest in the fruit trees. The banties, full of worms and contentment, flew into the low branches, too, so as to be safe from the coyotes who prowled the hills, keeping their eyes open for unwary and toothsome chickens. The cows bawled for the milkers for their udders were so full that the milk began to trickle of its own accord. Some kicked gently at eager calves who became too rough at the teats.

If it was full moon, the coyotes howled early, seeming to fill all the land-scape and ocean with their wailing as if they rode the waves as well as the slopes where wild mustard grew. A favorite trick of the coyotes, working in pairs, was to bite the tails off young calves. When the wailing started the calves and colts became nervous and kept close to their dams, their small ears flicking at the unearthly chorus.

Red fires danced in the cocina, visible now through the low windows as darkness set the stage for the evening's fun.

Tía Gracia and Felicita still presided at the cooking fires, but soon their roles would change. As soon as supper was over, Tía Gracia would become the queen of the rancho, and Felicita would emerge with bangles, castanets and her guitar to become the dancing and singing sprite of the fiesta scene.

Nobody ever knew for sure how many would be present, either for supper or the festivities afterwards, and nobody cared. It is true Tía Gracia used to glance just before dark at the long hitching rail outside the low adobe wall enclosing the kitchen garden, but it was an appraisal for hospitality's sake rather than any manifestation of worry over numbers. All who tied their horses there were welcome. It was merely a matter of making plenty of tortillas to go with the main courses.

If breakfast sent forth enticing odors, supper was a veritable blending and climax of the cooking art. Noon day dinner, of course, was supposed to be traditionally the "heavy" meal of the day but, to me, supper always seemed just as exciting.

From the mysterious cocina, with its perpetual fragrance of dried chilis ground on a large metate, came the procession of steaming dishes. Big pots of caldo de albóndigas (meat balls) with the bite and tang of the chilis in their soupy depths, led the parade. Then came the carne con chili—not chili con carne as it has been corrupted—giving due precedence to the meat which was its primary ingredient. Along with it was arroz, of course, also red-tinged with pepper fire and oregano.

The true tortillas, masterpieces in their own right, were larger than phonograph records and as thin as cardboard, waiting for the homemade butter to be folded in, and sometimes they were wrapped around frijoles, this being known as "burritos." Naturally, there were papas con chilis and chili relleno, the green chilis with the seed removed, covered with butter and ornamented with melted cheese.

But, above all, was the relish.

No meal, particularly one where meat was served, could possibly be considered complete without salsa, made with chilis: salsa de chili verde. It added the final touch to these wonderful suppers of which I speak. I do hope I am not confusing your gastric juices!

It is almost impossible to imagine the quick transition from the table to the impromptu fiesta almost every night. After the dishes were cleared away and the tables were set back toward the wall, the festivities began. If this was in the nature of a baile it always was held in the sala or reception hall. The mothers, fathers and old folks of the gente de razón gathered on one side of the sala. The young people congregated on the other, the girls in their mantillas and combs awaiting the young caballeros. The latter rode up in all their finery on their horses and hitched them to the long rack outside. The horses wore brilliant, sparkling headstalls and silver-ornamented bits, and the saddles also were decorated with silver, but this was not overdone or ostentatious.

At the baile there always were the inevitable cascarónes, the eggshells filled with coarse confetti which, when broken on the heads of the guests, made the whole room a fluttering mass of confetti, paper streamers and gaiety. On special occasions, when there was some particular guest of honor such as at a wedding or anniversary, there were a few doves' eggs filled with gold or silver dust as the final touch in this type of celebration.

All the young people joined in the famous traditional dances of California, the jota, the jarabe and the others which had come up from Mexico with the early settlers. The things I always enjoyed the most, though, were the individual dancing by Felicita and her singing of the songs which also dated far back into Mexican and Spanish history, *La Paloma* and *Cappotin-tin-tin* (the Rain Song).

These canciónes were simple, melodious, descriptive and sometimes religious—not a bit like rock and roll.

Felicita was so graceful in her dancing and her voice had such a compelling quality that she was the favorite entertainer when the young people congregated.

To the parties came families with great names and others with simple ones not known beyond the neighborhood—Lugos, Tallamantes, Angisolas, Arnazes, Cotas and Sighns. It little mattered what the names were. Everyone joined in the fun until it seemed that this era of contentment must go on forever. Happy people!

The guitar music resounding in the night, the stamp of dancing feet, the laughter, the songs and all the harmonious elements seemed to blend in my mind into a continuing pattern.

Perhaps, as with all things on this earth, a change was inevitable.

Vaguely, as the years went by, I began to sense that something was wrong at the Machados. Don Andrés and Tía Gracia were as friendly as ever, but an indefinable something began to cloud the happiness which always had reigned at the rancho. As in some of my stage plays, the curtain was slowly being lowered.

You could hardly call it worry. The Californians were almost incapable of worry. The abundant earth always had provided them with a living. Why should it cease?

Yet, from things said by my father and mother I knew all was not well. The fiestas became fewer and fewer. If there were cascarónes at all, there were no doves' eggs filled with gold and silver dust. The fruit trees in the orchard seemed to droop. Some withered and died. Even the weeping willow seemed now to sob. The gay murmuring song of Ballona Creek was somehow muted. Few horses were tied now at the Machado gate.

My father shook his head as he spoke in low tones to my mother. I heard the words "Andrés—trouble." Young as I was, it made me sad.

One morning, as the gray fog hovered in ghostly wraiths around the ranch-house and the brooding trees, Don Andrés stood on his verandah and squared his stooped shoulders.

He wore a flat yellow California hat made of the finest vicuña skin from South America, secured by a strap at the point of his chin. His copper-colored face, only a little darker than the hat, told the tale of the burdens he bore. Slowly he dry-rolled—no saliva—and kinked into shape a wheat-straw cigarette. Carefully he lighted it and inhaled deeply, then he expelled the smoke.

Through the cloud of fumo he called in a loud voice:

"Familia mía!"

With some alarm, they responded—Tía Gracia wiping her hands upon her apron, Felicita perplexedly, the sons Manuel, Alcala and Agustín hastening from the barn, always with their sombreros in hand when they approached their father. This was the call of a patriarch.

"Familia mía," Don Andrés said again, this time in a low voice and with tenderness as they stood before him. He paused as if reluctant to speak, then went on: "We must awaken to reality. The arms of a great octopus named prosperity are engulfing us in a wave of something called civilization."

He was speaking slowly in precise and expressive Spanish. He looked out towards the land.

"Our holdings have been encroached upon by a new thing called taxes. Unknown to you, I have been compelled to meet my tax bills with coupons of land. This has gone on for a good while. Our thousands of acres have been reduced to a small area hardly large enough for the casa."

His eyes looked far off, beyond what was visible. They seemed to say, how much is out there; one could go on forever seeing more and more; and what a lot has gone behind the curtain of Time.

Then, coming out of his reverie, Don Andrés said to his sons, "My great regret is that I did not prepare you for a business education. Your knowledge of horses and of agriculture does not prepare you for business. I hope you will have the acumen to carry on when I am gone. I fear further obligations. How will you care for your mother and sister?"

As his voice trailed away, Tía Gracia and Felicita took out their rosaries and walked to a niche in the sala where stood a statue of the Virgin and, kneeling, asked for guidance.

The sons, in silence, turned and moved toward the yard, fear in their eyes.

Don Andrés was left standing on the verandah.

Soon afterward, he died.

I remember going to the funeral: I was four years old. It was spectral: the horse-drawn hearse with black curtains on the windows which afforded a view of the simple coffin, the black-robed priests, the women with rebozos wrapped around their faces, the great concourse of buggies wending their way to the sacred burial ground. In those days they had what are called today "professional mourners," who screamed and mourned with great emotion, and frightened me.

Then life caught me up. First there was school, work on the railroad, San Francisco, New York, adventure, excitement, the stage. My childhood receded. Fifteen years passed.

Success came to me. I was a star on Broadway. Money was pouring in, with no income taxes. We started a road tour. Los Angeles was one stop. It was, I admit, a triumphant homecoming for me. A prophet is not without honor even in his home country; there was no doubt that in this case I *was* honored.

My friends all came to the theater and we had a party. All was gaiety and fun. I was happy I could make people happy. To be unhappy interferes with my pleasure! That is my philosophy.

Afterward, at home in Santa Monica, I asked my older sister Elisa something which had been in the back of my mind:

"What ever happened to Tía Gracia and Felicita and the boys?"

Elisa's face clouded. She sighed.

"Great troubles," she said. "First there was an earthquake which wrecked the old casa. Then the terrible flood which came down Ballona Creek and washed away even the debris. The remaining land was all taken over. The family moved away. We do not know where they are."

This haunted me. The memories of my early days at the rancho, a flash back to my boyhood, the sight and sound of the bailes and fiestas became very vivid again. But I was caught in a whirlwind. The theater overwhelmed me day and night. Great audiences! Applause! There was never much time for repining.

In those days, like all the young theatrical blades, I wore hand-made shirts of delicate Shantung silk from Japan. They were so fragile they were unable to stand the rigors of ordinary laundries; this was before laundromats.

Early one evening as I started for the theater in the shiny new sports car I had just purchased, the thought came to me that my supply of clean silk shirts was low.

Hastily, I gathered them up and thrust them in the car.

As I drove through a Hollywood side street I saw a crude hand-lettered sign on a little shack back from the street. I read:

HAND LAUNDRY DID HERE

I looked at my watch. There was plenty of time to stop. Gathering up the bundle, I went to the door and knocked. A bent little woman in a faded dress opened it.

"May I leave my shirts?" I asked. "Will you do them up nice?"

"I will be very glad," she replied in a low, tired voice with a Spanish accent. "Please write your name."

She held out a small piece of paper and the stub of a pencil. I scrawled my name.

She glanced at it, looked again, then stood transfixed. In a quavering voice, after a momentary pause she cried emotionally in Spanish, "Leo! Leo! God has sent you to us!"

"Felicita?" I answered in amazement.

I took her in my arms and felt her sobbing.

"It's so hard to believe," I told her. "I am thinking of the old rancho, your dear father and the boys—and your blessed mother! How long has she been gone?"

"Gone? She isn't gone. She's ninety-eight. Come see her. She is in the kitchen sewing on a crazy quilt. Come in."

Quietly we entered the house and went into the tiny kitchen. A small, intent woman was leaning over the quilt, laboriously stitching. She wore a pair of old square spectacles.

After a moment, she looked at me.

"Qué Dios te bendiga, Leopoldo!"

She held out her arms. I knelt at her feet. She took her rosary and touched my head and blessed me.

"Leo, I am looking at you through glasses your sainted mother gave me forty years ago. She must know this is the most welcome sight I have ever seen. God cherish that memory!"

Quietly we talked of the family, of the destruction of their home, of the troubles which had been visited upon them, of their faith through it all. Qué Dios quiere!

I left in a daze. My mind was busy with ideas of how I might help without wounding their pride. I knew it could be done.

Next morning I was still so overcome with emotion at the seemingly miraculous reunion that I got in my car and, instinctively, drove towards Ballona Creek and the old Machado rancho. Everywhere was change. Street cars and busses and automobiles clattered and roared through what had been open fields or country lanes. Ballona Creek had become a flood channel. The bending, lacy willows were only a memory.

Finally, amid business houses and homes, I did find the site of the gracious old adobe dwelling. Only a trace of one wall, where proud horses once had champed at the long hitching rack, still was to be seen.

Exactly where Tío Andrés' house had stood a giant oil derrick upreared against the sky, and a vast stream of rich petroleum was flowing 3,000 barrels a day. Oil! Oil!! The beginning of the Great Baldwin Hills oil discovery!

The Machados, proud and impoverished, had been sleeping on millions.

CHAPTER 9

SUNSET SHADOWS

Sunday—El Domingo—was like a pageant. Into town on their Palomino, sorrel, bay and black horses each Sunday morning rode thirty or forty dapper caballeros from all the great surrounding ranches, Aguages de Centinela, Ballona, and all the others.

Heading the group was Archie Freeman of Centinela. He was more than six feet tall, sitting his horse as if he were part of the animal itself. He wore snug blue broadcloth pantaloons with a definite bell at the bottom. Out of the bell came his small boots. Nearly all the rancheros had small feet because they were so seldom off their horses. What did they need large feet for? Certainly not for walking.

On his silver spurs was a twenty dollar gold piece as a rosette. His jacket of blue broadcloth was decorated with black and blue buttons and the studs on his white shirt were $2.50 gold pieces. His black hat was low crowned, tilted to one side with the barbaquejo, or chin strap, worn just below the lower lip.

Riding abreast, with full-length stirrups so all the impact of the horse was taken on the balls of the feet, the splendid phalanx would sweep into Santa Monica and up to the little church where there were hitching posts, not parking meters, for early morning Mass. The horses were tethered with mecates or ropes made of colored hair. The riders would loosen the cinch and throw one stirrup over the back of the horse so it could rest in comfort while they were in church.

The rumble of low, young voices would be heard then in the church in the responses to the service. Then the caballeros would emerge again en masse, tighten the cinches, remount, and dash away with whoops and yells to the old Pacific or Neptune Gardens for some refreshments. Then even happier than ever they would go over at noon for the big "dinner" which was served at that hour, rather than in the evening, at the restaurant of Eckert & Hoff. The full course dinner with plenty of beef, frijoles, tortillas, salsa, and all the rest was twenty-five cents but refreshments were extra. Beer was five cents and strong drinks—whiskey, aguardiente, and brandy—were ten cents. Then after a little rest to let their meal settle, the horse games would begin.

We kids and most of the townspeople gathered around to watch these sports which came straight out of the romantic past of California, of Mexico, and of Spain itself, dating back almost as far as that distant day when man first mounted a horse and discovered that with four legs instead of two he was one step nearer to being a demigod.

Indians and children would bring out buckets of water to wet down the unpaved street, the caballeros would come at full charge towards the long wet spot, rein up suddenly and start the horse in a long slide on all four feet, "skiing" in the mud. The object was to stop as close as possible to a line drawn across the street. Sometimes, but not often, a horse would go down as its back legs crumpled under it and the caballero would have to leap off and take his chances of falling in the mud himself. After the winners were finally chosen the whole troop would dash off pell-mell to the beach. There they would take the saddles off their horses, tie ropes around the horses' bellies, take off their own boots, and in their stocking feet, with their bridles off and riding the horses with loops Indian style, they would give the animals a dousing in the sea.

Thus refreshed, the most dangerous games began.

I can well remember the playing of the game which later was barred because of its alleged cruelty, but which we all thought of as the climax to the whole proceedings. The body of a turkey or chicken would be buried in the sand up to its neck, leaving only its head sticking out above ground. Then the rider would come at full speed "colgando"—the rider hanging from the mane, with his knees under the rope around the horse's belly—and leaning over with two fingers of one hand open, try to tear off the head of the turkey or chicken. Once again the whole town would be lined up to see the riders and to decide the winner.

After all this the young men with their spirits still demanding excitement would head out for the dance halls and gambling houses in the Santa Monica Canyon area where so many knifings, shootings, and murders took place. The day that began with Mass and singing in the house of God often would end in a wild melee. It was all part of the times; it was the way the Californianos lived.

The Freeman boys, Archie and Fred, along with the Machados and the Lugos became good friends of our family. They taught my brothers and me many tricks of riding. We had known how to ride after a fashion, as I've said, ever since we were babies, but these caballero-vaqueros were among the most skillful horsemen in the world and they imparted to us many little secrets which helped us in our endeavors to become true vaqueros ourselves.

We, too, learned to "ski" in the mud with our horses, to ride "colgando" to the consternation of our mother who thought for sure we were going to be killed as we swept along with our heads down hanging on to the horse's mane. It taught us self-reliance, fearlessness, and the other qualities which any good horseman must have.

During our time by the sea we learned horsemanship as well as fishing. We learned the code of the vaquero, the fact that a California caballero never showed fear under any circumstances, and that he was always ready to defend his honor, or that of any member of his family. It was a transplanting of the spirit of old Spain to the shores of the Pacific at Santa Monica.

Perhaps never again can there be such an era. We were living in the twilight of a great age. Sunset was coming for the pastoral era in California. But just as at sunset there are sudden brilliant illuminations lighting up the skies, so it was with us. We were fortunate to know the last vestiges of a magnificent time which can never return.

It was a time of horses, of quick anger, quick remorse, comradeship, and the knowledge that with the coming of civilization and progress we were to see the end of something grand on the stage of the Western world.

AÑO·1833

SEGUNDA

PARTE DEL LIBRO

&

SPIRIT OF THE LAND

LEO CARRILLO

&

THE VALLEY OF SAN LUIS REY

There is a valley that's bathed by the moon
Where living and love are in tune,
Where memory stays with the old Spanish days—
I long to return there soon.
In the valley of San Luis Rey
There are memories of yesterday,
Where the turtledoves coo,
And the meadowlarks sing
And the padres chant as the mission bells ring.
And the light from above shines a message of love
On the valley of San Luis Rey.

CHAPTER 10

THIS FRUITFUL EARTH

Two horsemen dashed madly across the rough ground. They seemed to be engaged in some strange game. Between them was a reata about 150 feet long. One would dash ahead until the reata was stretched taut, then leap off his horse, drive a stake in the ground, tie the reata to it and wait for the other horseman to dash past him. This rider, in turn, would go the full length of the reata and mark another spot on the ground and this would be continued endlessly on level ground, in arroyos, up hillsides, down steep slopes. It appeared senseless, but it was not.

This was the method of marking off the boundaries of a California rancho.

It was the method followed by my great-great-grandfather, José Raimundo Carrillo, in marking off his El Alisal Ranch in the neighborhood of Santa Barbara. All over California, in fact, the boundaries of the vast grants, sometimes amounting to tens of thousands of acres, were marked in the haphazard fashion by riders with reatas. The measuring was carried on under the supervision of a magistrate who was appointed especially for activities of this kind, with the necessary witnesses. Even the surveyors were required to take a serious oath, "By God our Lord and the sign of the Cross," before they started out on the measuring process.

Land and the fruit of the land seemed inexhaustible.

The valleys, hills, mountains and plains stretched to the far horizon. It appeared impossible that land could ever be as valuable as it later became.

59

On the lush grass of this vast domain grazed the endless herds, thousands upon tens of thousands of cattle. The Spaniards rarely castrated their calves and, as a result, nature and multiplication clothed the hills with a multitude of animals of all colors and descriptions, as the cows and the bulls ranged together all the year around.

The land itself was handed about with a lavish hand. My own people, as I say, were given the vast Rancho Alisal, then the Sespe Rancho, and other relatives received comparable tracts all over Southern California.

When Pio Pico, last of the Mexican Governors, was in debt, he casually gave his sisters the vast Santa Margarita Rancho where Marine Camp Pendleton now stands near Oceanside. One of the sisters married José Antonio Carrillo, and another Juan Forster.

Near the beautiful old adobe ranch house, which now is the headquarters of the Marine General commanding Camp Pendleton, was the bluff where horses were driven to their death so that there would be more grazing land for the cattle.

The San Vicente y Santa Monica Ranch of 31,000 acres, bought by Tía Arcadia and Senator John P. Jones of Nevada for $40,000, was an example of the low values placed on it even in the middle 1870's.

When my great-grandfather Carlos Antonio was Governor of California there was no money with which to pay him for his services. In place of this he was offered the huge Santa Rosa Island off the coast of Santa Barbara. He took it. But he regarded it so lightly that he traded it for 1500 head of cattle. It now is the range land for the immense Vail Ranch operations, in charge of Ed Vail, one of Will Rogers' closest friends.

Rancho Alisal of my great-great-grandfather, José Raimundo Carrillo, now has become a guest ranch near Santa Barbara. I am reminded too that some of the ranches, despite their early beautiful names in Spanish did not have English titles until around 1900. One forward-looking American, Promoter Wilcox, decided he was going to subdivide a portion of the enormous San Fernando Valley and see if he could sell a few tracts of land and some lots at cheap prices. He was driving along in a buggy with a Mexican boy looking over part of the property when he saw a number of beautiful plants growing on the hillside. They bore red berries in profusion.

"What do you call that?" he asked the boy.

"In Spanish it is toyon, but in English it is holly—wood."

This was a common expression in the Spanish mind because the identification of a tree or shrub usually was coupled with the word "madera" meaning wood, so it was quite natural for the Mexican boy to answer holly—wood.

"That might make a good name," mused Promoter Wilcox.

And so Hollywood with a capital "H" was born.

Possibly the most splendid wedding gift ever presented in California was not recognized at the time in its true light. When my grandmother, Josefa Bandini, married Pedro C. Carrillo, the Boston-educated lawyer who was my grandfather, Pio Pico gave Josefa the Coronado Peninsula as his personal wedding present. This included the present Coronado Island.

After the wedding Josefa Bandini Carrillo sold the entire Peninsula and Island for about $1,000 American money.

Just one little part of that enormous estate was sold later to the United States Navy for $7,000,000. It is known as North Island.

I guess the Carrillos sold too soon.

Much of the romance of ranchero life seemed to center around those great grants near the ocean. In one area, for instance, the tremendous Rancho Aguajes de la Centinela, the Rancho Sausal Redondo, Rancho San Vicente y Santa Monica, Rancho La Ballona, Rancho Rincon de Los Bueyes, and Rancho Rodeo de las Aguas combined to form a great semicircle around a trading center on the beach. This was the era of the mighty clipper ships from Boston which brought every kind of luxury imaginable to appeal to the taste of the Californianos. The Boston ships wanted the hides of the cattle which grazed in such tremendous numbers on the hills of California, and it was strictly a system of trade and barter.

The great ranchos of which I speak funneled their owners, their families, the native Indians and visitors down a "highway" known then as Calle de los Indios. Later this became known as La Brea Way and still later as Wilshire Boulevard, a showcase which today extends for 16 miles and displays the finest goods in the world. Wilshire Boulevard is merely an inland extension of the showcase on the beach below what is now Culver City in the days of which I speak.

Down the Calle de los Indios went the carretas, those two-wheeled awkward ox-drawn carts which formed the only wheel transportation in California. Their noise was almost paralyzing.

The wheels of the carretas were made by sawing the trunks of the huge California oaks or encinas. The axles were made out of this same wood. The roble or white oak was considered to be the best for this purpose. Some of the more discriminating people greased the axles with tallow from sheep and cattle, but many of the poor people didn't bother with such niceties, and the screaming and screeching of the wooden wheels on the wooden axle was terrifying when a caravan of the carretas was moving along the crude trail.

The commodities used in trading with the clipper ships included not only the hides of the cattle but also the tallow rendered down from the fat of both sheep and cattle.

The arrival of a clipper ship was the signal for days of fiesta. Romance reigned. Señoritas! Caballeros! Music! Dance! Love! Intermarriages! Gringos and Latins became one.

That is why some of my relatives are named Jones, Thompson, and perhaps even a Smith now and then—just a bunch of damned yanquis.

Amid the excitement when the clipper ship was standing off-shore and landing its treasures for inspection on the beach, the Californianos could see huge four-poster beds, splendid chairs from France and England, beautifully-decorated shawls brought from China and the Philippines and given the name "Spanish shawls" although they never had any connection with Spain; iron stoves, draperies, shovels, bolts of colored silk, high Spanish combs, saddles, guns, dresses, nails, powder, square rosewood pianos and shiny tin pans.

The bartering was active. In great piles were the hides which had been staked out and dried to be ready for shipment to the East. These were valued at about two dollars apiece in exchange.

The carrying of a piano in a carreta was something of a task, but when the purchase was made the proud owner managed it somehow.

The traffic up and down El Camino de los Indios was heavy whenever the clipper ship stood offshore. This was "bargain day" of that era.

On the ranches themselves there was not always peace and goodwill. Sometimes ranches were obtained by what we would call "adverse possession," or "squatter's rights." Out of these situations grew land feuds among the prominent early families of the whole Los Angeles area.

The reason for the feuds was simple. In the earliest days of the Pueblo of Los Angeles, certain lands were considered to be held in common by all citizens for the pasturing of cattle and horses. This was the case in regard to the thousands of acres lying to the south and west of the community and running all the way to the ocean. Included in these lands, which were more or less taken for granted by everybody, were the beautiful tracts known as Aguajes de la Centinela which meant "Sentinel Springs" and the Sausal Redondo, "Round Clump of Willows." Some enterprising citizens, though, were more attracted than the rest by the beauties of these spots and began to develop improvements which were certainly more than anything "in common" with the rest of the community.

Two of the great families at that time were the Avilas and the Machados.

Cornelio Avila had moved to Los Angeles just two years after it was founded. His five sons were energetic, enterprising men. One of them, Francisco Avila, built the famous adobe house in what is known today as Olvera Street near the Union Station in Los Angeles. This beautiful residence was known as the "House of the Revolutions" because so many plots were hatched there during the early days of Mexican factions contending for the rule of California. In 1847 this Avila adobe was the headquarters of Commodore Robert Stockton, one of the conquerors of Los Angeles just at the close of the Mexican War in this area.

A brother of Francisco Avila was Antonio Ygnacio Avila. The military commander of the area, Captain Noriega maintained headquarters in Santa Barbara, and Antonio Ygnacio applied to him for permission to keep his stock at Sausal Redondo. Captain Noriega said it was all right but that other people in Los Angeles also could use the area if they were willing to invest their work out there. Antonio Ygnacio Avila built up the ranch until he had 3,000 head of cattle which he and his children tended. Near the Sausal Redondo were the Sentinel Springs which flowed all the time and sent a little stream on its way down the Ballona Valley to the Pacific near what we know today as Playa del Rey, the site of the small craft harbor for which I voted as a member of the California State Parks Commission.

The Ballona Valley was a long flat stretch of land running to the sea. The creek meandered through it, taking the line of least resistance, an easy-going stream like the people themselves. The trail of the Indians brushed by the Springs of Centinela and went on down to Ballona Bayou which then was just a little inlet on the shore.

These beautiful springs attracted Ygnacio Machado of one of the other great families and he settled near them and began to cultivate the land along the creek. This Machado was a brother of the famous Agustín Machado who was on the Rancho La Ballona, the site of present Culver City.

Antonio Ygnacio Avila and Ygnacio Machado came into collision over their holdings. Avila protested Machado's presence at Centinela Springs.

Similar contests developed all over Southern California as the years went on, at first among the Californians themselves and later between the Americanos del Norte and the original owners of the grants, the Californians.

Some of the titles were fought over for many years until final settlements were made by the United States courts after California became a state in 1850.

A great battle developed also on the site of what is now Santa Monica in regard to the Rancho San Vicente y Santa Monica.

The famous names of the Sepulveda, Machado, Alvarado, Reyes, and Marquez families were involved in this dispute over lands between Santa Monica and Topanga Canyons.

As a sequel to this my great aunt, the beautiful Arcadia Bandini Stearns, wife of Abel Stearns, the cattle baron, eventually became one of the co-owners of the vast Santa Monica Ranch. Arcadia Bandini Stearns, after the death of her husband, married Colonel R. S. Baker—after whom Bakersfield was named—and Colonel Baker and Senator John P. Jones of Nevada bought the entire Santa Monica area in 1874. Just a year later a map of Santa Monica was recorded and the first lots were sold.

Later still, Tía Arcadia and Senator Jones gave 300 acres of the ranch for a soldier's home at Sawtelle. This is the great National Veterans Administration facility which still exists.

On the day of the dedication of the soldier's home, the American flag was run up and just as it was starting to flutter on the top of the flag pole a great eagle soared out of the blue sky from its home in the Santa Monica mountains and hovered over the scene as if pronouncing a blessing upon this humanitarian gift to the nation's heroes. The crowd stood in awe as this scene was enacted.

I have always liked to feel that this symbolic appearance of the American eagle marked the end of the great strife over land grants which once had marked the whole Santa Monica, Inglewood, Redondo area, and heralded a new era of peace and friendship among the grantees and heirs of the magnificent ranches which swept down between the mountains to the sea along El Camino de los Indios.

THE SOUND OF TEARS

As I sit beneath the arches of my home in the canyon where the sycamores twist upward to the moon there is one sound above all others which impresses itself upon me. It is the murmur of the little stream which runs through my place toward the sea.

It has the sound of tears.

This is not necessarily sad. Sometimes with tears there are associated scenes which in memory lend themselves to a different interpretation.

Tears flow for joy as well as for sorrow. Sometimes they are shed for the return of loved ones as well as for their departure. Emotions of the soul overflow in the eyes. This is what binds us together as human beings; a sharing of deep feelings. It is what lifts us above the animals. And, too, tears are related somehow to our idea of divinity, for the Mother of Christ shed them for her great tragedy when her Son died upon the Cross.

If there indeed be the echo of tears, in my little stream, I cannot always be sad on that account. Many times the sound uplifts me, as it did Robert Burns when he said to his beloved:

> *Ah, Jean, when I look into your twa e'en*
> *You can no tell me that I never heard*
> *The gurgle of your laughter in the ripple of the stream.*

As for me, the sound of the creek among the sycamores always brings back to mind the thought of a historic scene which was enacted almost within sight of where I sit.

On a day in the summer of 1769 just after the first Spanish settlers had walked up the 1000-mile-long peninsula of Baja California to the site of what is now San Diego, and had started onward in search of the Port of Monterey, a strange company was gathered in the great plain beyond my place.

It was along the Indian Trail, El Camino de los Indios, later called the La Brea Trail because of the brea or tar pits.

A little group of leather-jacketed Spanish soldiers stood there confused and uncertain about what route they should attempt to take. The commander was Don Gaspar de Portola.

On the left lay hills, a short distance ahead lay the sea, to their right the larger mountains. They did not know whether they could go along the coast or whether they would have to scale the mountains and try to find some pass to an inland valley for their journey north.

Portola looked about him in the noon-day glare and decided to dispatch some soldiers ahead to find whether there was a way along the coast, forbidding as it appeared.

The tremendous surf breaking on the sands seemed to defy human encroachment. It was a terrifying watery barrier and off to the north Point Dume where the glowering mountains and the sea come together was raised like a great clenched fist, signifying, "You shall not come this way!"

As the scouting party marched away Portola stood where he could look at the heavy growth of the hills and the beautiful meadows extending in every direction.

Only one thing was lacking on these meadows. There were no cows or horses. The only ones in California were the few recently brought by the Spaniards themselves, for horses had not been introduced before to this part of the world from Mexico, the Caribbean Isles, and Spain.

In the strange silence broken only by the sound of water birds in the marshes or ciénagas along the way, and with red-winged blackbirds flying overhead, Portola meditated upon the hardships which inevitably faced the little party in the long journey up the coast.

As the soldiers wearily went ahead to explore the possibilities of the coast route, Father Crespi, the diarist of the expedition, decided to investigate the countryside in the immediate vicinity of where they stood. He walked off to his right toward what now is the city of Santa Monica.

As he went along in his long robes he, too, was awed by the immensity of the country into which they had penetrated. He felt as if he needed some divine sign to give him courage in the midst of this vast land so that he in turn could transmit it to the soldiers who were in his charge and to the heathen whom he hoped to encounter along the way and convert to Christianity.

As he walked he looked about him at the plants and the small animals.

Rabbits skittered here and there, doves and quail flew from trees and brush, ducks and geese rose from the expanses of marsh-lands along the shore of which he walked.

The marsh-lands were not beautiful in themselves, rather to the contrary. They appeared dismal and foreboding.

But as Father Crespi trudged along his eyes suddenly beheld a remarkable sight. He felt as if his prayers had been answered. There before him glistening in the midday glow were two clear pools of water shaped almost like the eyes of a woman.

Father Crespi stared at them with adoration. Words came almost instinctively to his lips.

"Las Lágrimas de Santa Monica!" he exclaimed.

"The tears of Saint Monica!"

He was thinking of the legend of Saint Monica who, with tearful eyes, mourned for her son Augustine because of his waywardness and evil deeds.

Father Crespi remembered that the tears of the mother had been effective. She so mourned for her son and prayed so deeply for his salvation that he turned from his wickedness and began a life of a different kind. He, too, was later made a saint because of his humility and the innumerable good deeds which he performed, all because of the tears and prayers of Saint Monica.

As the little priest meditated upon the beautiful story he walked slowly in reverie along the stream which flowed from the two pools which he had named "The Tears of Santa Monica." Willows grew along the banks and the waters rippled over golden sands. Tiny minnows could be seen frolicking in the water. On the surface were insects darting and skipping. Dragonflies with all the colors of the rainbow in their flashing wings swooped towards the calm surface of the water.

The scene was so peaceful that Father Crespi was transported in memory to his childhood. He remembered wading in little streams like this when he was a tiny boy.

Suddenly the desire came over him to wade once again. He realized how strange it might appear for a priest, sent into the wilderness to save the heathen and to help the soldiers find a route through a new land to a distant port, to be seen wading in a stream like a child. Still the afternoon was warm and the water looked so inviting he could not resist. He removed his sandals, lifted his cassock to his knees and stepped into the stream.

The water bubbled and gurgled around his weary feet and he was reminded of the biblical story of Mary Magdalene washing the feet of the Saviour. He could appreciate how much water meant in a desert land through this experience of his own. He held his breviary and rosary in one hand and his cassock in the other. The water ran between his toes. He felt again the sensations of his early youth.

The waters laving his feet made him feel as if he had been washed clean by the glorious tears of Santa Monica.

After a few minutes he emerged upon the bank and walked in the grass so that his feet would dry and he could put on his sandals again. He felt refreshed and uplifted as he prepared to rejoin the men. It was as if some spirit had laid a calm and assured hand upon his heart and soul here in this distant land where man seemed so small and God so great.

With a final glance backward at Las Lágrimas de Santa Monica, Father Crespi rejoined the soldiers, rejoicing.

The good father found an air of gloom in the camp. The scouting party had returned with word that it was impossible to find a way between the raging sea and the great cliffs extending down to the water's edge. Captain Portola was faced now with the necessity of going inland, over the mountains. Even the Captain himself was dejected at the prospect of the long weary march through that forbidding region.

But Father Crespi, inspired by his experience at the pools and uplifted by the message of hope which he felt he had received from Santa Monica, spoke vigorous words of encouragement.

He was so confident in his own faith that his feeling was transmitted to Captain Portola and to the soldiers themselves.

With strengthened spirits they started towards the mountains and ascended an Indian trail which led to the valley beyond, now known as San Fernando

Valley, and eventually arrived safely at Monterey itself. The trail they took is what we call today Sepulveda Boulevard.

And all along the weary miles to Monterey, through every sort of danger, the faith and courage of Father Crespi provided the spark which made the journey a success.

I heard this story from my father and mother when I was a little boy. When we moved to Santa Monica, named for these same two pools of water, I felt a mysterious sense of kinship with the past. I, as a barefooted boy, also stood in the little stream flowing from the "Tears of Santa Monica" and felt the clear water ripple over my feet as it had done so many years before over the feet of Father Crespi.

These sycamores which grow upon the bank of the little stream which I have loved so much seem to me to be God's antenna for the broadcasting of the beautiful sound of music, compounded of the murmur of the waters and the rustling of the leaves. It is as if nature were transmitting the strains of *La Golondrina*, my mother's cradle song to the purple mountains in the evening glow, blessing the memory of Father Crespi and the vision which prompted him to give the name to these springs of pure water, "Las Lágrimas de Santa Monica."

CHAPTER 12

STRIFE IN EDEN

WE Carrillos have never been known to neglect a damsel in distress. It may have been due to our Castillian lineage, with a dash of Don Quixote, or just plain romanticism and knight-errantry. At any rate, the appeal of a woman who needed help always elicited instantaneous response from my forbears and kinsmen in California.

So it was with José Antonio Carrillo, a most accomplished lawyer as well as military leader, when he was asked to aid a woman who was being hounded unmercifully in a financial way by a relative.

This resulted in one of the longest legal fights and strangest verdicts in law annals.

It all began long before José Antonio was born, in a situation involving Juan Valdez who was one of the soldiers under Portola. Valdez was marching along with the little band on the way from San Diego where the Spaniards had just arrived with Father Junipero Serra, to seek the famous port of Monterey to the north. On this particular day they were walking wearily through a country between hills, the old Indian Trail, later La Brea Trail, and still later Wilshire Boulevard. A great flat plain lay ahead of them. Beyond the plain was the Pacific Ocean.

This Valdez was a leather-jacket soldier who was quite alert and always on the lookout for the unusual in nature. Lifting his eyes now toward the hills on the right he saw the rounded crests seemingly melting into the brilliant blue of the sky.

On the hills, in addition to the vast masses of yellow from the flowers of the mustard, were great numbers of mountain lilac bushes. Valdez recognized the lilacs although it was too late in the summer for them to be in bloom. He thought the hills formed a beautiful spot to which he might like to return some day. That evening, as the weary men camped beside the springs of Saint Esteban, he approached Portola and asked whether he could make formal application for a land grant.

"What land is it that you want?" asked Portola somewhat brusquely because he had enough troubles on his mind without wishing to add to them.

"Over there," said Valdez simply, pointing to the hills now cloaked in shadows from the approaching night.

The next day the group continued on its way but Valdez could not get the vision of the beautiful land out of his mind. He served faithfully in the Spanish Army in this new land and then when it became possible for him to carry out his desire to own the spreading tract he did so. He made a formal application which was attested to by Don Gaspar and presented it to the Governor. Then he waited for the slow machinery of the Government to operate.

Finally to his great joy he was given a formal grant to the very hills where he had seen the innumerable lilac bushes.

These ceanothus plants burst into full bloom in many shades of lavender in the early spring of the year that Valdez took over the property. The land was marked off and surveyed in the crude manner of the period, with the use of a reata strung out behind a horse as a measuring device. The Spanish league, which is about three miles in modern terms, was used as the basis of measurement. The amount of land which Valdez actually acquired was about 4,000 acres. He moved onto it with his young wife from Sonora and they spent many happy years building up the property, constructing a home and stocking it with a modest number of cattle and horses.

The law provided that for a grant to be held it must be providing nourishment for at least 150 head of cattle. Sometimes Valdez had this many and sometimes he did not. Finally he grew old and died and so did his wife. The property was inherited by their daughter whose name was María Rita. María fell in love with a young man named Vicente Ferrar Villa who had come to California as a six-year-old boy from Mexico at about the time Los Angeles was being founded. María Rita and her husband occupied the ranch and tried to keep it going as a prosperous rancho. But they had difficulties. They found themselves with a large number of children and without enough cattle to meet the law requirements.

María Rita had changed the original name of the rancho, Rodeo de las Aguas which meant literally "The Roundup of the Waters" because of the fact that the turbulent floods which came down the canyons which now are known as Coldwater and Benedict flowed together on the property. She gave it the new name "San Antonio."

Their difficulties became acute and María Rita appealed to her kinsman Luciano Valdez who had been the schoolteacher in Los Angeles for several years. Luciano, who saw an opportunity to be included in a potentially fine piece of property, suggested that some cattle be obtained from the Mission San Gabriel which had more than it needed, so the required 150 head could be running on Rancho San Antonio.

The good padres at San Gabriel were glad enough to help out a deserving family and provided enough cattle so that a large drive was held and the cattle were taken around the base of the hills through the Verdugo Rancho, which is now Glendale, close to Los Angeles and to María Rita's spreading acres.

Luciano now decided that his kindly gesture should be rewarded in a more tangible fashion. He demanded a portion of the ranch. María Rita was grateful but she did not feel that her cousin deserved as much property as he was demanding. She objected to his demands and this touched off one of the longest feuds, both personal and legal, in the history of California up to that time.

Luciano made himself objectionable in every possible way, building a house so close to María Rita's that it shut off the view and in many other ways harassing her until she became desperate.

It was then that she enlisted the aid of José Antonio Carrillo, the most eloquent man in the Pueblo of Los Angeles and the most distinguished lawyer, and asked him to help her settle the difficulties with her unruly kinsman. Whatever there was in Southern California, José Antonio was it!

For an entire decade, then, the kindly José Antonio worked on the case, trying in every way to get it settled satisfactorily. Witnesses were heard and the whole history of the transaction was raked over again and again. Finally the time came for the verdict.

Ten full years had elapsed, much bitterness had been created, many people who had taken sides either with María Rita or Luciano refused to speak to one another when they met on the street, and all sorts of evil consequences had flowed from the struggle. José Antonio won a truly remarkable settlement. The verdict was for $17.50 American!

Upon payment of this, María Rita came into undisturbed possession of the great Rancho.

Once more she could sit in security with her husband and children on the front porch of their home and look out over the lowlands to the present Baldwin Hills across the area where the generous waters came together to form a great ciénaga where my father often went in later days to shoot ducks and geese. She enjoyed this tranquillity after all the trouble through which she had been to establish her title.

So, for many years she was able to continue in this happy condition, worrying no more about the past and unmindful of the future which was hidden from her by the mists of time.

Actually, if she had lived beyond the normal human span and been able to sit on her front porch a hundred years later she would have been able to look out and see, not the ciénaga where wild ducks and geese flew into the sky as the shots resounded, but rather a great boulevard crammed with honking automobiles and noisy buses and on the signposts marking that boulevard would have been the words "La Ciénaga," a thoroughfare of restaurants and fine shops known throughout the world.

And if she had cared to look close by she could have peered down into the magnificent gardens of the home which once had belonged to Wallace Beery, the actor. For the Rancho Rodeo de las Aguas, sometimes known as San Antonio, had been subdivided by a Boston syndicate and named for a little town in Massachusetts.

It was what we now call Beverly Hills.

And my kinsman, the good José Antonio, got not one acre of it for ten years of labor.

He *was* invited to a barbecue, though—I think!

CHAPTER 13

THE OWL WOMAN

In the days of his youth, my great-great-grandfather José Raimundo Carrillo was a mighty hunter.

He carried a shield made of a young bull's hide and with this in front of him, he approached even the fiercest animals, including the dreaded grizzly bear, for combat. He killed many a grizzly with a sword or knife while using the shield as his only protection. Such creatures as mountain lions and wild-cats he considered to be merely small game.

After his days of service as a leather-jacket soldier for the King of Spain in Alta California, he decided he wanted a rancho for himself where he could settle down and raise a family—the beautiful tree-studded area, near present day Santa Barbara, which he had seen on the way to Monterey with Portola and had already named, in his mind, "El Alisal."

Taking his horse and his musket, he started out on a leisurely trip along the coast and into the inland valleys to hunt and fish on his way to "El Alisal." One day, in the region of what is now Santa Monica, he began to see the tracks of a great number of mountain lions. The mountain lions were not new to José Raimundo but they were always good sport and he thought that the presence of so many must mean a lot of deer and other game in the area, so he decided to camp and see what he could find.

He stopped beside a rushing stream in a canyon which seemed to wind far inland; we now know it as Malibu Sequit Canyon. Great oaks and sycamores bordered the stream and there were many wild birds flying overhead as well as the sign of much game in the region.

José Raimundo took care of his horse and camped for the night. The next morning before it was light he started out on foot for a hunt. During the night he had heard the sounds of animals in the woods around him, the wailing of coyotes, and two or three times the screams of the mountain lions themselves.

He kept close to the stream and went inland, walking noiselessly along as all soldiers had learned to do in those days. As it began to get light he saw doves flying and heard the whir of quail wings in the chaparral.

The skies became lighter and lighter but, strain his eyes as much as he could, he did not see a single mountain lion. A number of deer were grazing on the hillside but José Raimundo was not in need of food at the moment and he did not shoot them. He did want the pelts of a couple of mountain lions for decorations in the home he planned to build so he kept on the lookout.

As he went along he suddenly thought that he saw in the dim light a human form in the shadows against the cliff-like bank of the canyon. But his eyes seemed to have deceived him for there was absolutely no sign of anything when he looked closely again.

He went on up the canyon, glorying in the beauties of the scenery as well as in the fun of the hunt. It was spring and the lilacs were in bloom in many shades of white, lavender and purple. The scent of wild flowers was in the air and on the hillside great masses of yellow mustard bloomed so that the slopes appeared to be painted with gold.

At last José Raimundo decided he was not going to find any mountain lions that morning and turned back. As he went along, noiselessly as a wildcat himself, he suddenly stopped and stepped behind a tree. He could hardly believe his eyes but there ahead of him was a human form straight out of the Stone Age.

A woman stood before a carefully-concealed entrance to a cave in the side of the canyon. By straining his eyes José Raimundo could see two babies playing on all fours and frolicking almost like kittens. They were stark naked. The woman wore a garment made of deerskin. Inside the entrance to the cave from the particular vantage point where he stood, José Raimundo could see a pile of goatskins that apparently served as a bed. Hanging by the cave entrance were a bow and a number of arrows. Beside these were a lance with a stone point and a crude implement which he thought must be used as an axe.

The woman was grinding acorns in a stone metate and in the nearby waters of the stream there were little sacks made of some kind of close woven fibre in which evidently the ground acorn meal was being leached; that is, the bitterness was being taken out as the water ran through the acorn meal submerged in the stream.

When José Raimundo stepped from behind the tree and started to go down the canyon the woman disappeared almost as if she had been swallowed up in the earth. She evidently was extremely agile and fearful of human beings. My great-great-grandfather did not wish to intrude upon her so he went back to his camping spot wondering about this strange female hermit in so isolated a region.

Most of the Indians of California seemed to prefer to live in groups if for no other reason than to share their misery. They were usually hungry and dirty and this seemed to give them the only common bond which they possessed. But José Raimundo had noticed that this woman and the babies appeared to be clean and that there was no sign of any man about the place or anyone at all, for that matter, living close by.

Later that day José Raimundo shot a deer and left a portion of the meat near the cave. The next morning he noticed that the meat was gone, the gift evidently having been accepted in the spirit it was intended. He remained in the neighborhood several days, intrigued by the mystery of this lonely woman and each day he left some little gift of meat close to the cave. Each time it was taken.

Finally on the fifth day José Raimundo was placing a gift of some tree squirrels on a rock near the stream when he glanced up and saw the woman close by looking at him. He was astounded at her appearance. Her eyes were large and round and the pupils were very large as if she were capable of seeing in the dark.

Involuntarily José Raimundo exclaimed: "La Lechuza—the owl woman!"

The woman gazed fixedly at him.

My great-great-grandfather bowed in courtly fashion and pointed to the squirrels. She nodded and came forward, apparently without any fear, to accept them. He saw that her hands were pliable and strong as if she were capable of any feat of strength. But the thing which attracted him most was those eyes, the unbelievable eyes with the tremendous pupils. She gazed at him without any fear now but after he had presented the squirrels he turned and went back to his camp. The next day, just to show her trust further, the woman brought her two little babies with her, both boys, and another child whom my great-great-grandfather had not seen up to this time, a boy about fifteen who had the same kind of eyes as his mother. The boy appeared more distrustful than the woman or the babies and refused to come close to José Raimundo. This boy carried a bow and arrow of his own and was dressed in a sort of G-string made of deerskin.

My great-great-grandfather was so impressed by all of this that he tried during the next few days to converse with the woman. It was impossible for him to understand her dialect. She spoke only a few halting words as if language were something foreign to her. She conveyed most of her meaning with gestures of her hands even when conversing with her own children.

Several times after that, during the night, José Raimundo saw two great shining eyes in the woods surrounding his camp. At first he thought they were the eyes of some wild animal. Then he realized they were those of La Lechuza herself.

"She has the eyes of an owl!" he said once more, crossing himself, and remembering the stories of witches and oracles from ancient times.

But the woman appeared to have no evil designs or any intention of using witchcraft to cast a spell on him. Actually, in a dignified manner, she once more indicated friendship the next time he encountered her with her children in the daytime.

By means of signs, she thanked him again for the meat he had left for her at the cave. She also gave a sign which he interpreted as the Indian equivalent of the Spanish phrase "Vaya con Dios," (Go with God), accompanying it with a gesture as if she were blessing her benefactor.

After ten days, José Raimundo decided he must proceed to his ranch site. He decided to reconnoiter from the top of the bluffs. He had not seen La Lechuza for a day or two but he had been so busy preparing some carne seca to carry on his horse as he journeyed toward the inland valleys that he had not paid any particular attention to her absence.

As he climbed the hill towards the crest he came into some heavy woods.

It had puzzled him all during his stay that he had not seen any of the mountain lions although the tracks had appeared in great numbers when he came into the region.

Now as he made his way into the oak forest his mind came back to this subject and he was more puzzled than ever about the absence of the mountain lions. He came out into the edge of a little glade near the top of the hill where apparently there were some springs. The grass was extremely green and the trees around the open space very large. As he came to the edge of the glade he suddenly saw a sight which almost paralyzed him. La Lechuza, carrying both babies in her arms, was walking down the path carrying some mountain fibres which she had gathered apparently for weaving. She was passing underneath one of the large oaks when suddenly, with a terrifying scream, a mountain lion leaped upon her back.

Instinctively she tossed the babies away from her onto the grass and they scrambled away as fast they could. She was pinned to the ground by the mountain lion which was clawing at her and trying to reach her throat for the kill. Just at this moment her son appeared and with a great leap, while José Raimundo also was rushing toward the scene, landed on the back of the mountain lion. With tremendous strength, the boy hooked his arm around the neck of the mountain lion and then with a bear grip pulled it off of his prostrate mother and wrestled with it on the ground.

José Raimundo was running uphill and he was afraid the boy was going to be killed before he could arrive.

But to his amazement, before his startled eyes, a fountain of blood shot up from the lion's neck and fell in a crimson spray on the bushes and grass and La Lechuza herself. The boy was hacking at the lion's neck and even as José Raimundo watched the lion began to grow limp in the boy's arms.

At this moment José Raimundo arrived but saw that there was no use to shoot the beast. It was near death, for a great stream of blood poured from the jagged gash in its neck.

The boy stood over it with what José Raimundo saw was a rusty piece of a Spanish sword, his only weapon.

In his excitement, José Raimundo found himself swearing great Spanish oaths at this incredible sight.

La Lechuza was crawling towards her son with blood running out of the wounds on her back but apparently not seriously injured. José Raimundo helped her to her feet and patted the boy on the head and said to him, "Muy hombre!"

He and the boy dressed the wounds of La Lechuza with herbs—yerba del golpe—found near the springs after washing them in the stream.

Then the Owl Woman gathered up her babies who had remained calmly on the grass during the whole frightful event, and she and her son started on down toward their cave again.

The whole thing had happened so suddenly José Raimundo was dumbfounded. He had seen a Stone Age boy with only a piece of rusty metal subdue a mountain lion before his eyes. It seemed as if the whole event must have happened in another era and in another world. But as he looked down the mountainside there indeed were La Lechuza with her two babies, and the boy supporting her as she went back to her lonely dwelling.

José Raimundo prepared to depart the next day.

As he led his horse up the canyon to start on his way towards the ranch of his dreams, "El Alisal" to the north, night was beginning to fall. His path led him by the cave.

He wished to find whether La Lechuza was recovering from the attack of the mountain lion. He stopped and peered.

It was very dark inside the cave. A fire was smouldering but it cast no light. At first José Raimundo could see nothing. Then the great shining eyes of La Lechuza became visible. They affected him strangely as always.

Involuntarily, he crossed himself again.

The fire flared up momentarily. He saw then, with the enormous eyes shining into his, that La Lechuza was smiling and that she was making the sign of good fortune and farewell. My great-great-grandfather went on, uplifted and full of faith. He felt sure now life would be good to him on his great land grant "El Alisal" because he had been given the blessing of the Owl Woman, La Lechuza, the cave dweller of California.

My father told me this story at the cave itself in Malibu Sequit Canyon when I was very small.

The Owl Woman lived not far from my present adobe home.

I think perhaps her spirit has blessed me, as she in person blessed my great-great-grandfather. At least I like to believe so and to express my thanks, too, to La Lechuza.

CHAPTER 14

ROMANCE OF A PIRATE

BUCCANEERS . . . . pirates . . . . marlin spikes . . . . shanghaiing . . . . cutlasses . . . . pillaging . . . . love . . . . romance . . . .

So goes the chronicle of the invasion of California by the doughty pirate with the splendid tongue-curling name, Captain Hippolyte Bouchard in the days of long ago. It was the first time a foreign foe ever set hostile foot upon these Western shores.

Legends have been built upon it. Let me tell you mine.

And, strangely enough, it all begins in Boston on the faraway New England coast. . . .

A young man was groping his way home through a blinding Atlantic fog. The crooked streets of Boston were engulfed in the mist. The young man, a science student and skilled in many trades, was thinking of his studies and the future he wished to build for himself as an engineer. He was moving along in the area close to the docks. Here and there yellow patches of light from lamps inside taverns and grog houses tried feebly to penerate the fog. Shouts of drunken sailors and the squeals and tipsy songs of women of the streets came to his ears. He was too engrossed in his own thoughts to pay much attention.

Suddenly, at a street corner, rough arms seized the young man, a cloth was flung over his head, and he felt himself choking from chloroform fumes which made him feel as if his head were going to burst. He lapsed almost instantly into unconsciousness. Three men picked him up and carried his limp form towards the docks.

When he regained consciousness he felt waves of nausea sweeping over him. His head hurt, his muscles felt cramped and sore. He tried to move his head and then winced and almost fainted as agonizing pains shot through his brain. In a moment he became aware of a motion beneath him. At first he thought it was merely the nausea giving him the impression of movement. Then he realized he must be on a ship. This was the unmistakable roll and toss of a vessel under sail.

The young man was right. He was on a vessel. He had been shanghaied for sea duty, as happened quite often in those days.

When he was routed out by fierce commands, some of them in Spanish, he began to realize the seriousness of his situation. He still was sick and weak but he was forced to go on duty. He found he was on board a vessel bound for Buenos Aires, Argentina. This was at a time—the year 1818—when the provinces of Spain in the New World were in revolt, both in South America and in Mexico. For eight years the series of revolutions had been underway. Buenos Aires was a kind of informal headquarters and outfitting point for all the insurgent forces.

The young engineer was a skilled seaman as well as a technical man. He had been aboard ships of his father and uncles ever since he was a child and the feel of the sea was in him. He was questioned by the captain of the vessel on which he had been shanghaied. It was at this time he discovered their destination of Buenos Aires and a little about his prospects for the future. He was ordered to prepare to be the second-mate of a privateering vessel which was to set forth in a few days.

When the vessel left Buenos Aires it was one of two heading for the Sandwich Islands in the Pacific. The craft were under the command of a skilled seaman indeed, Captain Hippolyte Bouchard, the Frenchman of whom I have spoken. One ship was the *Argentina* and the other the *Santa Rosa,* called respectively the "Fragata negra" and the "Fragata chica." Their objective, the young engineer learned from gossip among the other officers although he was never told anything directly, was an attack upon California and its seizure for the revolutionary forces.

California at this time still was under rule of Imperial Spain through the intermediary, Mexico. It is true that a revolt against Spain under the heroic priest, Hidalgo, had started in 1810 but by 1818 it was still four years short of success. So, nominally, California was still a Spanish province and fair prey for the privateers or pirates.

When Captain Bouchard and his two ships arrived at Honolulu in the Sandwich Islands they began to put on stores of all kinds for the trip across to the California coast. The young engineer from Boston was kept on board ship all the time under constant surveillance so he could not possibly escape. His seamanship had been duly reported to Capain Bouchard and the Captain determined not to lose so valuable a technical man in the project on which he was embarked.

It so happened that the American brig *Clarion* was in the port of Honolulu at the time Captain Bouchard's vessels were outfitted. The Captain of the *Clarion*, Henry Gyzelaar, who formerly had been on the American vessel, the *Lydia*, was a good friend of the Californians because he had been hospitably received there on previous voyages. Captain Gyzelaar learned everything that he could about the hostile intentions of Bouchard's men and then hastily sailed for Santa Barbara. He stretched every sail on the vessel and made the best time possible across the Pacific.

On October the sixth, 1818, he arrived at Santa Barbara and immediately gave the startling news to Commandant Guerra of the Port of Santa Barbara. Guerra went into action at once. He sent a correo violento—emergency dispatch rider—to Monterey and began to issue orders for the civilians in the Santa Barbara area and to the priests of the Southern Missions.

The dispatch riders, using relays of horses, reached Monterey in less than two days and reported the startling news to Governor Pablo Vicente de Sola. This touched off a chain reaction through all of California.

Governor Sola issued his orders swiftly and with evidence of great thought. Cavalrymen, artillerymen and militia were ordered to their places. Twenty-five lookouts were set up along the coast, preparations were made for the placing of food supplies at the interior missions so that the women and children could be evacuated quickly, and every possible precaution was taken.

For the first time, probably, on the American Continent in modern times medieval archers were mobilized on a large scale. The Indian bowmen, the neophytes of the missions, had been trained with their bows and arrows so that they formed regular companies. Now these archers were ordered on duty all along the coast, and the sight of bowmen alongside the Spanish soldiers with their guns and cannon formed one of the strangest contrasts ever seen on these shores.

Both the Governor and Commandant Guerra at Santa Barbara voiced defiance of the prospective invasion.

"Under the protection of the god of battles I believe I can destroy all such villains as may have the rashness to set foot upon this soil," announced Commandant Guerra.

At first the arrival of the pirates, or privateers, was expected within five or six days. Actually, a month went by without any signs of the expected vessels. Then, late in November, a lookout on Point Pinos near Monterey saw two strange craft under sail heading for the coast. The alarm was sounded and immediately the soldiers and archers assembled and the flight of the women and children began.

The next few days were bloody and frightening. Cannon battles took place between the vessels and the shore batteries at Monterey. The pirates finally swarmed into the town, burnt the Presidio and other buildings, killed cattle, seized provisions and ransacked homes. Everywhere was the sound of flames and the screams of the drunken sailors who had discovered the brandy hidden in the warehouses.

The archers with their bows and arrows never got a chance to fight the pirates. They were ordered to retreat when Bouchard's men swarmed ashore in overwhelming numbers.

On the ship the young Boston engineer—now let us call him the Young Pirate—looked with horror upon the sacking and burning of the city. Even amid the confusion and the firing, however, he was impressed by the beauty of the California scene. Within sight of the ships the beautiful hills, made green by the early fall rains, glistened in the sunlight. Placid cattle could be seen grazing even while the cannonading went on. The hills and valleys stretching in that beautiful emerald garb appealed to the sense of beauty of the sensitive young Bostonian.

In a few days Bouchard ordered his two vessels southward. He had heard of one of the great ranchos in California which reportedly was extremely rich with stores of gold and provisions and hides and cattle. He thought the seizure of this wealth might assist him in the over-all objective of taking over California for the insurgents.

In a few days the vessels anchored off shore opposite this beautiful Refugio Rancho, just north of Santa Barbara.

The Young Pirate now received a strange order.

He was ordered to go ashore in a boat with some of the men. This was the first time he had been allowed off the vessel since it left Buenos Aires. It seemed strange after having been so long aboard the pitching, rocking vessel, through storms around Cape Horn and across the mighty Pacific.

As the small boat was rowed toward the shore the Young Pirate looked fascinatedly at the magnificent scene before him, the green hills rising in successive rows, the innumerable cattle of all colors grazing in the grass and the yellow flowering mustard, the beautifully spaced groves of oaks and sycamores, with the blue skies forming a magnificent backdrop for the pastoral scene.

As the pirates stepped ashore they were unaware of the preparations made for their reception. Word, of course, had been sent by Governor Sola from Monterey and Commandant Guerra had made his preparations well. A young sergeant, Carlos Antonio Carrillo—my great-grandfather—with thirty men had been sent to lie in ambush near the Ortega Ranch because prisoners taken from the Bouchard ships at Monterey had indicated that it was to be one of the targets of attack.

These men sent out by Commandant Guerra under Sergeant Carrillo's command were hidden well in the peaceful countryside upon which the Young Pirate gazed with such admiration.

When the small boat was run up on the sand of the beach the officer in charge ordered the Young Pirate to remain with it. He and the rest of the men moved forward to reconnoiter the Refugio Ranch in preparation for the attack by a larger body of men.

The Young Pirate strolled along the beach looking at the countryside and speculating about what was happening to his pirate companions. Just then he heard pounding hoofs and looked up to see the pirates running towards the boat with horsemen twirling reatas about their heads in close pursuit. Most of the pirates succeeded in pushing the boat into the water and rowing away, but two were lassoed just as they were clambering into the boat.

Just at this moment the Young Pirate, who stood horrified by this sudden onrush of the horsemen, felt a sudden burning sensation on his arms and he was jerked off his feet. He realized dazedly he, too, had been lassoed. A horseman dragged him along the beach as the Californians yelled insults in Spanish at the retreating pirates.

The Young Pirate was jerked to his feet and still in the tight embrace of the loop around his arms was ordered in Spanish, and with gestures, to march inland. The reata was kept taut so that he was unable to move his arms and he went along at a half-run trying to keep from being pulled over and dragged by the horse. In this discomforting situation he was out of breath after the first quarter of a mile because of his long inactivity on the vessel. In a little meadow the Californianos dismounted and came up to surround him in a circle. He was almost too dazed to realize what was going on but he did notice that one of the vaqueros had roped a wild horse which was struggling against the rope around its neck.

He had learned enough Spanish while on board the vessel to hear a vaquero who was apparently in charge call out: "Bring him here."

The Young Pirate was pulled towards the struggling horse and in a momentary flash he realized what his fate was to be as he saw a short reata being tied around the tail of this wild mustang. The Young Pirate was trussed with a reata wrapped around and around his body. Then this reata was secured to the short one tied to the horse's tail, and the leader of the vaqueros prepared to give the order to turn the horse loose.

The Young Pirate's whole life seemed to flash before his eyes as he realized he was about to be dragged to death in a fashion of which he had heard but never believed. He thought again of his Boston home, of his mother and father, of his sisters, of the quiet streets, the Common, and all of the familiar sites of his childhood and young manhood. The voice of the chief vaquero was raised giving the order to liberate the horse.

Just at that moment a scream was heard.

A lovely girl with her long dark hair hanging about her shoulders ran forward calling out to the chief vaquero.

"Wait," cried the girl in a tone of authority. The vaqueros hesitated.

"Why do you wish to save this anemic thing?" asked the chief vaquero.

"What are you doing?" exclaimed the girl. "You must not kill him! I order you to stop this madness, Esperanza!"

"Sí, señorita Concepción," replied Esperanza, the leader of the vaqueros, suddenly emerging from the blood-thirsty state of mind in which he had been intending to kill the Young Pirate, and deferring now to the daughter of the owner of the great Refugio Rancho.

Almost unable to realize his miraculous good fortune, the Young Pirate looked with gratitude and admiration at the beautiful young woman who stood before him. She touched his hand, pointed inland toward the old adobe house visible behind venerable trees and asked in her beautiful low voice in Spanish, "Are you able to walk?"

"Sí," replied the Young Pirate, stretching his arms as the reata was removed. He moved forward, tottering and forcing one foot after the other because he was weak and shaken from his close brush with death. The girl watched him carefully as they moved towards the house. She spoke to him again asking him if he felt all right and he replied that he did.

The Young Pirate didn't know what to expect when they reached the house. He remained dazed and groggy from his experience, almost unable to believe this beautiful girl was by his side, tenderly assisting him.

He took a few deep breaths, tried to walk proudly like a man as he entered the gracious adobe home.

The whole family was there—the father, the mother, brothers, sisters, servants who had been prepared to fight off the attack of the buccaneers.

Gravely, but with complete courtesy, the father greeted the Young Pirate. Evidently judgment was being withheld until he could offer explanations.

Concepción herself directed the preparations for his comfort. He was taken to a lovely room, provided with hot water and soap, clean clothing of the California type, boots and even a flat-crowned hat. He was given food and the ruby wine of the rancho. He bathed, shaved, combed his hair, put on the fine clothing. Then he went to face his hosts—or captors.

He showed the scar from the marlin spike blow when he was shanghaied in the Boston fog. He told his story. He was believed.

"We need engineers in our new land to build mills and aqueducts and ships and roads," said the father, offering his hand. The Young Pirate shook hands with everybody.

Concepción let her hand linger in his for a fleeting moment, but it was long enough.

He looked deep into her lovely eyes. She looked trustingly into his.

What do you think, amigos?

Of course they fell in love.

The Young Pirate stayed. He married Concepción.

And he blessed the night he was struck on the head in Boston—the strange prelude to California, romance, and bliss. . . . .

CHAPTER 15

BLACKBIRDS OF THE TEMESCAL

W**HEN** I sit in my oficina, a part of the rambling adobe home nestled against the hills I love, tranquillity seems to flow around the house, almost as tangibly as the little stream tinkling in the arroyo below. I am never lonesome because of the voices of nature talking to me.

The occasional thump of an avocado falling off the tree sounds on the roof over my head.

Out of the window I can see giant golden delicacies like oversized grapes against a little building containing possibly the finest collection of Early American glass in this country gathered by my wife Edith and daughter Antoinette from Cape Cod and other parts of the nation. These "over-sized grapes," of course, are naval oranges. Besides the orange trees are date palms with their long fronds waving gentle salutes in the breeze. And always the tall sycamores, native of this canyon, stand in their majestic proportions as if they realized the lordly role they fill in the arboreal world. Giant Luther Burbank cactus, without thorns, are here too, so smooth you could run through them in a bathing suit without looking like a porcupine.

Banty chickens with their new babies run around grubbing for worms, the dogs lie dozing in the sun and occasionally there comes the shrill cry of a peacock from out near the adobe barn.

This is a tranquillity I enjoy.

But it did not always exist at this spot.

The lower portion of Santa Monica Canyon, in fact, was the nesting place at one time of evil characters. Here were all sorts of dens of iniquity scattered among the beautiful trees; saloons, houses of prostitution, dance halls, beer gardens. It was such a tough area that the more sedate citizens in nearby Santa Monica and on the surrounding ranches said that, just as was true around the Plaza at Los Angeles, "they had a man for breakfast every Sunday morning." It certainly was a fact that many times bodies were found slumped beside the trunks of the sycamores or even in some instances dangling by a rope from the limbs of an oak tree where unknown characters had taken care of a horse thief or a murderer.

Drunken parties went on every weekend. A wild steer would be lassoed by the young fellows, killed and cooked in the blazing barbecue pits all the same day. The vaqueros would drink the blood of the steer to impress the señoritas, and supposedly to add to their manhood.

One of the characters, Alejandro, got drunk on dago red, interrupted a card game and one of the players slapped him so hard he was knocked to the ground. Alejandro jumped up drew his revolver and killed the gambler on the spot. Alejandro resided in San Quentin a long time after that although he was lucky and did not get the noose, but he was lonely because he was a great rider and couldn't get his horse in the little cell.

Down by what is now Brentwood a lot of irate ranchers hanged an Indian from a sycamore tree and let his body stay there until the buzzards picked the bones clean so it would be an example to the children not to steal.

The very worst criminals of all, though, who lived near here were two blue-black Indians who were such desperate characters that the law officers seemed to be afraid to invade their hideout. These Indians were known as "The Blackbirds of the Temescal." The Temescal was a canyon in a wild and wooded area which we know today as Pacific Palisades, and the Blackbirds operated on the site of what is now a Methodist meeting place.

These "Chanates del Temescal" became so daring that every decent person was in terror of them. They were guilty of murder, horse thievery, rape, and every crime on the list.

Near this site there lived at the time of which I want to tell a respectable family of considerable wealth. The family loved its horses, its spreading lands, the games in which the young people indulged, the balls and fandangos held at the ranch house. Yet, as happens sometimes in the most select families, one of the young men of this clan, who had been a friend of Alejandro, was inclined to wild and wicked ways. Finally his escapades grew so serious that they were climaxed by a charge of murder. The family was shocked but even its influence could not save its young member from being apprehended.

He was taken to Los Angeles and put in the jail in the old Bullard block, and a heavy ball and chain was riveted to one of his ankles.

This was the jail where justice was administered quite simply by putting a condemned horse thief or murderer on a carreta with a rope around his neck, and then driving it out from under him so that he was left dangling to choke to death. The new prisoner was thankful he was not under sentence of execution.

In the adobe cell he was not allowed to languish to any noticeable extent. He had special privileges which were afforded by the jail in return for cash payments surreptitiously slipped to the jailer, but there were other privileges which even the jailer did not know about.

Of course, the jailer did see the masses of flowers which were sent to the young man by admiring damsels of Los Angeles who caught a glimpse of the handsome prisoner through the prison bars. Sometimes his cell was so loaded with these offerings from the beauties of the town that he seemed to be more a guest of honor than a suspected criminal. The place looked like the site of a gangster's funeral.

The thing which the jailer did not know was that the magnetism and personality of the young man had exerted itself on someone besides the señoritas of the town. The jailer's wife herself had been smitten by the charms of the wealthy prisoner who bore such a proud name. The young man was no fool, and he made every effort to capitalize on this prospective conquest which he sensed from certain coquettish glances and from the particularly generous portions of tasty dishes which she cooked for him.

The affair proceeded to the point where the wife agreed to elope with the prisoner. As a prelude she obtained a pair of revolvers from the jailer's private arsenal and slipped them to the prisoner. Then one day when the moment had arrived she put knock-out drops in the coffee of her husband. As soon as he lapsed into unconsciousness she obtained his keys, unlocked the door of the prisoners' cell, and opened the other doors of the jail so that they were free to slip out the back.

She had obtained a horse ready-saddled for the occasion and she assisted her lover to mount as he was handicapped somewhat by the ball and chain, and then she too got on the horse and they galloped away.

The open-mouthed citizens of Los Angeles were astonished to see this strange apparition of a speeding horse with the prisoner holding the ball and chain with one hand and the woman with the other.

The pair fled along the old Indian trail—now Wilshire Boulevard—to the area of what later became the Doheny Ranch in the vicinity of my own home. There, hidden in the thick woods of this region, they panned enough gold from the granite sands of the creek to buy a meager amount of frijoles and tortillas which the woman bought under cover of darkness at little tiendas on the edge of Santa Monica.

Manuel, the prisoner, was greatly feared by the law officers. He was known to be a fine shot and to be utterly contemptuous of human life. He also was an expert with the knife, a weapon much favored by the Spanish race and was reputed to be able to pin a butterfly to a tree at a distance of 15 feet. This kind of reputation naturally caused hesitation among the authorities in attempting to recapture so notorious a character.

Manuel and his paramour lived in a primitive shelter, ate their frijoles and tortillas and he dragged the ball and chain with him wherever he went. He was always armed with the two revolvers and a long-bladed knife which he was ready to use at a moment's notice.

It was becoming a disgrace that Manuel and the Blackbirds all were defying the law.

The officers would have liked to take the Blackbirds in particular but it was too scary an undertaking to invade the hideout in the Temescal.

In the Pueblo of Los Angeles, however, there lived a smart man. I have heard that it was one of my great uncles, but on this point I am not sure. It sounds as if what was proposed might have been one of his ideas. At any rate, word was sent to Manuel offering a "deal." Manuel was pretty tired by this time of carrying around the ball and chain and he yearned to be more active. But he lacked the necessary equipment to file off his iron attachments.

Maybe, too, he would have liked to go down to the tiendas for tortillas himself, and have a glass of tequila with the boys.

The "deal" was that if Manuel would "take care" of the "Blackbirds of the Temescal" he would be given a pardon, all charges would be dropped against him, he would be freed, and the jailer would get a divorce so Manuel and his girl friend could be properly married and quit scandalizing the neighborhood with the prospect of a lot of little illegitimate Manuels.

Manuel thought it over carefully. He at first feared a trick, but he really loved the jailer's wife and a written offer was sent to him—in diplomatic language, of course, about what he was supposed to do to the Blackbirds—yet it was sufficiently clear to remove his suspicions.

He agreed. "Bueno," he said.

A man was sent up with a file, a horse, a rifle and plenty of ammunition.

The man filed and filed and at last the shackles fell off and Manuel was able for the first time in months to move without dragging the weight after him. He jumped around for sheer joy at first, waving his leg like an adagio dancer.

"Here is the rifle," said the man as he prepared to leave.

Manuel took the rifle, mounted his new horse and started for the Temescal.

The Indians saw Manuel coming but they knew he had been in trouble with the law too and they figured they might team up with him. Three outlaws are better than two.

When Manuel got to their camp he suggested a deer hunt.

The Indians, complimented by having so notorious a character join them, readily agreed. They set out up the mountain.

Soon, two shots sounded. But when Manuel returned he carried no deer. He did look satisfied, though.

And what became of the bodies of the Blackbirds of the Temescal?

I used to ask my father this question when he told me the story.

"My son," he replied, "the 'Blackbirds' were taken care of by superior birds. We had those great vultures, the California condors in our canyons then. For days we saw them hovering over the mountainside where Manuel went 'deer hunting.'"

CHAPTER 16

AN ELOPEMENT SECRET

Now is the time, I have decided, to tell the secret of the most beautiful Carrillo señorita in the history of our family in California. This secret has been guarded in my family for almost a century and a half but I feel no harm can be done by divulging it now, since the sentimental statute of limitations has run out.

She was Josefa Carrillo, daughter of Don Joaquín and Doña María Ignacia Carrillo, of the admirable city of San Diego, first spot in California on which the foot of civilized man was set in the settlement of this remote province. The essential fact which I am now about to tell does not take away in any degree from the romance of the story which has come to be known as the most famous elopement in the history of California.

It all happened because a Governor became lovesick like a youth in his teens. He had ants in his pantalónes.

The Governor bore a name almost too heavy for his puny frame to carry —His Excellency Don José María Echeandia. He was appointed ruler of Alta California by the officials in Mexico City who were never too worried about how things turned out in the distant province and were not too careful in their selection of governors.

The capital of California at that time was Monterey and Governor Echeandia went there. But on the way something disturbing happened. He met a vision of loveliness in the old town of San Diego.

In San Diego there were comfortable homes with red-tiled roofs clustered around the Plaza and there was a semblance of high society as the Bandinis, Carrillos and the Estudillos and other notable families indulged in fiestas, bailes, fandangos, and tertulias to the music of square rosewood pianos, violins, and guitars imported from Spain.

The most beautiful woman the Governor had ever seen was Señorita Josefa Carrillo. He had met her at a party and was smitten at once.

Her flashing dark eyes, the laughing mouth with the full red lips so inviting to look upon, the tender oval of her face, the raven hair, all bewitched the new Governor and made him neglect his official duties so he could spend more time in the pursuits of Cupid.

Monterey did not appeal to him at all. The fogs came in and the attempts of the local people to beguile the Governor with parties and bailes proved unsuccessful. His thoughts were elsewhere. He made a decision. He would transfer the capital to San Diego.

Of course, Don Joaquín and his wife considered it an honor for their daughter to be courted by a Governor, even if he looked like a shrunken version of a modern method actor. He probably weighed 123 pounds with rocks in his pockets. His features were pointed and, in general, he made a very bad impression upon everyone except other politicians who were seeking favors from him.

He fancied himself as a Beau Brummel and a glamour boy and dressed in the height of fashion as news came through from Mexico City of the latest styles there and in Spain. When he arrived in San Diego Governor Echeandia pretended to have a terrible cough. He would suffer coughing spells whenever he thought of it. Sometimes, though, his memory was so bad that he forgot for a long period and then would force himself into an unusually severe fit so as to make good on his excuse that the damp climate of Monterey had forced him to bring the capital to San Diego. The northern people continued to be furious at him for abandoning the proverbial capital of California, but this meant little to him because communication was so slow he really received very little word, good or bad, from Monterey.

Anyway, he was so busy courting Josefa, who was the Marilyn Monroe of her day without the calendar, that he had little time to think about political affairs. The Governor's courtship was the sensation of California.

The sight of this thin little squirt out singing love songs in the streets before dawn under the window of his beloved Josefa set tongues wagging from San Diego to Sonoma.

Many people chuckled at the Governor's plight.

"He is like the little paisano who said about his sweetheart, 'She has eyes like soft-boiled eggs turned upside down floating in olive oil,'" laughed Pío Pico, Josefa's rollicking cousin.

All the Carrillo clan eagerly awaited the latest developments in this affair. Everyone knew that a legend was in the making and wanted to be in on every possible detail as it happened.

I can remember myself, as a child, hearing the story told over and over again whenever my relatives got together, as they did so often in family gatherings. It became a part of my inheritance to hear about this famous love affair and even as a child I was fascinated by the romance of my great-great-great-Aunt and her strange little hummingbird lover. I shouldn't use the word "lover" because Josefa refused to take the Governor seriously.

This was something of a trial to her father and mother although Don Joaquín was not the foot-stamping, ranting type as some fathers of Spanish blood of that period were.

In fact, Don Joaquín rather fancied himself as a diplomat. When the Governor's suit seemed to be approaching the serious stage, Don Joaquín spent all his time trying to think up some way to influence his daughter in behalf of this splendid match without absolutely ordering her to be married.

Whenever her parents attempted to talk to Josefa about the Governor she giggled and made some irreverent remark which shocked her mother and convinced her father more and more that he must take some action soon to set the path of love on the true course.

"I could never love a funny, ugly little Bantam rooster of a man like that!" Josefa exclaimed. "He makes me want to laugh at him. I am willing to wait a long time for the man I can truly love. He must be somewhere and I'm not going to marry someone that I could never care for."

Marriages were mostly "by arrangement" in those days as they had been for so many centuries in the best families of Spain and Mexico. It was almost unheard of for a young girl to be so outspoken in her opposition to her parents' choice, particularly when it involved the Governor of the entire province.

"Why do you have to be so obstinate, my daughter?" asked Doña María Ignacia. "You must realize the wonderful time you would have—a fine carriage, servants, a loving husband, and think of what it would mean to your father and me."

"But you and Papa are not marrying the Governor," replied Josefa as she prepared one day to go out with her cousin, Don Pío, one of the young dandies of the town.

Sadly shaking her head, Doña María Ignacia watched her daughter go out into the sunshine and then she herself retired to her bedroom where she wept bitter tears over the stubbornness of young girls.

When Don Joaquín was told that evening by his wife of the absolute refusal of Josefa even to consider Governor Echeandia, Don Joaquín decided the time had come for action. A plan had been forming in his mind and now was the moment to put it into execution.

That very day there had anchored in San Diego Harbor one of the magnificent clipper ships from Boston fitted out as a traveling department store. The *María Esta* was ready to trade with the townspeople. This always was an event because it gave the women the opportunity to look at the beautiful items which the sea captains had brought with them not only from Boston but from the ports of South America, Mexico, the Sandwich Islands, China and the Philippines.

Don Joaquín said casually to his daughter, "We are having a tertulia, you know, and I am to play the violin. It will be one of our finest parties. The Governor and his staff and all the rancheros from miles around will be here. Don't you think, my daughter, that you should have a new dress for the occasion? If so, why not go out to the *María Esta* and buy the finest silk one you can find?"

It was a summer day when Josefa set out shopping. The brilliant sun shone down on the blue expanse of San Diego Bay and was reflected off the white walls of the Mission Church on the hill above Old Town.

In the lowlands, Indians worked in the fields and on the hills the cattle of the rancheros grazed in the high grass and mustard stalks.

Riding quietly at anchor, the *María Esta* presented a busy scene. Rowboats were plying back and forth to the vessel carrying all the leading women of the area to look over the splendid cargo aboard. Each one wanted some particular thing—a new piano, beautiful pre-Victorian furniture from Boston, shawls from China, serapes from Mexico, the great pearls of the Sea of Cortez, Chinese silks and all the luxuries for house and table including even shiny tin pans which formed almost as much of an attraction as the dresses themselves.

Don Pío Pico, resplendent in his California caballero's garb, proudly escorted his cousin out to the ship. He helped her up the ladder and then stood by as she looked around in wonder and astonishment, her eyes sparkling and the color in her cheeks mounting as she saw the beautiful objects displayed before her in the Saks Fifth Avenue of her time. It was her first experience as a buyer on one of the great ships, her mother always before having made whatever purchases were needed for the family. As she stood looking at the dresses displayed on racks as if in a store, she became aware that someone was looking at her.

She turned and looked into the violet eyes of Captain Henry Delano Fitch of Massachusetts, who sailed out of New Bedford in this splendid clipper ship over which he had command.

The Captain caught his breath as he looked into the dark luminous depths of the black eyes of Señorita Josefa.

Impulsively, when they were introduced by Don Pío, Captain Fitch took the small hand of the girl in his and continued staring into her eyes as they stood, without saying a word, on the deck in view of all the townspeople who had stopped their shopping to watch the little tableau.

In a moment, trying to regain the proprieties, Josefa withdrew her hand but her cheeks were scarlet now and she smiled shyly as the Captain spoke to her.

"What is it that you would desire, señorita?" he asked in Spanish. "I hope we have something aboard worthy of you."

Josefa was too overcome by the strange sensation which had gripped her heart to decide upon any of the beautiful objects shown her by the Captain. Her mind was in a whirl. All she could think about was the handsomeness of the young man with ojos violados, his air of splendid independence, and the admiring glances which he apparently was unable to keep from casting in her direction.

The sun continued to illuminate the polished decks and all the gay array of clothing and luxuries but, after a few minutes, neither one of the young people paid any further attention to the pretense of the shopping tour. They stood by the rail, side by side, and looked out over the sparkling water toward the beautiful hills, Point Loma. The murmur of conversation from the shoppers came to them but they were unaware of it. They talked of the Captain's voyages, of his parents far away in New Bedford, of the strange ports he had visited, and the hopes he had for building up a whole trading fleet of his own. His tongue seemed loosened by the presence of the gorgeous young woman by his side and he talked on dreamily, hoping that she would remain on board as long as possible.

Josefa, herself, once they were virtually alone at the rail told him of her sheltered life, of the fiestas when the creaking carretas came in with their shouting, laughing cargoes of young people from the rancheros, of the gay dances in the moonlight, the guitar music, the castanets, and the odor of night-blooming jasmine in the air so heavy it was almost intoxicating. He listened raptly to every word she said, gazing at the animation of her features, her even white teeth, the color which still lingered in her cheeks, the gloss of her black hair, the swelling curve of her bosom under her modest dress, the little feet almost hidden beneath the many folds of the long skirts.

Captain Henry Fitch had never felt like this before. Suddenly he turned and gazed intently at the San Diego shore and said to Josefa, "Who is the sneaky little fellow peering out here with the spyglass?"

Josefa, coming momentarily out of the dreamy languor into which she had plunged at the first sight of the young captain, looked closely, and smiled.

"That is my suitor, His Excellency the Governor of California," she said demurely. "My father and mother are giving a tertulia for him in three days."

"He's nothing but a little runt," exclaimed Captain Fitch contemptuously. "Do you love him?"

"No," she said, "but it is necessary for me to be present at the party or there will be a great scandal." Then she added hastily, "Would you care to come to the party, Captain Fitch?"

Captain Fitch in turn looked deep into her eyes.

"I will be there," he said quietly.

I remember that as a child when the story reached this point my excitement always would be at fever pitch imagining the meeting of Captain Fitch who had fallen so suddenly in love with Josefa, and his rival, the little Governor of California. The unfolding of the story always was new and fresh to me no matter how many times I had heard it, just as children listen over and over again to nursery rhymes and stories which they already know by heart.

And if San Diego had been scandalized by the sight of the Governor serenading Josefa in the moonlight, it was going to be scandalized a lot more by what happened in the next few weeks.

This period ever afterward seemed like a dream to Josefa and to young Captain Fitch; sometimes a beautiful dream, sometimes a nightmare.

During the few days between their meeting and the tertulia Josefa and the young sea captain fell more and more in love. It would have been unseemly for Josefa to repeat her visit to the ship but there was nothing to prevent Captain Fitch from coming ashore. He seemed to find compelling reasons every day and evening to row to San Diego. Although he did not have the ability to sing beneath the window as Governor Echeandia had done, he still made it plain in many ways where his affections lay.

Sea captains mingled with the elite of the town, of course, and naturally Don Joaquín became acquainted with Captain Fitch. The father of Josefa was compelled to admit that the young Captain was a fine upstanding figure of a man but still there were all the other considerations which entered into the matter.

The alliance with Governor Echeandia would mean tremendous social and political power for the Carrillo family. This was not something to be dismissed lightly. Then, too, it was against the law for a California girl to marry a foreigner or a non-Catholic. Captain Fitch was a transgressor both ways.

So Don Joaquín was carefully polite to Captain Fitch but went no further than that.

Governor Echeandia, humiliated and angry, did everything he could to embarrass Captain Fitch. The Governor talked to Don Joaquín and made it plain that any attempt on the part of the Captain to make a serious matter out of his casual acquaintance with Josefa would result in the most serious complications and that he, as the Governor, certainly could not take part in such an illegal procedure as to permit a union of a Yankee and a Protestant with the beautiful Josefa.

On the evening of the tertulia, flares lighted the way of the guests through the patio of the Carrillo home into the grand sala where the festivities were to take place. Don Joaquín had been tuning his violin all day and was ready to give the greatest concert of his career. He hoped that perhaps the influence of sentimental music might make the stubborn Josefa change her mind at the last minute and permit the engagement to the Governor to be announced. Doña María Ignacia guided the group of Indian servants in preparing the greatest feast she could think of, in the hope of creating such an atmosphere of happiness and well-being that Josefa would give up her stubborn ways. Great haunches of beef were being barbecued outdoors, and inside the cocina the smell of chilis, roast pig, kid and lamb mingled with the sounds of the tapping of fresh tortillas as a whole corps of young girls prepared the masa for the final cooking on the heated iron.

Flowers bedecked the sala, candles gleamed softly on the old silver and the beautiful linen of the table. The rosewood grand piano in the corner shone with the patina of age and was ready to join its dulcet tones with the violin of Don Joaquín when the proper moment came.

All of San Diego was agog over the tertulia. It was rumored that Captain Fitch had been given an invitation at the insistence of Josefa, and everyone wondered whether he would have the temerity to respond and actually appear in person.

The Governor was dressing in his most fashionable clothes, spraying perfume on himself and kicking his servants for not polishing his boots properly as he, too, prepared for the supreme moment in the romantic duel with his young upstart rival.

When the party started, Josefa quickly took care of everything. Young Captain Fitch was among the first arrivals, coming in just late enough not to seem too eager and yet early enough to show his appreciation for having been invited. Don Joaquín and Doña María Ignacia greeted him with smiles and polite phrases but the Captain was keen enough to see the worry in their eyes. As yet the Governor had not appeared and, as the sala filled up, everyone present began to await the entrance of His Excellency.

Finally he did appear. If it had been medieval times he probably would have come in with the sound of trumpets and pages carrying the long train of his royal robes, but as it was he came in and divested himself of his long cape with such flourish and such disdain for the servants who took it that he gave the impression of a reigning monarch instead of the mere appointed governor of a distant province of Mexico.

As the music for the first dances, the violins and guitars began to be heard, Captain Fitch presented himself before Josefa and asked her permission to be her partner. She accepted at once, the color rising in her cheeks, setting off the beauty of her features and the exquisite dress and the necklace of pearls which she wore.

The Governor glowered as he stood talking to Don Joaquín and his wife, but he did not deign to glance in the direction of Josefa and the Captain.

All evening the scandalous event went on. Josefa was openly defying her parents and making sport of the Governor as she danced time and again with

Captain Fitch. The Captain himself was trying not to appear contemptuous and smug. He was simply a young man deeply in love, and to many of the townspeople this became apparent. His conduct, even though he did continue to dance with Josefa, was so faultless that by the time midnight came he had won the tacit support of many of the women in the room and even some of the older men who normally would have sided with parental authority in such a situation. When the tertulia was over and the couples dispersed into the night and the families made their way homeward, it was generally agreed that the Governor had lost the contest and that Josefa would never be his.

The next few weeks continued to be a dream to both Josefa and Captain Fitch. A few days after the tertulia Captain Fitch formally asked for the hand of Josefa. The parents were polite but pointed to the law of California which forbade such a marriage.

"I can take care of that," said Captain Fitch. "I can apply for Mexican citizenship and become a Catholic. We people of the sea don't have much time for religious services but any religion which pleases Josefa would please me."

The parents were more reasonable than most and finally agreed to permit Captain Fitch to be baptized as a prelude to a more definite understanding about matrimony. A kindly Dominican Friar was living in San Diego at this time and he agreed to perform the baptism. The Franciscans who had settled California and were considered its spiritual godfathers held aloof, but the Dominican was touched by the obviously genuine affection of the young pair and it was this which influenced him to go as far as he could to help in the situation.

The baptism took place at the Chapel of San Diego.

So anxious was the young couple to be married that it was agreed the ceremony would be performed the next evening at the Carrillo house.

Never was there such confusion and bustling and hurrying as went on the next day. The servants all joined in the excitement and Josefa herself seemed to be the only calm person in the entire household. She was so happy she was unworried about details or the little trivialities which were so important to her parents. It was decided that because of the embarrassing situation regarding the Governor there would be no large ceremony but only a few members of the family present. Captain Fitch's full name had been Henry Delano Fitch, but when he was baptized he was given the name Enrique-Domingo Fitch, the Domingo being used because Domingo Carrillo, uncle of Josefa, was going to be one of the principal witnesses at the marriage.

That evening the family assembled in the sala: the servants and everyone connected with the establishment, Captain Richard Barry of the Boston clipper ship *Vulture* which also was in the Harbor, young Pío Pico who had introduced the lovers, and Maximilian Bernstein, not a Spanish relative but a family friend.

Padre Menendez was standing ready to pronounce the wedding ceremony but Domingo Carrillo was late. Finally he came in. He looked extremely agitated.

"We are ready to proceed," said Don Joaquín.

"I cannot do it," stammered Don Domingo. He looked so pale and frightened that Don Joaquín at once suspected he had been threatened by the Governor. Padre Menendez stood irresolutely for a few minutes amid the confusion. Josefa burst into tears. Fitch lost his self control and demanded angrily why he was being discriminated against in this fashion. In the meantime Don Domingo slipped away and it was impossible to proceed with the ceremony.

The kindly priest blessed the distracted young pair and himself went away, shaking his head in sorrow.

In a few minutes Captain Fitch led Josefa outside and in the silent patio they sat on a bench with the almost overpowering odor of night-blooming jasmine about them. It could have been the lovely fragrance which blessed their marriage but as it was it seemed merely to mock them in their despair.

They talked in low tones for awhile and then Fitch went determinedly into the house and motioned to young Pío Pico to come outside. The three young people talked in whispers and then Fitch led Josefa to the door, kissed her tenderly goodnight, and went out through the silent deserted patio and the gate into the street.

Don Joaquín and his wife were so upset that they retired to their room to talk over the whole situation and try to arrive at a solution.

Silence descended upon the house, all the lights were extinguished, and even the night itself seemed to brood over the sorrowful affair.

Just before dawn the figure of a man slipped silently into the patio. Out from the door came Josefa muffled in a long black coat with a black rebozo over her head. With her she carried a tiny traveling bag.

Without a word, the man led her outside where a horse was waiting. He ,ed the horse down the road for several hundred feet remaining in the shadows as much as possible. Then he assisted Josefa to mount and got on the horse himself. They rode to the harbor where in the blackness a boat was waiting, only faintly illuminated by the small shining wavelets on the beach. Captain Fitch rushed forward and took Josefa in his arms and they clung to one another. Then he picked her up gently and carried her into the boat. He shook hands with Pío Pico and the boat silently pulled away heading not for the *María Esta* but for the *Vulture* of Captain Barry. Immediately and as silently as possible the *Vulture* got under way. She slipped out of the harbor entrance and headed south.

At the rail stood Josefa and Captain Fitch looking back at the dark town. Only one or two pinpoints of light showed. Captain Fitch put his arm around Josefa's shoulder and she nestled close to him.

"My ship is well taken care of," he told her. "I have put the first mate in charge and we will return with another vessel later."

The next morning the discovery of the scandalous departure prostrated Doña María Ignacia. Vainly Don Joaquín tried to comfort her although he himself was stricken. It was the most shameful thing that could happen to a California family to have a daughter run away with a foreigner, a cursed Yankee.

Doña María Ignacia went into mourning as if her daughter were dead and refused for many weeks even to leave the house. San Diego and, indeed, all of California were shaken by the event. The Governor raged mightily but there was nothing that could be done. The *Vulture* had disappeared into the vastness of the Pacific and no one knew where it was headed. Captain Fitch's own vessel, the *María Esta*, also sailed away under command of the first mate.

A year elapsed with no word of the lovers. Then one bright day the vessel *Leonor* appeared at San Diego. On board were Captain Fitch and his wife Josefa and a tiny infant son.

The family of Josefa consented to see her but the meeting was strained and awkward. The mother, Doña María Ignacia, was still so ashamed of what had happened that she could hardly face her daughter. Don Joaquín was more tolerant but he too felt keenly about the whole affair because he had been shunned by all of the Governor's followers and even by some of his own friends.

Josefa and her husband remained only a few days in San Diego and then sailed on up the coast. By this time Governor Echeandia, of course, had heard the news and he began to prove how long was his memory and how deep his revenge.

The Governor worked closely with Padre Sanchez at San Gabriel Mission, Vicar and ecclesiastical judge of the whole territory. Orders were issued for the arrest of Captain Fitch on charges of abduction and on other serious counts. He was arrested and placed in a cell at San Gabriel Mission. Josefa and her baby were left stranded in Monterey. Finally, though, Josefa was permitted to go to San Gabriel for the trial.

She was placed in the care of Eulalia Perez, the famous and kindly old woman who looked after the Mission of San Gabriel but Josefa was not permitted at first to see her husband.

Then Josefa and Captain Fitch were questioned at length before the ecclesiastical court. Arguments flowed back and forth, there were reams of Latin tomes read into the record and all sorts of charges made.

Captain Fitch pleaded eloquently for the marriage of himself and his wife which had been performed at Valparaiso, Chile by Curate Orrego, with Captain Barry of the *Vulture* as one of the witnesses. He particularly urged the recognition of the legitimacy of the baby son. There could be no doubt about the authenticity of the marriage certificate, but this did not satisfy the court completely.

Scandal had rocked California. A foreigner had sailed away with one of the most beautiful women of the province in defiance of the law and the court was determined to do something about it.

Finally, after more than a month, Padre Sanchez rendered the verdict. He recognized the validity of the marriage certificate but set up a number of punishments anyway. He ordered that the pair go to the Mission Chapel the following Sunday and receive the Sacraments which he said should have preceded the marriage ceremony. He also ordered that they should go to church with lighted candles in their hands for High Mass on three festival days and also recite for thirty days, one-third of the rosary.

Most important of all, in his written sentence he provided that:

"Yet, considering the great scandal which Don Enrique has caused in this province, I condemn him to give as a penance and reparation a bell of at least 50 pounds in weight for the church at El Pueblo de Nuestra Señora la Reina de Los Angeles de Porciuncula which barely has a borrowed one."

After making all of these pronouncements, the Padre freed both Captain Fitch and Josefa and they were joyously reunited. Captain Fitch had not seen the baby for so many weeks that he was astounded to see how much he had grown.

As soon as he could arrange it, Captain Fitch bought the bell for the Church in Los Angeles.

It was this identical bell which tolled joyously at the wedding ceremony of my parents and also on the occasion of my own baptism in the little Plaza Church.

Shortly after the bell was installed, Captain Fitch asked permission for a consultation with Don Joaquín and Doña María Ignacia, in private. They went into the sala of the San Diego home in formal silence. Josefa and the baby remained outside. They talked for a long time.

It was noted that when Doña María Ignacia and Don Joaquín came out it was as if a great burden had been lifted from their shoulders. Their faces shone with joy which could hardly be explained even by the release of Josefa and Captain Fitch; it must have been something more than that.

So now at last, feeling it can do no one any harm after this lapse of almost a century and a half, I am going to tell the secret which Captain Henry Fitch confided to his wife's parents that night in the sala.

He revealed to them that the courageous priest, Padre Menendez, had risked his ecclesiastical standing by marrying Josefa and Captain Fitch in the middle of that horrible night after the originally scheduled ceremony had been prevented by the refusal of Don Domingo to proceed as he had promised. Pío Pico had arranged for the midnight ritual with the necessary witnesses sworn to eternal secrecy so the ceremony could be performed in valid form.

It was the disclosure of this news which took the burden of shame from Doña María Ignacia and Don Joaquín, and the secret having been buried in the bosom of my family, it has never been told until this moment.

CHAPTER 17

CLIPPER SHIP LAWYER

MAYBE the oft-mentioned "call of the sea" has more of a romantic tone than most of us suspect. Anyway, the Carrillo women seem to have been attracted by seafarers. At least that certainly was the case in the days when California was young and the great Boston ships with their stately masts towering toward the skies came around murderous Cape Horn, over to the Sandwich Islands, and back along the California coast for trade.

I never had the chance to sail before the mast myself, but there certainly would have been precedent if I had heeded the call of the sea because of the great influence which the Boston sea captains had on my family.

The Danas and the Carrillos have been particularly intertwined in their family trees.

Everybody has heard of Richard Henry Dana and his *Two Years Before the Mast*, a nautical masterpiece, greatest early-day description of the voyage to California and the life of the people here. Because of Richard Henry Dana's prominence some people have overlooked the Danas who had an even greater part in the growth and development of California.

I have always been fascinated by the Dana story because of my own friendship for Juan Francisco Dana, called "The Blond Ranchero," who spent all his life on the famous Nipomo Ranch up near San Luis Obispo. Don Juan lived to be almost one hundred years of age and was keen and alert even in his ninety-eighth year when he loved to reminisce about his childhood, dating back to his birth in the year 1838.

It was his father, Captain William Dana, who began the Carrillo-Dana association in California.

Captain William Dana and the later Richard Henry Dana figured in the visits of the *Alert*, the *Penguin* and the *Pilgrim* to this coast. Captain William Dana was so interested in California that he started a store in Santa Barbara in 1825 while he was still continuing his trading missions as an active sea captain. These Boston rovers certainly had trouble when they tried to marry California girls. I have already told of the elopement of Josefa Carrillo and Captain Henry Fitch from San Diego, and it appeared for a while that the same sort of incident might be involved with Captain Dana.

By chance, too, the same little amorous Governor of California, José María de Echeandia, was the villain in both the Fitch and Dana romances. Governor Echeandia tried his best to win Josefa Carrillo in San Diego but was foiled. There is no record that he wished to marry this other Josefa Carrillo, this one a daughter of Don Carlos Antonio Carrillo, my great-grandfather who served for a time in 1837 as Governor of California and was living at the Presidio of Santa Barbara with his wife and five daughters. But it happened that Captain Dana fell in love with the Santa Barbara Josefa Carrillo and sought permission to marry her.

The girl's name actually was María Josefa Petra del Carmen Carrillo and she and her sisters eventually all married Americanos.

Our family legend is that Captain Dana met Josefa on his first trip to California in 1824 but that it took three years for him to win her hand in marriage, partly because of the necessity to gain the permission of Governor Echeandia, which was so difficult to obtain. Although my own people were of Spanish origin it was necessary for them to assume Mexican citizenship so they could carry on normal activities in California. Captain Dana was neither a Catholic nor a Mexican citizen and this made it nearly impossible for him either to marry a California girl or to obtain a land grant. I say "nearly impossible."

Anyway, before the romance had blossomed publicly and possibly while it was in progress, the leading citizens of Santa Barbara decided they should give a fiesta and dinner in honor of Captain Dana because he had done so much for the town with his trading vessels. All the caballeros and dons of the region joined in the preparations.

Seizing upon an old Spanish custom, the townspeople took the opportunity to proclaim a fiesta. Cascarónes were prepared. The señoritas and dueñas put on their black earrings—aretes—and their high Spanish combs and bright mantillas. All the musicians tuned their guitars and violins, and the singers and dancers attired themselves in their finest clothing. Enticing odors were wafted from many kitchens as the women vied with one another to prepare delicacies for the feast.

At last, all was ready, and Captain Dana was escorted to the seat of honor at El Paseo, a grand home in the center of the pueblo amid the singing of gay Spanish songs and the shouts of the fiesta crowd.

During the festivities and at the main dinner Captain Dana was attracted by a teen-age boy, Pedro C. Carrillo, younger brother of Josefa. The Captain had not previously met Pedro. The boy, although he could not speak English, was so bright in his looks and possessed such an air of a Spanish grandee that Captain Dana decided to ask his parents, Carlos Antonio and Señora Carrillo whether he might take Pedro East for further education.

He approached the subject with great formality the next day after the fiesta.

"My dear friends," he said to Don Carlos and his wife, "I have observed with interest the fine appearance and eager mind of your son Pedro. I know he has had splendid educational opportunities here and in the Sandwich Islands. But may I take the liberty of suggesting something further?

"In Boston we have a great Catholic college where he could perfect himself in the English language and study the law and become an attorney. It would be my great pleasure to take him to Boston on my ship if it meets with your favor.

"This added education would give your son an insight into the bigger world so he will be prepared when the gates of commerce open in California."

Pedro had graduated from the Santa Barbara Mission School and from Santa Iñez School. He, of course, was anxious for the adventure and the family went into consultation on the matter. Finally it was decided that he could make the trip.

He accompanied Captain Dana around the Horn on the same ship in which Richard Henry Dana was busy writing *Two Years Before the Mast.*

On the morning he left, Pedro's mother walked to the gate of their lovely home with him.

She was a devoted parent, and she was grief-stricken at the thought of the long separation from her boy. The odor of roses was in the air as they halted at the gate. Tenderly the mother enfolded her son in a last embrace, and they spoke their farewells in Spanish.

"Mi hijo, ahora vas a estudiar a uno de los grandes colegios de Boston. Regreserás un abogado graduado. Qué orgullo reina en el corazón de tu madre!"

"My boy you are now leaving to study in the great colleges of Boston. You will return a graduate lawyer. What pride reigns in your mother's heart!"

For the family, the intervening years seemed very long. First he went to parochial, then to preparatory, then to law school and graduated. Scollay Square became as familiar to him as Santa Barbara. All this took 12 years.

In the meantime, Captain Dana continued his three-year courtship of Josefa. One obstacle after another was thrown in the way of true love by Governor Echeandia and the law. Many times impatient Captain Dana must have wished, if he had used a modern phrase, that he had Josefa on a slow boat to China. But finally his persistence triumphed, romance won, and they were married in the old Mission.

Then, after complying with Mexican law, the Captain was granted the huge Nipomo Rancho of more than 37,000 acres in Southern San Luis Obispo County.

Age, of course, had come upon Governor Carrillo and his wife as they awaited the return of their educated son from the great American city in New England.

It was hard for them to believe that the great day had come when the bells rang at the Mission and everyone began running toward the waterfront when the vessel of Captain Dana carrying Pedro C. Carrillo, Attorney at Law, was sighted entering Santa Barbara Harbor.

Young men on horseback, girls playing castanets, barefooted children screaming with excitement all ran toward the waterfront.

Pedro's mother stood at the gate where she had told her son goodbye so many years before and as he came forward, elegantly dressed to greet her, she embraced him tenderly again and cried in Spanish:

"Oh, hijo mío, otra vez has vuelto a los brazos de tu madre! Ahora tu eres un abogado graduado en uno de los grandes colegios de Boston. Qué orgullo reina en el corazón de tu madre."

"Ah, my son, once more you have returned to the arms of your mother!

Now you are a graduate attorney from the great colleges of Boston. What pride reigns in your mother's heart."

Looking at her coldly, the splendidly dressed young man with his fine mustachios and air of authority replied with a heavy Boston accent, "But, Motha, I've been in Bawston so long I cawn't understand a word you say."

"The devil you can't," replied his mother, making in a moment the transition from Spanish to English.

And she seized a rawhide quirt and gave him such a licking on the seat of his fancy Boston pants that he forgot all his Boston airs and begged her pardon with great humbleness.

The truth was, too, that ever after he spoke English with a beautiful Spanish lilt. The rawhide cured him of his superiority and New England accent at the same time.

He never ate Boston baked beans again—just California frijoles!

CHAPTER 18

LIVELY PATRIARCH

THE William Dana family was a fruitful one. The Captain and his wife became the parents of twenty-two children.

The most famous of these was my tío, Don Juan Dana, of whom I have spoken.

The strange thing was that I had never met Don Juan before I went East to start in my theatrical career. Relatives who lived at a distance didn't visit among themselves as much when I was growing up as they do now. It was a long way from Rancho Nipomo to Los Angeles and we rarely saw that branch of the Carrillo connection.

Once, years after my start in show business, I was in San Francisco with my company when we were playing Lombardi, Ltd. We decided to go to Los Angeles by automobile. Our route ran close to the Rancho Nipomo and I decided that at last I would try to meet the famous old gentleman of whom I had heard so much.

My father had told me of the Dana place and it was not difficult for me to recognize it when we got there. The family was no longer living in the old 14-room adobe constructed during the days when Don Juan and his twenty-one brothers and sisters were living there. Don Juan's home, at the time I made this visit, was a gingerbread sort of house smacking of New England, possibly a reminder of his father's Boston heritage.

It was a warm bright day as I went up and knocked at the door. My company, tired from its long theatrical run and from the journey over the crude roads, sat on the lawn and relaxed in the sun. I heard rapid footsteps approaching in the house at my knock. They sounded so peppy I thought it must be a young person. Then the door opened and before me stood a little man with blue eyes, white hair, white beard, weighing possibly not over 130 pounds, and gazing at me with an almost startling directness. He spoke with a New England-American-Spanish combination of accents.

"How do?" he said inquiringly.

"Pardon me," I answered, "my father told me if I ever came this way to be sure and stop and call on you—"

"Who are you?" he broke in.

"Leo Carrillo," I replied. He hesitated, looked searchingly at me, sniffed and rubbed his nose.

"The actor?"

I nodded.

"Ain't you ashamed of yourself! You must be John's son then."

"If I wasn't an actor I might be selling tamales in the Plaza at Los Angeles," I said defensively.

His eyes twinkled.

"That might not be so bad, you might eat better than you do as an actor."

I could tell that he was joking and I entered into the spirit of the occasion.

"I know you don't want to be degraded by being seen associating with theatrical people," I said, "but part of my company are out here and I know they would like to meet you if you wouldn't mind."

He looked out and saw the girls reclining on the lawn and his interest quickened immediately.

"Pardon my appearance," he said, "I've been doing some work with my little boys. We've been chopping wood."

He called loudly, "Boys!"

Out from behind the house came the two "boys" to be introduced. One was John, seventy-four years old, and the other was William, sixty-eight. Don Juan himself was ninety-eight.

Don Juan lived up to his name as he kissed the hands of the girls with a courtly gesture, and presented his sons.

After we had chatted for a few minutes he pointed to a gigantic eucalyptus tree, fully 150 feet high, and said, "See that tree. I saw my father plant it more than eighty years ago when the first ones were brought in from

Australia. I used to have to carry the water to keep the little tree alive. It started to grow right away and shot up like a weed.

"When General Frémont was marching down to capture Santa Barbara and then go on to Los Angeles, he camped across the ravine over there.

"My father went over to the camp and I sneaked over there too. General Frémont spotted me and said to my father, 'Who is that child with the blonde hair and the blue eyes?'

" 'He's mine!' replied my father. 'I told him to stay out of here and not bother you.'

"General Frémont said, 'Oh he's not bothering us,' and beckoned me over. I went up and he lifted me and I sat on his knee while he discussed the campaign with my father. I still had long hair and I was crying because some of the soldiers as I came into the camp had taunted me by calling me 'little girl.'

" 'Why don't you cut his hair?' asked General Frémont.

" 'I think we ought to!' replied my father.

"So while I sat on the General's knee a soldier took a big pair of scissors and cut off my hair. I felt like a man after that. And I've never forgotten meeting the General—even if he was just a Lieutenant Colonel then."

We sat on the grass in the sunshine and listened to the fascinating tales of the early days flowing from the lips of the colorful old man in his mixture of accents. His mind was sharp, his recollections exact, and his choice of words beautiful.

The girls in my company were particularly absorbed in his reminiscences. He had a tremendous masculine charm even at ninety-eight.

He told us how in his youth he used to ride the 90 miles from Nipomo to Santa Barbara for a weekend of sport, particularly for the bull and bear fights which took place on Main Street. The bears were giant grizzlies lassoed by the vaqueros in the San Marcos Pass country.

"Do you still get to Santa Barbara?" I asked him.

Don Juan, who by his glances obviously had been wishing my leading lady was wearing a Bikini, sighed reminiscently, "Hombre!! I wish I was eighty again!" And then, to me, "What was it you said?"

"Do you still get to Santa Barbara?" I inquired again.

"Oh, I get down there once in a while but not as often as I used to. Not so much fun now, no more bull and bear fights."

"We've got to go pretty soon," I told him, "but I certainly would like to have you visit me in my home at Santa Monica. How long has it been since you were in Los Angeles?"

"Quite a while," he said.

"How long?" I persisted.

He screwed up his eyes and thought for a moment.

"I guess I haven't seen the damn place in seventy-five years! It must have grown some. I'll call on you."

We went reluctantly to the car and said our farewells to Don Juan and the two "little boys" who stood waving to us as long as we were in sight.

"What a man!" said my leading lady with a dreamy look in her eyes.

Don Juan affected all the ladies like that. Muy hombre!

Less than a month later I was sitting one evening in my patio with a comforting fire going for a barbecue. My dogs barked and I heard the sound of feet approaching on the baked tiles. They were rapid feet sounding peppy like a young person. I knew immediately who it was. Sure enough, there was Don Juan in his early California cape, "La Capa de Antes," his black hat turned up on one side, a cane in his hand and a smile on his lips.

"Here I am like I promised!" he exclaimed. "My grandson Rocky, you know the one who is a judge in Nipomo, brought me down."

We sat under the sycamore trees and talked.

"I just went out to the County Museum to look in the glass case out there where they have the wedding dress of my wife," Don Juan said. "It was shantung silk, you know, from China and they've also got my cut-away suit made up special in San Francisco for the wedding. I guess they sort of think they're relics already."

He chuckled as if dismissing the idea of being a relic.

"Say," he went on with a wink and in a half whisper, "what about these Earl Carroll Follies I been hearing about down in Hollywood? Do you think we could maybe go over there tonight and see the girls?"

"I don't know why not," I told him, "if you think you would enjoy it."

"Sure, I'd enjoy it," he said. "That is if Rocky will let me go. He's a lot stricter than I am."

As the sun went down over the western hills and the soft glow of twilight enveloped my little ranchito, we sat in silence for a while and listened to the murmur of the water in the tiny creek gurgling on its way to the sea. The hoot of an owl sounded. A light breeze touched the long fronds of the palm trees and whispered through the sycamores.

A scent of orange blossoms was in the air. The chickens were making their way towards their roosts. The dogs lay sprawled around the patio. All was quiet.

"I guess I've got to go now," Don Juan announced. "Rocky gets tired if I keep him up too late."

"Wait a minute before you go," I urged. "You've got to sign my guest book. Have you got your glasses?"

"Glasses, hell!" exploded Don Juan. "I don't need any glasses. It's these damn electric lights ruin your eyes. I've never had anything but lamps in my house. The soft lamp glow saves your eyes. I can see as good as anybody."

We went inside and I got out the guest book and put it on the table. Don Juan squinted a moment at the offensive electric light I had switched on and then turned to the book. In a firm steady hand he wrote "Juan Dana, ninety-eight-years-old."

I think it is the most treasured autograph I own.

CHAPTER 19

HORSE RACE LAMENT

A HORSE that had been dead for more than a quarter of a century caused me to give up gambling before I even got started.

My father always considered it a stigma to have any member of the family associated with gambling. The angriest I ever saw him was when he caught one of my brothers in a poker game. We finally discovered the reason behind this feeling. Father had good cause for his emotional reaction to gaming.

The race horse of which I speak flourished long before the immortal Man of War of the Dangerfield Farms of Kentucky, Seabiscuit, Assault, Citation and Swaps, but Californians always loved a good horse race more than anything else.

A lot has been said about the short dashes, perhaps of a few hundred yards comparable to our modern quarter horse races, which took place with the old mustangs off the plains when rival vaqueros or caballeros believed strongly enough in the speed of their mounts to bet on them. But these short dashes were not by any means the only kind of contests staged.

My grandfather, Pedro C. Carrillo, the very same one who had gone back to Boston College on the ship of Captain William Dana and returned to California a full-fledged lawyer, was a young man then beginning his practice in Los Angeles. He was struggling along because clients were few but he always managed to dress well for appearances. His son Juan, my father, was ten-years-old at the time. He idolized his father and wanted to follow his example in everything. That was what started the trouble with the horse race.

This all happened just two years after California became an American State. Southern California was a strange mixture of native Californians and Americans.

For the most part everything was cordiality between them although the Mexican War was over only four years before and the Treaty of Cahuenga had been signed near Los Angeles by José Antonio Carrillo, my great uncle, on behalf of the California forces, with Lt. Col. Frémont for the Americanos del Norte.

The population of Los Angeles was small and it was always ready for anything which promised fun and sport.

Don Pío Pico, the last Governor of Alta California who had served right up to that moment on July 7, 1846, when the Americans raised the Stars and Stripes at Monterey under the leadership of Commodore Sloat, was one of the leading citizens of Los Angeles. In fact, he and my great uncle, José Antonio Carrillo, were among the most respected of all the native Californians.

One day my father tagged along with my grandfather to the courtroom down near the Plaza. At the court my grandfather met Tom Mott, an American who had come out in the gold rush of '49 and then had wandered on down to Los Angeles and was beginning to be one of the notable citizens here.

Mott had married Chona Sepulveda and this alliance caused him to be literally "one of the family" in business and racing matters involving the great Sepulveda dynasty which owned Rancho San Joaquín, now the famous Irvine Ranch in Orange County, as well as Rancho Palos Verdes.

"Did you hear about Don José Sepulveda's new horse?" asked Mott.

My grandfather shook his head.

"He has gotten the greatest race horse I ever saw," said Mott proudly, "and I'm going to have a share in it."

"Do you mean that he might even think about racing Don Pío Pico's Sarco?" asked my grandfather with a smile.

Sarco was considered the greatest race horse ever produced in California. He had never been beaten at a distance. Every Californian believed he was invincible.

Tom Mott looked my grandfather straight in the eye and said, "Sarco wouldn't have a chance."

My grandfather was too polite to enter into a public dispute over the matter but he shook his head and went on about his business in the court and then back home. But the matter stuck in grandfather's mind and he decided that he would find out more about the wonder horse which Sepulveda had obtained.

Sepulveda was one of the great land barons of the day. He owned, among others, the vast Palos Verdes Rancho, thousands of head of cattle, hundreds of horses, sheep, goats, and every kind of property. His wife and children dressed in the height of fashion and the carreta in which the wife of Don José rode around Southern California was the finest in the whole region and squeaked the least because the wooden axles were kept greased with tallow so as to reduce the fierce sounds which usually came from the protesting oaken wheels of carretas which were neglected in this respect.

My grandfather, with my father following him around eagerly to hear all the details, made inquiries about the Sepulveda horse. He found it was a rarity indeed in this part of the world.

Don José had imported it all the way from Australia. The animal was a dark mare named Black Swan. She landed in San Francisco and Don José himself and his trainer Bill Brady, a remarkable horseman who seemed to have the ability almost to talk to horses, went up to meet her at the ship.

Carefully the Black Swan was unloaded and Don José looked at her with great satisfaction.

He turned to the trainer and said, "Guillermo, I charge you to take this magnificent creature to Los Angeles and to treat her as if she were a princess."

Bill Brady patted the neck of the emaciated mare which had suffered a great loss of weight on the voyage and nodded his head. Don José was satisfied. He knew the Black Swan was in good hands.

Brady lived up to his trust. He rode the Black Swan himself all the 450 miles from San Francisco to Los Angeles over winding trails, being careful to avoid sharp stones or any impediment which might injure her in any way. He came to know the horse as a gentle and responsive creature and he was sure that as soon as she had gained back some weight she would be ideally fitted to go into training.

Naturally in Los Angeles the news of the arrival of Sarco's rival in the northern city had caused a sensation. My grandfather and father, of course, were highly partisan in favor of Sarco because Don Pío Pico was so closely connected with the family both by blood and sentiment. It was he who had assisted in the elopement of our kinswoman, Josefa Carrillo of San Diego and

Captain Henry Fitch, and my grandfather and father were fully aware of his loyalty to all members of the Carrillo family. In turn they showed their loyalty by enthusiasm for Sarco. It seemed a natural thing to do, anyway, because the great horse had simply run away and left all his rivals in the southern portion of the state. His fame, now that he faced a potential challenge, reached a new peak.

My father was just at an age to enter into the passionate enthusiasm of each side for its horse. It so happened that the young son of Don José Sepulveda, Ygnacio, also was ten-years-old and he was just as wild in his support of Black Swan as my father was in behalf of Sarco. The town was so small that the boys saw one another quite frequently and the subject of the horse race began to cause friction between them. Ten years is a pretty bellicose age and when you are loyal to your father's interests in such a tremendous matter as a match race of horses, kids are liable to get even more excited than their elders.

When Brady, the trainer, rode into Los Angeles with Black Swan there were hundreds of people waiting at the Sepulveda stable to see what the horse looked like. The crowd included supporters of both the Sepulvedas and the Picos and there was a sharp division in their reaction.

Black Swan certainly did not look too formidable when she arrived. She still was suffering from the effects of the sea voyage and had not gained back her full weight. While Brady had taken good care of her on the ride from San Francisco there still had been no opportunity for him to get her back into condition.

Some of the Black Swan supporters went away shaking their heads rather sadly in disappointment after they had gotten this first glimpse of her. On the other hand, the followers of Don José were jubilant because they felt now that Sarco was bound to win against such a mangy-looking creature as this imported foreigner from Australia.

My father and young Ygnacio were too young, of course, to sit in on the deliberations concerning the terms and conditions of the race, but these immediately were relayed to them afterwards so they kept fully aware of all that was going on.

The negotiations were conducted with all the formality and punctilio for which the Spanish race is famous. Don Pío Pico and Don José Sepulveda and their principal aides would meet in long sessions to talk over the minute details of how the race was to be run. Finally the conditions were agreed upon. The course was to be about 3 leagues or 9 American miles. The course was to start at a point on San Pedro Street and run south 4½ miles to a post around which the horses would run, and then return. The stakes were to be $25,000 in gold slugs on each side, 500 mares, 500 heifers, 500 calves and 500 sheep, all of the live stakes to be penned near the scene of the race so they could be delivered to the winner after the race had been decided.

One of the strangest conditions, although it was indulged in sometimes in those days in long races, was that each side could have outriders to go along and whip the racing horses at will.

Absolutely no restriction was placed on either horse concerning the amount of weight to be carried. That was left up to the discretion of the owner. It was decided that, in order for all the preliminaries to be taken care of, the race would be run in three months from the time the agreement was signed.

This three months was one of the most tempestuous in the history of California. Word spread all over the state. The interest definitely was not confined just to Southern California. It extended all the way from the Mexican border to the Tehachapi Mountains and from the Pacific Ocean to the Colorado River.

It also extended as far north as San Francisco, Sacramento, Hangtown, and all the other gold camps where the adventurous miners loved to sit around their fires in the evening and talk over the events of the day. Hardly any other topic came up except the respective merits of Sarco and Black Swan.

Sarco was known as a horse with great bottom, that is with long lines and a tremendous stride. He was of the native stock which had evolved from the horses of the Conquistadores in Mexico imported to California, which of course meant he had Arabian and Barb blood. He was what might be called a mustang although he was longer and rangier than most of these compact little horses which were used on the cattle ranges.

Black Swan was credited with being a genuine English thoroughbred which had been sent to Australia before having been imported to California. She supposedly traced her lineage back to the famous Godolphin Arabian of the previous century, the sire of nearly all English thoroughbreds.

Her record in Australia had been impressive but that country was so far away and so unknown to the Californians that they dismissed the whole matter with a wave of their hands.

The training procedures of the two horses were extremely different.

Tom Mott and Sepulveda, who jointly owned Black Swan, treated her gently, building up her weight and exercising her with discretion, sometimes after dark so her runs could not be observed by too many people.

On the other hand Sarco was treated in the manner that most California race horses were compelled to endure at that time.

He received virtually no training at all. It was considered that he was such a powerful animal he was ready for a race anytime.

As the date neared for the great event, the excitement grew higher and higher. In saloons on Main Street and Los Angeles Street, in the Bella Union Hotel, at the Plaza, and all over town the rival factions talked of nothing else.

The number of bets made before the day of the race was so tremendous that a month ahead of time the amount exceeded anything that had ever been bet in California on a single event before.

A week before the race date, my father and Ygnacio Sepulveda, surrounded by a ring of screaming boys egging them on, met in a wrestling and fist fight in the dirt of new High Street. They fought until my father had two black eyes and a bloody nose, while Ygnacio bled all over his face and had taken such a pummeling in the stomach that he was doubled up and had to walk home with his head bent over.

It would have been difficult for the two boys—Juan Carrillo and Ygnacio Sepulveda—to believe, bloody and sore as they were, that in a few years they would be traveling together to the Isthmus of Panama, across it by mule-back, and then to Boston by side-wheel steamer to attend Holy Cross in Worcester, Massachusetts as classmates. Yet such was to be their later path in life.

Now, though, their bitter thoughts were entirely on the race and their personal differences.

Horses, cattle, sheep, goats, houses, ranches, household furniture and all imaginable items were included in the bets being made everywhere.

Particularly in evidence among the people who had money were the famous octagon $50 gold slugs which were being minted in San Francisco. The gleam of gold as it passed from hand to hand in bets was a common sight in all the saloons and hotels.

The days dragged by and it seemed that the date of the race never would arrive. Finally, though, the morning of the contest did dawn due to the sheer inevitability of the calendar.

Long before daylight the roads and trails coming into Los Angeles were crowded with ranchers riding their horses, carretas with families, sheep-herders on foot, people on donkeys, some riding mules. A shipload of enthusiasts had come down from San Francisco, others had ridden in from the San Joaquín valley and from the distant lands of the Colorado River.

On San Pedro Street, where the race was to start, the scene was one of wild confusion. Hawkers went through the crowd selling pinoche, tamales, hot tortillas wrapped in clean white cloths, and colored drinks.

Almost as if by instinct, the backers of each horse gathered together. There was little mingling of the supporters of Sarco and of Black Swan. The only time they came together was for the placing of last-minute bets. One German who was carrying money for Mott and Sepulveda sat in a buggy with coins all around him in boxes. Nearly all of it was gold.

The custom of the Californians in making a bet was to give the amount of the wager to one of the parties to hold in the presence of witnesses. Then after the race the person holding the money kept it if his horse had won or gave back double the amount if the other side had triumphed. The Californianos crowded around the buggy, pressing their money on the German so fast that thousands of dollars were wagered in this final rush.

My grandfather, with my father tagging at his heels, was among those making a bet at the buggy. My grandfather was so convinced that Sarco would win he took all of his savings, $400, which had been hidden in a metal box buried under one of the baked bricks of the kitchen floor and put the whole amount on Sarco. My father's eyes were as big as black saucers as he watched the gold coins being counted out; he felt a personal responsibility for the money his father was wagering. My father's eyes were still swollen and black from his fight with Ygnacio Sepulveda, and the two boys might have started in all over again before the race if their parents had not kept a restraining hand upon them.

Some taunts were hurled back and forth between the two rival adult groups as the horses were prepared for the course.

Just then Señora Sepulveda in her almost-squeakless carreta came into the race area surrounded by a retinue of servants, friends and admirers, with dozens of barefooted children running along in excitement and squealing and screaming out of sheer exuberance. The great lady carried a huge handbag which she seemed hardly able to lift. She sat on a gilt chair in the carreta and surveyed the scene around her with the air of a queen.

As the carreta stopped it was surrounded immediately by the friends of the Sepulvedas. Señora Sepulveda motioned to her servants and they too gathered around.

Then from the handbag she began to give to the servants the distinctive octagon shaped $50 gold pieces which were minted in San Francisco and formed the most popular currency among the wealthy residents of the Los Angeles area. The servants rushed into the crowd to bet the gold.

Besides the noise made by the thousands of people there was the baaing of the sheep, the bleating of the goats, the snorting of the heifers, and the wild antics of the mares where they were penned near the start of the race. The dust raised by the animals formed such a heavy cloud that it drifted over the crowd, and many people were sneezing and wiping their eyes.

The officials called Don José and Don Pío together to make sure that everything was understood about the start and about the whipping of the horses during the running of the race.

Everything seemed to be well understood. This was far from being the first contest between the Pico and Sepulveda families. Races had been going on between them for a long time and the balance having been rather in favor of the Picos, the Sepulvedas were confident this time of evening the score.

Tension and excitement in the crowd mounted moment by moment as the hour of the start approached. People were moving about munching tortillas and chili rellenos almost without seeming to know what they were eating. The hawkers selling candy and fruit were doing a big business but some of the young gamblers had become so enthusiastic that they had put every peso in their possession on the race, and had to borrow a few centavos from their wives to pay for the sweetmeats they were buying.

The greatest secret of the whole affair still remained to be revealed.

Who was going to ride Black Swan?

The Sepulvedas, contrary to the usual custom, had refused to indicate who was going to be the rider of their horse. Ordinarily, there was much bragging about the capability of the rider of the race horse and many people based their wagering in part upon the skill of the rider as well as upon the speed of the horse. But this time for some reason the Sepulvedas were refusing to discuss the question.

Even when Black Swan and Sarco were led out towards the finish line for inspection by the officials there was no indication who the rider would be.

This secrecy caused some concern among the supporters of Sarco although others said they did not care who rode Black Swan because Sarco was going to win anyway.

Now that the three months of training had gone by Black Swan had filled out to her true proportions again, her coat was sleek and she shone in the brilliant sunshine as if she were an animated black sapphire from her land of Australia.

Some of the backers of Sarco, in fact, began to feel a little doubt when they saw how beautiful Black Swan had become. It was a transformation. She was no longer the sickly nag she had appeared when she arrived from San Francisco.

The hour of the race was at hand but still no rider for Black Swan was in sight.

At this moment José Sepulveda was seen to motion toward the doorway of one of the buildings on San Pedro Street and the eyes of the entire crowd turned in this direction.

A gasp of astonishment was heard as the rider appeared.

He was a tiny Negro dressed in bright clothing similar to that of a modern jockey, with a small cap turned backwards on his head.

"Carramba!" somebody cried. "Un corredora negra y un chalán negro!"

Indeed that was it—a black race horse with a black jockey.

A flutter of new excitement ran through the crowd. Such a sight had never been seen in an important race in Los Angeles.

Some of the supporters of Sarco, noticing the small size of the jockey in comparison with the large Mexican youth who was to ride Sarco began to voice some doubts about the outcome. Uncertainty was on many a face. Almost as great consternation was caused by the saddle now brought forward for Black Swan as had been caused by the appearance of the strange jockey. The saddle was a small one of the English type, extremely light and looking like a postage stamp in comparison with the heavy, conventional saddle on Sarco.

All around my grandfather and father there were exclamations of bewilderment and some of actual fear in regard to the outcome.

But they remained enthusiastically loyal to Sarco, feeling that the horse's great strength would give him the advantage after the pole had been turned at the half-way mark despite the light weight of the Negro rider.

Now the Chief Official looked at his watch and mounting on a stand held up his hand for quiet. The crowd even to the outermost fringes calmed down for a moment, appearing almost frozen in its attitudes as the people looked up expectantly towards the official.

"Señores and Señoras," he called out. "We are now ready to proceed with the race between these two great animals. Will you please remain quiet until the signal for the start has been given?"

He then nodded to the trainers of the two horses who led the animals up to the starting line. The riders adjusted their spurs and mounted. The crowd watched fascinatedly as the little Negro got into the strange, light saddle on Black Swan. Amazement still was evident on many faces.

The riders poised themselves in the saddles and leaned over the necks of their mounts. The starter raised his hand and in the momentary deathly hush cried out the magic word in a great shriek:

"Santiago!"

As if they had been shot out of a gun, the two horses plunged ahead.

Behind them and alongside rode their supporters in a pell-mell shouting mass. Instantly the backers of Sarco began to whip him and it appeared for a moment that he would take the lead, but the mare without even being beaten sped swiftly to the front. She opened a wider and wider gap as she sped along the San Pedro road, the crowd along each side yelling and screaming encouragement as the racers themselves and their followers thundered by. The sound of quirts landing on the hide of Sarco sounded almost like drum beats.

At the instant of the start my grandfather had leaped on his horse which was being held by a servant, and with my father clinging behind him started out after the racers. They kept the two animals in sight for awhile and at a point about four miles out they stopped on a little rise where they could see the pole around which the racers were to turn for the four and one-half miles of the return trip.

My grandfather had decided that if he could see the animals circle the pole then he would start back and be at the finish line to watch the climax of the race.

The mare was opening up a long lead by this time and as she approached the turning pole she was perhaps 150 yards ahead of Sarco.

As my grandfather and father watched, the mare did reach the turning pole. Mott was stationed there and as the mare approached he watched her stride and general appearance carefully. As the little Negro pulled hard on the reins to turn the mare, Mott reached up and grabbed the reins. He looked into the nostrils and foam-flecked mouth of Black Swan and then, seeing the speed with which Sarco was approaching, he jerked the reins, turned the mare around the pole and struck her with his quirt. She leaped ahead and started on the long weary grind back towards the starting line.

As soon as this happened my grandfather turned his horse and began to gallop back along the San Pedro road. My father hung on behind, occasionally looking back over his shoulder to see whether the race horses were catching up with them.

The pace had begun to tell on both Black Swan and Sarco, though, by this time, and they were not gaining on my grandfather's horse which of course had a half mile head start on the return trip. People were perched on top of gates, on the flat rooftops of the occasional houses in the countryside, and on every possible vantage point. Some trees were so loaded that the branches appeared likely to break under the weight of the spectators. As my grandfather and father neared the starting line the crowd was so great that they could hardly get through. My grandfather hastily tethered his horse to a fence and then he and my father ran towards the finish line. Already they could hear the shouts of the crowd along the way and then the yells and curses of the supporters of each horse as they came in sight.

Black Swan was still ahead but Sarco with great strides and apparent new strength was gaining with every leap. The mare was bleeding at the nose but still the little jockey struck her only occasionally because he seemed to feel that she was exerting every bit of strength she possessed.

Frenzy gripped the crowd as the animals entered upon the last furlong. Black Swan now was five lengths ahead, with Sarco straining every muscle, desperately trying to close the gap. Most of his backers had been lost in the mad scramble because their horses had given out but two or three hardy souls were whipping the great horse frenziedly as he attempted the seemingly impossible feat of overtaking Black Swan. Then Black Swan, bleeding from the nose and mouth and almost staggering, swept across the finish line four and a half lengths ahead, with Sarco still gaining a fraction.

Part of the crowd was stunned.

The rest screamed, jumped up and down, waved their arms in such a pandemonium that my grandfather and father were almost deafened.

They could not believe their eyes. The calamity of Sarco having been beaten was more than they could comprehend. My father—boy that he was—looked up despairingly at my grandfather. Grandfather Carrillo had put his hands across his eyes as if attempting to shut out the sight of the victory which meant he had lost every centavo the family possessed. On his face was a look of such agony that my father could not restrain his own emotions and began to cry.

At this, my grandfather removed his hands from his eyes, looked down at the weeping boy, put his hand upon his head and patted him gently.

"We will never bet again," said my grandfather simply . . .

When my father in later years told me the story his own face would contort at the still-vivid memory of that horrible moment. It so impressed itself upon my youthful mind that I could never forget the scene there at the finish line when Black Swan in her moment of triumph had wiped out the savings of the Carrillo family.

I swore I would never become a gambler.

And I never have, all because of a horse I never saw.

CHAPTER 20

TEAR FOR A BANDIT

A BEAUTIFUL girl was riding her chestnut horse at a gallop over the rounded hills of beautiful Rancho San Joaquín, a neighbor of vast Rancho Santa Margarita between Los Angeles and San Diego. Sheer enjoyment shone on her face as the horse seemed to soar over the crests and float through the hollows.

The girl rode superbly. She was putting the horse through various evolutions with hardly any discernible touch of the reins. She seemed to be in complete accord with the animal and he responded without any urging.

It was a spring day. The earth was bursting with new green growth. The mustard stalks were growing high and a few already were in golden bloom. The alfilaria was so high that the grazing cattle moved through it as if they were treading some green jungle.

Clumps of live oaks dotted the hills. Overhead a few fleecy white clouds lazed in the intense blue sky. The sun beamed down with just enough warmth to create animation rather than lethargy. Nature seemed to be bursting with kindness and generosity. The girl and the horse were sharing in this seasonal upturn of life as if both felt youth in their veins and the beckoning of a bright future unmarred by trouble.

In one of the clumps of oaks on the crest of a higher hill nearby, three men were hidden. Their horses were tied on the far side of the hill and they crouched in the undergrowth watching the girl as she and the horse came nearer. They whispered among themselves. Their faces were evil and scarred.

One was pock-marked, another had a deep slice down the side of his face from the eyebrow to the point of the jaw. The third, with loose slobbering lips, appeared as if he might be almost an idiot.

Silently the men worked further back in the undergrowth as the girl came closer. Then at a signal among themselves they jumped on their horses and waited tensely for the approach of the beautiful rider. As she came bounding along on the horse just below the crest of the hill, the three horsemen dashed out with their reatas whirling. One of them threw a loop over the head of the girl's horse before she realized what was happening. The men closed in around her. One on each side seized her arms. She shuddered and tried to shake them off. There was only defiance in her eyes as she cried out, "Let me go. What does this mean!"

"You'll find out," said the man with the scar. He pointed towards the oaks and the man with the reata around the horse's neck began to pull the girl's mount in that direction. The girl gazed scornfully at her captors, refusing to show any sign of fear.

"My father and brothers will kill you if you harm me," she said calmly as if stating a fact beyond any doubt.

The men, looking lasciviously at her rounded figure paid no attention to her words. Lust was in their eyes. They neared the oaks, the men on each side holding the girl tightly.

"In there!" ordered the man with the scar.

They moved faster.

Just at this moment another rider appeared from beyond the clump of oaks. He rode a magnificent black horse. On his head was a large sombrero with silver ornamentation around it. His bearded face was shadowed by the hat brim.

The men obviously recognized him. They hesitated for a moment and then came to a full stop. The man on the black horse came up and gave an order in tone of command so stern that the three captors of the girl seemed to wilt in their saddles.

"Let her go!" he ordered.

Immediately the men released the girl's arms and the reata was taken from the neck of her horse.

The man with the sombrero removed it with a sweeping gesture, bowed low, and said courteously:

"Señorita, I humbly beg your pardon. I was watching you ride. You are magnificent. My men shall be punished for this affront to you. I hope you will convey to your father my apologies for this conduct. It is fortunate that I appeared at this moment."

And he glanced witheringly at the three men who slunk off into the oak grove. The girl sat erect in her saddle and flashed a smile at her rescuer.

"I thank you, Señor, from the bottom of my heart. My family will be grateful to you. May I tell my father to whom I am indebted for this kindness?"

The horseman bowed again, put his sombrero back on his head, and as he started away said:

"Señorita, tell your father you have just met Tiburcio Vasquez." . . . . .

The girl was Chonita Sepulveda, whose father owned the gigantic San Joaquín Rancho, now known as the Irvine Ranch in Orange County. The bandit, who for once had proved to be decent in some of his inclinations, had been terrorizing all of Southern California with his band.

Vasquez originally was from Monterey where he became incensed at the gringos because he said they always danced with the prettiest girls at the fandango.

His real career of bandit began at a little settlement called Panama, a few miles south of Bakersfield. A dozen bandits were "whooping it up" at a dance in this Mexican settlement and under the influence of aguardiente and pulque which gave them false courage, they decided to hold up a railroad pay car. They all piled out onto their horses and made the attempt, but were driven off.

They wanted to vent their disappointment in some manner so they rode to the little village of Tres Pinos, robbing the stores and killing three men. Then they went on to the little town of Kingston in Tulare County and terrorized it and stole all the money they could find from the storekeepers there. Then they vanished into the mountains.

Law officers learned from gossip in the Mexican communities that Vasquez was the leader of the group.

One of the informants was the husband of a man in Monterey whose wife had run away with Vasquez.

The bandit leader rarely stayed in one spot. He recruited new bands of outlaws in various places. He was so careful that he would not even sleep in the same camp with his men for fear of being betrayed. The only companion he trusted was an outlaw named Chavez.

Vasquez was so daring that he would try any kind of trick, sometimes apparently just to aggravate the law men. One day he rode up with three companions to the ranch of Alessandro Repetto only nine miles from Los Angeles. Vasquez and his men were disguised this time as sheepshearers. They held up the entire Repetto household and then made old man Repetto sign a check for $800. Vasquez then sent a boy into town with the check, telling him that he would kill Repetto if it was not cashed.

This check was taken to the Temple and Workman Bank. Mr. Temple was shown the check and he became suspicious. He notified Sheriff Rowland. The boy told the whole story but begged the officers not to go to the Repetto place because Mr. Repetto would be killed.

Finally the boy was permitted to go back and the officers followed some distance behind him. But Vasquez was so wily that his scouts saw the approaching officers, and he escaped.

During the years of his activity Vasquez struck up some strange friendships. One of these was with "Greek George," a camel driver from Smyrna who had come to the United States to help drive camels from Texas to California where they could be tried out by the Army as beasts of burden.

Greek George had a little house with a lean-to at one end about ten miles from Los Angeles in what now would be Hollywood. Vasquez visited him quite frequently. Vasquez' organization was so wary, however, that Sheriff Rowland and other law men were almost helpless because every movement they made was reported to Vasquez and if they so much as started in the direction of Greek George's he would get away.

One foggy night a strange drama began to unfold in the wooded countryside. Some horsemen silently made their way on a roundabout route to the mouth of Nichols Canyon which was about two miles from Greek George's house. Charles Knowles, an American, lived here. The men hid in Knowles' house waiting for morning.

A little distance away, some Indians with an old wagon were cutting firewood. The members of the posse who had gathered so silently at Knowles' house went to the Indians and by a display of guns so terrorized them that they agreed to do whatever was wanted.

The Indians were given strict instructions. They were to drive to Greek George's house and to ask whether he wanted to buy any wood.

The members of the posse hid in the bed of the wagon between the pieces of wood so they were completely concealed. During the morning the Indians finished their work and in a state of terror drove toward Greek George's.

They apparently aroused no suspicion because they came quite close to the house and saw two gray horses and a black one tethered outside. One was recognized by the posse members peering through the holes in the side of the wagon as belonging to Vasquez. In a moment, in fact, they could see Vasquez through the open door eating breakfast. He was being waited upon by a beautiful Mexican girl. No one else could be seen, not even Greek George. One of the Indians went up to the door to ask about the wood.

"Quiere madera?" quavered the old Indian.

"No," replied the Mexican girl in English.

Vasquez hardly looked up from his meal as the conversation went on. The old Indian, though, had been given instructions to continue the conversation as long as he could in order to give the posse an opportunity to observe Vasquez. So he asked again:

"Por favor, señorita, quiere madera?"

At this Vasquez himself became impatient.

"Andale!" he exclaimed, waving his knife.

This was too much for the old Indian. He started back toward the wagon, looking helplessly at the concealed posse.

Just then the men of the posse leaped out of the wagon and started running to surround the house. Vasquez was as quick as a cat. He jumped out a window on the far side and ran for his black horse which was a considerable distance away. The posse opened fire with both rifles and shotguns. Vasquez was hit in the leg and cried out "Boys, I've been a damned fool! I give up!"

He held up his hands, and the posse approached carefully and took his guns.

"What is your name?" asked one of the posse members.

"Alessandro Martinez," responded Vasquez.

The posse men assisted Vasquez who was bleeding quite heavily back into the house. The girl was screaming and begging the officers not to kill her lover.

"We're not going to kill him now," said one of the men as they started to search the house.

In a few minutes Vasquez, claiming that he was going to die, confessed his identity. In the house was found his vest containing a watch stolen from Charley Miles of the Los Angeles Water Company who had been robbed just a few days before. Vasquez, pretending to be desperately wounded, asked the posse men to write down his will. He said that he was single but that he had two children living near Elizabeth Lake. To prove his statement he showed pictures of these children. He claimed never to have murdered anyone and begged for mercy.

He was taken to jail in the old Bullard Block in Los Angeles.

At first some of the admiring women of the Pueblo sent him bouquets of flowers and his cell was filled just as had been the case with the prisoner I mentioned before, Manuel, who tricked "The Blackbirds of the Temescal." But Sheriff Rowland was not going to tolerate floral displays for Vasquez. He ordered the flowers thrown away as they arrived, while the bandit sat dejectedly awaiting his fate.

Finally Vasquez was taken to San José for trial.

He was found guilty and ordered to be hanged.

The day of his doom came in March, 1875.

He had few mourners. One of these was a girl.

On the great Rancho San Joaquín a little tear trickled down the cheek of Chonita Sepulveda.

She was one of the few people in the world who could remember a good deed connected with the name more feared than any other throughout all of California—Tiburcio Vasquez, the bandit who once had a tender spot in his heart for a helpless girl.

CHAPTER 21

THE DWINDLING STAIRCASE

GRANDFATHER used to tell us when we were kids that it was tough being a judge in Los Angeles in the early days. He knew what he was talking about. He was one. This all was a good while before I was born. But if grandfather had been a judge in an even earlier day, he might have done better financially.

Long before his time, when the pueblo of Los Angeles was very young, there were a lot of pauper Indians called cholos who hung around the Plaza all the time and tried to mooch a little money so they could buy the awful wine and worse brandy which was sold in a cave close to where the Union Station now stands. Grandfather, when he was telling us about it, never knew exactly who thought up the idea, but quite a system grew out of the poverty of the Indians and their craving for liquor.

Slavery came to Los Angeles.

This resulted from the need of the well-to-do vineyard owners for cheap help. They and the early-day judges worked out the combination.

On Sunday night all the drunk cholos lying around the Plaza would be dragged up to the horrible filthy little jail on Fort Moore Hill. Then on Monday morning they would be herded with their hangovers down to the courtroom. The judge would set bail for each one and this would be paid by a vineyard owner who would get the services of the Indian for a week for a very cheap price. The Indians would work straight through till Saturday night when they would be given just enough money to get roaring drunk until Sunday night. Then the whole process would be gone through again.

It was very handy for everybody and the Indians didn't seem to mind too much themselves. Maybe that's the trouble with slavery; you get sort of used to it and you have to fight against it to appreciate freedom. I'm sure my grandfather after his strict upbringing and his training at Boston College would never have participated in this slavery situation, but he had other troubles to contend with. It was perhaps two or three decades after the slavery condition was ended that grandfather became a judge.

The system in his day was that the judge paid for his own courtroom out of the proceeds of the fines levied against the prisoners who were brought in. The court which grandfather used was a second-story room above a store on New High Street. The landlord was a volatile Frenchman. The rent was $50 a month.

This doesn't sound like much when there was so much crime and so many potential prisoners to be brought in. Still, grandfather had his difficulties in meeting the rent out of the proceeds of the fines. This was due to a number of causes. The chief one was the laxity of the law enforcement officers. It was a free and easy age then. Common drunkenness and gambling and a few minor vices were taken for granted. To many of the law officers it just seemed like a waste of time to drag drunks into court and then to bring them in all over again in a few days. The repetition became monotonous.

So the result was that the law men spent most of their time around the Plaza at the cock fights or watching the bull fights on Sunday, or hanging around the Bella Union hotel on Main Street listening in on the conversation of the tinhorn gamblers and politicians.

Grandfather needed business. Sometimes he would go days at a time without a prisoner being brought in. It wasn't exactly his function to barge out and arrest people, and it might have appeared a little bit self-seeking on his part if he had done so just to get fines. But things were pretty bad in the rent situation.

Lots of times grandfather just couldn't raise the $50 for the Frenchman.

This Frenchman was excitable. He used to wave his arms and scream and it was all very unpleasant for grandfather who had added Boston culture and poise to his native dignity as a Spanish gentleman. He disliked being screamed at and being told that he was in arrears in the rent.

Finally things got so bad the Frenchman not only screamed but resorted

to practical and inventive reprisals against grandfather. Apparently the landlord was not able actually to evict the judge because a court did have some
slight standing even in those days. Yet he thought up an ingenious way to
embarrass grandfather. Whenever the rent was unpaid he would cut off one
step of the staircase leading up to the courtroom. Pretty soon the number
of steps which had been taken out left a huge gap so that grandfather had to
build a kind of catwalk to get up to the remaining portion.

This made it even more inconvenient for drunks, too, because sometimes
the law officers had to push them up the catwalk from behind or haul them
up with ropes into the courtroom.

People began to talk about the undignified proceedings, and grandfather
became more and more embarrassed.

At last came the showdown. There were only a few steps left and a huge
gap between the sidewalk and the second floor. Then the Frenchman took out
these final steps . . . and dragged them down the street, adlibbing cuss words
in French, complete with gestures of his one free hand as he gripped the steps
with the other.

Grandfather had to add a new section to the catwalk.

The whole trouble was based on the lack of cash in the pueblo. Coins and
paper money were extremely scarce. Most transactions were carried out with
hides at the prevailing rate of $2 each. But grandfather didn't have any hides,
and he would have considered it rather embarrassing to lug 25 hides down
to the Frenchman for rent money, anyway.

By this time both sides were pretty angry about the whole thing and grandfather wasn't speaking to the Frenchman and the only time the Frenchman
spoke to grandfather was when he screamed at him to demand the rent.

At this time grandfather decided that he had to resort to stern measures
to restore his respectability and self-esteem in Los Angeles. He conferred
with the bailiff. The next day grandfather and the bailiff climbed up the long
catwalk into the courtroom without any prisoners there at all.

Quietly, grandfather called the court to order with only the bailiff and
himself present.

On this particular morning the Frenchman had a fight with his wife who
had discovered him carrying on an affair with a little seamstress down at the
Plaza, and he was in a fuming, fighting mood. He decided it was time to dun
grandfather for the rent again.

Always before, the Frenchman had held in his anger and never actually invaded the courtroom. He had accosted grandfather down on the sidewalk and demanded his money, often in the presence of grinning witnesses, but on this particular occasion he was so beside himself with rage that he climbed up the catwalk and poked his head through into the courtroom.

He saw grandfather and the bailiff gravely sitting in their places as if waiting for some prisoners to appear so court could be called to order.

With a howl of rage, the Frenchman climbed on into the courtroom and ran up and shook his fist under grandfather's nose on the bench.

"I want my money," he screamed. "You're cheating me all the time. I want my money."

"Silence," roared grandfather. "This court is in session."

The Frenchman waggled his finger under grandfather's nose and screamed again, "I don't care what is in session. I want my money."

With the greatest gravity grandfather turned to the bailiff and said, "Arrest this man for contempt of court."

The astounded Frenchman felt the bailiff's hand upon his arm and looked up at grandfather in total astonishment. He could not conceive of this possibility. Then he tried to fling off the arm of the bailiff.

The bailiff who was a big man held on all the tighter and shook the Frenchman until his teeth rattled.

"Bring the prisoner to the bar," ordered Judge Carrillo.

The bailiff pushed the Frenchman up in front of grandfather who looked at him sternly.

"You have invaded the sacred precincts of the court and it is mandatory that I punish you," said grandfather severely.

The Frenchman's face was the color of a beet, the veins stood out in his neck, and he was absolutely speechless with rage for the first time in his life.

"Bailiff," said grandfather, "you were a witness to the unseemly conduct of this prisoner. He violated the sanctity of the court and showed disrespect for the judge and the process of law."

Then grandfather turned again to the prisoner.

"I sentence you to pay a fine of $50," he thundered.

The Frenchman was so overwhelmed by the whole procedure that he almost involuntarily reached into his pocket and took out a $50 gold slug. The bailiff promptly grabbed this and handed it to grandfather.

"Court's adjourned!" grandfather snapped before another word could be said. Then descending from the bench he came up to the Frenchman. With his most winning smile and in a Boston accent he said, "Monsieur, I believe that the rent date has arrived on the courtroom. Here is a month's rent."

And he handed the Frenchman back his $50 gold piece.

"I will appreciate a receipt," he added sweetly "—and then you can start rebuilding the stairs!"

CHAPTER 22

IMPETUOUS PAISANO

JUDGE Juan José Carrillo was father-confessor to all the little Mexican ranchers who lived around Santa Monica.

I am speaking of my father, of course.

When he was judge he had the authority to handle those who came before him in a legal way, but there was always a little something in his eye and in his heart indicating a lot of sympathy and understanding for the poor people who didn't understand the seriousness of certain offenses. He always took those things into consideration, and in that way won the love and respect and confidence of everyone who met him.

I can remember the day before Thanksgiving one time, some of the old veterans from the Soldiers Home, at Sawtelle, came into town and got drunk and spent all their money and wound up in jail. Three of them came up before my father and he reprimanded them for their behavior and told them they were a disgrace to the uniform they were wearing. He called attention to the fact that his aunt gave the land for the home they were using as a last haven of rest. Then he fined them $10 apiece.

All of a sudden, though, he thought: "Heavens! Tomorrow is their big Thanksgiving feast and they won't be there because they haven't got the $10 to pay, and they'll have to go back to jail!" So he dug into his own pocket for $30 and paid their fines and sent them home so they could enjoy their Thanksgiving.

That was typical.

The paisanos who lived in the neighborhood used to call him Tío Juan, instead of Judge. It was an affectionate term.

It happened that there was one little Mexican named Jacobo who had a habit of doing certain things and one of his worst offenses was too-frequent matrimony. He had been before the priest many times to get married. Then maybe the wife would leave him, or maybe he would leave the wife. Anyway, there was a process of elimination. The marriages never stuck.

Finally, though, Jacobo found himself a great big fat Mexican girl in her twenties and fell desperately in love with her. He lived in a place called Calabasas, very populated now but in those days just an old ranch. The only access to it was over the Santa Monica Mountains through a swale called Calabasas Pass. It was a cleared road for wagons to bring firewood and one thing and another to sell in the city of Santa Monica. That's how the Calabasas people made a living.

This fellow Jacobo fell for a big, fat, beautiful, healthy, Mexican girl, full of frijoles, and he came in one day to see my father in the courtroom. He started, "Tío Juan," but my father interrupted him.

"You call me Judge in this courtroom and speak English because whatever you say has to go on these books in English and not in Spanish. Habla inglés?"

Jacobo struggled a bit and tried to explain it in English:

"Judge, I want to get married. I come to you because I go to the priest and the priest says he don't want to marry me because I been there too many times to get married. Sometimes I have to go away from here out-of-town to get married, some other place, but I know if I come to you and you know if I'm in love, I want to know please if you will help me. I drive all the way from Calabasas. If you want to make me happy, only marry me today."

My father said, "Who are you going to marry?"

"Well, Judge," and he looked at father sheepishly and pointed out the window, "I'm going to marry the lady sitting out in the lumber wagon."

Father could see this fat girl sitting in the lumber wagon pulled by a couple of horses. The wagon had a little straw in the back where two or three children were playing.

My father said, "You're going to marry this lady sitting out in the wagon?"

Jacobo replied, "Yet, I know you want to help me."

"Well, let me see."

Father got up from his chair and looked out the window and he observed the children playing in the back of the wagon.

"Who do those children belong to?" he demanded.

And very sheepishly, Jacobo half-bowed his head and looked up rolling his eyes and said, "Well, Judge, they're ours but it took us a leetle while—the roads was very rough!"

CHAPTER 23

INCREDIBLE LOTHARIO

QUITE often, you may have noticed, I have spoken of the great institutions of learning in the East which attracted the sons of California families. We Carrillos favored Boston College and Holy Cross.

But now there is another I must mention.

What courses they must teach at Yale University!

It so happened once when I was on the stage in San Francisco a letter was delivered to me with a message so provocative I could not resist checking its truth. This was no perfumed note from some damsel to a matinee idol, which I might in all modesty admit to having been at that time. Instead, it was a letter from a man on a subject which is dear to both sexes. It spoke of an old California love story.

Or, I might say, love stories!

It seems that one of my distant kinsmen known to my grandfather in his earlier days had returned to California after being graduated from Yale to settle upon the great rancho where his family had resided for many years. He came back conversant with the ways of the world. I shall not mention his real name—I might be besieged by a million alleged relatives.

It was one of his duties to travel throughout the great rancho area to see that everything went well in the camps of the vaqueros and at the homes of the distant overseers. Also he visited other ranches. The young ranchero was married and raising a family but he had a roving eye. In a few years it began to be noted throughout the entire region that, although it was before the day of bicycles, there were a great number of children bearing a striking resemblance to the Yale graduate. Indeed, as the years went on the number of these children increased.

The young man had another liking, too. Food was a great passion with him. He instructed all his servants and ranch people to be on the lookout for delicacies. He imported special Virginia Smithfield hams from San Francisco, pineapples from the Sandwich Islands, even tin goods such as truffles and mushrooms from distant France. At a meal he often ate an entire sizzling broiled kid—the favorite meat cooked over coals in the early California days—washed down with a gallon of the fine wine produced in the region near his home.

As the number of his children increased so did his own size. He alternated between eating and rolling over and sleeping; with castanets as his alarm clock for amorous interludes. By the time he was in his early forties, he was a mountain of fat. It was impossible for him to get on horseback but by using a carreta and a discreet driver he managed to keep up his circuit which might have been described as a sort of honeymoon orbit with a very large perimeter. He seemed to be related to a Chesapeake shad or a Belgian hare.

More and more his physical ills forced him to confine himself to the pleasures of the table rather than the bed, however, and as was inevitable, he began to suffer palpitations of the heart and other indications that the pace of his life was killing him. He was a one-gut wonder with king-size cholesterol.

At this point he called in a famous physician from San Francisco and the doctor was frankly astounded that the ranchero had lived as long as he had.

"If you continue to gorge like this and to chase so many women you will not live out the year," his physician told him.

This Yale man was very brave. Instead of being crushed by the doctor's warning he took it as the signal for a fiesta. To all his friend throughout the countryside, the rancheros and caballeros who had looked somewhat askance at his love pranks, he sent a message of kindest terms requesting their presence at the great fiesta on his ranch.

For miles around the word spread.

"El Señor Too-Many-Frijoles is giving the greatest celebration of his life."

Some people came out of friendship, others out of curiosity to see the immense ranchero himself, still others wondering what could be the occasion of so elaborate a fiesta.

Everything was mirth and jollity for a long time. The ranchero, seated at the head of the table in a giant chair lined with a bull skin still bearing the hair, was wreathed in smiles and ate with such gusto that it seemed impossible any human frame could contain the amount of food and drink he consumed. When the party was at its climax the ranchero rang a sheep-bell for silence and all the guests looked toward him expectantly.

"I want you to know that my doctor thinks I shall not live long. He says I am digging my grave with my teeth. This matter in itself is of no great importance for me. I have lived a full life and enjoyed every moment of it. We all must die sooner or later; perhaps my death is to be sooner.

"The thing I want to ask you all is this: Do you consider me to be in my right mind?"

"Of course," responded the chief guest, another rancher of great importance in the area. This was echoed sincerely by all those present. Although Señor Too-Many-Frijoles was known for many eccentricities and irregularities of living, nobody could possibly question his sanity. His eyes looked forth steadily into those of his friends, and he seemed satisfied with the answers.

"Remember this night," he admonished his guests. "The reason I have asked you this question is a good one. I wanted you all to attest to the soundness of my mind when I made my will. It has been duly witnessed by the necessary number of witnesses but because of certain items in it which may be considered strange I want the courts to know that I was indeed a sane man when I wrote down its provisions. Come now, let us drink again and thank you all for your attestation of my sanity!"

The guests considered it rather strange to be drinking a toast to a will when they did not know its terms but Señor Too-Many-Frijoles had proved himself a brave man by his declaration, and everyone emptied his glass and expressed the hope that their host would live far longer than he believed.

The doctor knew what he was talking about, however, and Señor Too-Many-Frijoles had known the truth of the warning given him.

Within six months he died, having had one last gargantuan meal with a wench on his lap and the gravy of a great beefsteak on his many chins. He at least died fat and happy.

Throughout the countryside there was great expectancy in regard to the reading of the will. What did it say? What were these strange provisions of which Señor Too-Many-Frijoles had spoken so guardedly? Why had it been so important that his sanity be unquestioned when the document was filed with the courts?

The mystery was soon solved. When the will was filed it contained provisions which shocked all of California.

Señor Too-Many-Frijoles made provisions for his own widow and children, speaking of them in fond terms. Then he added: "During the years I have shared the couch with many a lovely lady throughout this beautiful region. This was no casual affair with me in any instance. Each beautiful señorita or señora who bestowed her favors upon me did so with the full knowledge that I was appreciative of the great honor so shared.

"As a result of these wonderful amorous adventures I have numerous children as well as many fond memories.

"It is my last will and testament that after adequate provisions for my family a substantial bequest be left to each of the following lovely ladies and, if they were fruitful, their children also. This is done in full possession of my faculties and with the knowledge that the friends who gathered at my final fiesta will testify to my essential soundness of mind."

The will then named one hundred and thirty women of the region. . . . .

In a codicil it was stated:

"Also for my zeal and to make amends I leave bequests for 19 broken beds."

The next time I saw my grandfather Carrillo, the judge, I asked him about the truth of the information contained in the letter.

"I know the case well," he said, judicially. Then he added with awe: "There were 130 authenticated bequests to mistresses!

"And Señor Too-Many-Frijoles was a Yale man you know."

Grandfather sighed:

"Por Dios! What a man! Think of my wasted years at Boston College!"

CHAPTER 24

THE LOST TREASURE OF CAHUENGA PASS

IF, some night when the cars are whizzing along the glittering freeway through Cahuenga Pass on the edge of Hollywood, you see me in the hills with a lantern and a shovel, do not be surprised. I will not have lost my mind. I will be there for a definite purpose. Let me tell you why.

Once, long ago, there lived at Paso Robles a sheepherder. He was a peaceful man of that calm temperament which sheepherding requires. He wished nothing more than to be with his flock by day, guiding them to the best grazing grounds, and then watching over them with his faithful dogs at night. He was devoted to his calling.

A simple diet was all he cared for, a broiled jack rabbit now and then breaking any monotony which he might have felt from the tortillas which he baked on a hot rock and the red wine which he squirted into his mouth whenever he felt like it from a wine sack made of the bladder of one of his animals.

Old Juan, for that was his name, had no ambition in life except to continue living as he was doing. The stars spoke their message to him at night, the sun warmed him in the day, and he was content.

One night, though, a strange thing happened. Juan was watching over his flock as usual when he thought he saw a light in a nearby arroyo.

Leaving his dogs in charge of the sheep, he went quietly towards the light which proved to be much farther away than he had thought at first. As a man of the hills and the plains, he moved silently as a ghost without even being aware of taking precautions. But in this case it was fortunate that he was careful because he saw a paralyzing sight. Around a small campfire was grouped a bunch of rough-looking men whom he recognized at once from their descriptions as desperados who had been robbing stage coaches in the area of Pacheco Pass.

At first the robbers appeared only to be eating their evening meal but in a few minutes they did something which caused Juan's heart to beat fast and his fingers to clench into fists. They scraped aside the remnants of the fire and dug a hole and from sacks in their pockets they took out glittering objects and placed them in the hole. Juan recognized these objects as gold and silver coins and he was sure he saw the flash of diamonds and rubies.

The robbers carefully pushed the dirt back over the hole and then put the embers themselves over it so that to all appearances there merely had been an innocent fire at this spot instead of the burial of stolen wealth. The robbers looked all around to make sure that everything was all right and then went to their horses and rode away into the night. Juan could hardly wait for the hoof beats of the horses to die in the distance before he crept down to the site of the fire. Carefully he pushed back the still smoking coals and with trembling hands began to dig in the warm earth beneath. Soon his fingers struck little leather sacks and he pulled these out and in the moonlight poured some of the coins and gems into the palm of his hand.

Even in the pale light the gems winked and glittered as if they were animated with some inner fire.

Juan dug up all the treasure and loaded it into his pockets so that he could hardly walk. As he started back to his flock he began to think for the first time in his life of all the wonderful things he could do with the money and the gems. He began to build in his mind a fine house. He had been a temperate man but he now envisioned beautiful girls he would install in the house in succession as if he were some Oriental monarch.

He looked with disdain at the bladder of cheap red wine and threw it down in disgust. He decided he would drink nothing but the finest wine from golden goblets and eat venison off silver plates brought to him by his servants. He was so fired up with his thoughts that he forgot to eat his simple breakfast or to look after his flock. The sheep wandered away and he paid no attention to where they were headed. He was through being a sheepherder.

Dreaming of the luxuries he would have, he walked in a daze to the home of a friend three miles away and borrowed a horse.

"I find it necessary to travel to see a sick relative," he lied glibly, forgetting in a moment his lifelong truthfulness.

The friend thought he was acting strangely but gladly let him have the horse because Juan always had been kind and generous in the past.

Juan rode south, his mind ablaze with wild plans for the future.

About noontime his belly began to remind him that he had not eaten since the night before. He wondered what to do. He felt it would be unfitting for anyone of his wealth to cook his own meal over a campfire even if he had any meat, which he did not. At the same time he was afraid to go into an inn because he was still so near his home region that someone might wonder how he was able to pay for a meal with gold.

Momentarily, too, he wished he had kept his cheap wine sack, but then he thought again of the luxuries which awaited him as soon as he was in new territory where he could spend freely without arousing suspicion. All that day he traveled beset by hunger and thirst but undecided how to satisfy it. The treasure in his pockets weighed him down but he kept fingering the golden coins and gems and thinking what they would mean in a day or two.

Finally on the second day he bought a meal with the smallest of his gold coins and was reassured when he apparently did not arouse any particular interest in the innkeeper.

When he came close to the settlement of his relatives and friends he selected a spot deep in the woods where he was sure he could remember the location, and carefully buried all his treasure except enough for a fiesta which he was fully determined to give for all those in the neighborhood. He scattered leaves over the spot where he buried the gold and gems and walked carefully back to his horse which he had tethered at a distance, so as to leave as few tell-tale footprints as possible.

Then he went to the cantina where he knew he would find his old cronies.

"Amigos all!" he exclaimed as he went into the cantina and embraced his friends. "I want you to join me in a fiesta this evening, for which I shall pay. An old uncle has died and left me some money and I wish to share my good fortune with you."

His friends slapped him on the back and sent word for all the musicians to gather that evening.

"Come, let us have refreshments!" invited Juan. "Bring out your best wine."

And he threw several gold pieces on the bar.

All day he and an increasing number of friends who gathered as the word spread, drank steadily from the dust-covered bottles of old wine brought from the cellar. By mid-afternoon Juan was drunk.

He waved his arms and staggered among the tables which were being loaded with food and embraced all the pretty girls, while he constantly urged everyone to have more drinks.

When the sizzling meat was on the table and the fresh tortillas were being brought and the wine glasses were filled once more, Juan took his place at the head of the table like some Oriental monarch, just as he had imagined when he found the robbers' loot.

For a couple of hours now he had been dropping hints that his wealth exceeded that which he had first indicated.

He talked so wildly of sacks of gold and handfuls of diamonds, rubies and emeralds that his friends began to suspect he was making up the whole thing. But he did keep bringing forth gold coins from his pockets to pay for the drinks and some people believed he might be telling the truth.

Juan was not interested in eating. He kept drinking the wine—finer and more mellow than any he had ever tasted in his life—until he felt he owned the world. He also wanted to make a speech.

With an effort he pushed himself up from his chair, and swaying unsteadily called out in a loud voice:

"Amigos, parientes," he hiccoughed slightly, "I have not been honest with you. I have a great fortune—."

A tremor ran through his body, and he placed his hands on the table to steady himself.

In a choking voice he tried to continue as the guests half rose from their chairs and looked fearfully at him:

"... big fortune ... diamonds and rubies ... much gold ... buried in the forest in Cahuenga Pass. . . ."

The veins in his neck stood out as if they were going to burst and his face became crimson and he began to choke.

From the guests came cries of alarm as they rushed toward him.

A babble of voices sounded:

"Fortune . . . buried . . . where can it be? . . . diamonds . . . gold. . . ."

They lifted up Juan's head.

He was dead, killed by a stroke.

That is the reason you may see me any night now, with a lantern, searching the woods of Cahuenga Pass for the lost treasure of Juan the sheepherder—the victim of good fortune.

CHAPTER 25

THE BELL THAT NEVER RANG

Always in those days of my youth we heard the sound of bells. Some were for worship. Others were for evensong. At times, they rang in wild alarm for fires or riots. A few seemed to ring just for joy, as if the clapper were animating itself to say a musical word of cheer to everyone within hearing.

The bells fascinated me even when I was small. I would stop, and put my head on one side, and listen as if a personal message were being spoken to me in notes fashioned from bronze and silver.

Once, in the evening, I was sitting by my father on the verandah at Santa Monica looking out towards the ocean, and watching the people strolling along the street as the shadows deepened. We were alone. The sweet-toned bell in the church tower began to ring.

I listened intently. My father watched me drink in each separate note, clear as a bird call. He smiled and tousled my head.

"Did I ever tell you about the bell that never rang?" he asked gently.

I came out of my reverie, induced by the bell, and looked at him and shook my head.

"It was when I was a younger man, before you were born," he began slowly as if conjuring up pictures deep within his mind.

I was riding through the great thorn jungle of Sonora, Mexico, my father went on. Some men here in Los Angeles wanted me to inspect mining properties for them, and I was nearing the town of Magdalena where I was to hire pack mules and go into the wild mountains.

The great cactus were in bloom. Some had white flowers near the tips many feet from the ground, others bore scarlet flowers close to the ground. On the bushes were flowers of many colors, purple, blue, yellow, pink, and red. The combined scent of the flowers hung over the whole area as I rode along.

It occurred to me that it was from this very region that there had come a young man of whom we had heard a great deal in California. He had become the most feared bandit in the whole state.

His name was Joaquín Murrieta.

Many of us in California knew the story of Murrieta and what drove him into the terrible life of a bandit. It all began there in Sonora where he was born. He was a mild-mannered young man, very deft with his hands. People liked him and predicted that he would have a fine future.

He fell in love with a beautiful young girl who was only sixteen. Her family wanted her to marry a rich hacendado who was more than seventy-years-old; he owned vast grants of land and thousands of cattle and horses. The girl's parents thought it would be a grand match for her and they insisted that she marry him. But she was in love with young Joaquín. The young couple decided to elope.

They were married at a little mission church in Sonora and then fled on horseback towards Alta California. The parents and the hacendado were furious and pursued them but the couple escaped across the border into the United States. They made their way to the gold country of California and lived in Angels Camp. Joaquín's brother already was there so Joaquín felt he would be able to get a job. As I said, Joaquín was very deft with his hands. He had a fine personality and was honest, so he got a job dealing Monte in one of the big gambling halls.

He lived with his bride in a little house out on a beautiful stream and he staked out a mining claim where he had control of much of the water. Just below his claim was one owned by five rough Missourians.

They resented the fact that a "Mex" had the water rights and the control of the stream which flowed on down to their claim. One night all five of them got drunk and went up to Joaquín's house and pounded on the door and demanded that he move away and leave the claim to them. He refused and barred the door again and the men went away cursing and threatening him. In the morning Joaquín who was of a peaceful nature, rode into Angels

Camp town where there was a law officer so that he could ask protection for his wife and himself.

He was gone all day.

When he returned in the evening he found his wife lying on the floor of his little cabin. She was almost unconscious. She had been abused and raped by the five Missourians and as the horrified Joaquín came in and picked her up she died in his arms. He was blinded with grief. Almost unable to breathe or to speak, he rocked in silent agony, holding the body of his beloved bride. Just then he heard the noise of a large crowd outside crying:

"Death to the man on the mule!"

He heard cries of "Horse thief!" "Hang him!" and louder and louder screams, and then the voice of his brother. He laid his wife gently on the bed and rushed outside to see what was happening. He saw then that his brother was being dragged towards a tree by a mob. The threats he had heard were directed against the brother.

Joaquín pushed into the crowd calling out to explain that his brother was not a thief and that he had bought the mule from the man who had actually stolen it. No one would listen to him, and he was shoved aside. Then, before Joaquín's eyes, the brother was hanged to an oak tree until he was dead.

The crowd, knowing Joaquín was kin to the victim, turned on him and lashed him with rawhide whips until he was almost senseless. Finally the crowd left and Joaquín dragged himself bleeding and bruised into the house where lay the body of his bride. After he had partially regained his strength, he buried his wife and erected a little cross over her grave in the woods nearby, and bade her farewell. Then he went out into the night armed with all the guns of his brother and himself.

He had but one aim.

That was to exterminate the gringos, the hated Americans, the damned scoundrels who had committed the crimes against his wife and left her dying on the floor of the little house where she and Joaquín had enjoyed so many happy moments. This crime and the hanging of his brother awoke a beast inside Joaquín—he lost all feeling of mercy. He was filled only with a deadly thirst for revenge.

He vanished from the area.

The miners were so busy with their own business that they hardly realized that he had left. A few days later people in the area noticed a great swirl of buzzards over a rough area in the mountains nearby.

These buzzards circling round and round always indicated death. Often it meant a cow or a bull or a deer—sometimes a human being. There were so many buzzards some of the more curious miners investigated.

There they found the five Missourians who had killed Joaquín Murrieta's wife, each one with a hole in his forehead and a sign on his breast in Spanish saying "Revenge!" This frightened all those who had been in the mob which hanged Joaquín's brother because many of them knew they had been recognized. The name Joaquín Murrieta came to be dreaded throughout the whole gold country. He killed many of those who had unjustly executed his brother. He gathered around him a group of desperados who had fled from the law for one reason or another. They began to rob the rich and in many instances fed the poor.

Joaquín Murrieta became known as "the Robin Hood of Eldorado."

The state put up posters offering to pay $10,000 for his capture, dead or alive.

Along came Murrieta and wrote with a flourish underneath:

"And so will I.

(signed) Joaquín Murrieta."

His own thirst for vengeance was directed at first mainly against those who had wronged him. But the wild and lawless men who congregated around him had no scruples at all and no particular objective for their evil passion.

By far the worst of the criminals who attached themselves to Joaquín Murrieta was Three-Fingered Jack. He was utterly cruel, without a spark of mercy and he had one particular hobby which he carried to the point of obsession. He collected Chinamen's ears. Every time he got the opportunity he would cut off the ears of any Chinese he encountered and add them to the long necklace which he boasted as his proudest possession.

My father shuddered as he came to this part of the story, recalling the vividness of his memories in those early days when California was terrorized by the Murrieta band of outlaws. Father felt a great compassion for Murrieta himself as a person who has been driven out of his mind by the horrors heaped upon him in the country to which he had fled with his bride and where he expected kindness and protection.

As father rode along in the gathering dusk in the Sonora wilderness, the thoughts of Murrieta kept coming to him. He tried to figure the difference between right and wrong. How could Murrieta's deeds be justified? Yet how could the crimes committed against Murrieta and his bride be overlooked?

Just as father reached this point in his thoughts in the Sonora thorn jungle he saw ahead of him the first lights of evening in what he knew must be the little town of Magdalena. It took his mind off the horrible story which he had been recreating almost involuntarily because of the reminders in this area where Murrieta once had lived.

Father's horse, tired and hungry after the long day's ride twitched his ears and hurried his steps as they neared the village. The first sound father heard were those of a guitar and half-drunken voices singing. He surmised that it must be coming from one of the cantinas on the straggling main street of the pueblo.

He saw a corral and arranged with the Mexican owner for feeding and watering his horse. Then with his cramped muscles aching from the long ride he walked down the street towards the sounds coming from the cantina. A gush of light poured out of the half opened door and the sounds of merriment inside now increased to a din as father came closer. He saw that the place was connected with a little inn where he was to stay.

He peered inside. The place was crowded. Smoke from innumerable cigarrillos made it almost impossible to see. But there were gaudily dressed women, vaqueros, miners, townspeople, gamblers and all sorts of individuals cramming the place. The clink of glasses and bottles sounded at the bar. Aguardiente, pulque and tequila were being drunk like water.

Father decided he would go in to make inquiries so he walked through the door and tried to get up to the bar so he could ask the man there about some of the persons he was supposed to contact.

As he came in he noticed an old man look up suddenly with a startled expression and then stare at him fixedly. In a moment the old man moved over towards him through the crush of people and clouds of smoke.

The old man wore his hat tilted over his eyes, so that he looked out from beneath the brim with a piercing stare. With a slow almost calculated gesture he brought his brown cigarrillo to his lips and puffed and blew out the smoke.

His face was covered with a beard and long moustaches. To my father he said in Spanish, "You are a Californian—I can tell by your clothes."

"Yes," answered my father, glad to meet any sort of friendly response in this place which looked like a den of iniquity and sounded like bedlam.

"I'm a Californian myself," said the old man, his voice trailing away as he added, "but I've been away a long, long time down here in the horse and cattle business—quedando ganado. I sometimes long for my home region of Alta California."

"California is a wonderful place," responded my father. "I'm just here on some business and then I am going back."

"Would you do the honor to allow me to sit with you?" asked the old man.

"With pleasure," replied my father. He accompanied his companion to a little table in a corner where they were surrounded by the babble of conversation, the loud plunking of guitars, the rattle of castanets, and the sounding of Mexican horns as the people in the cantina joined in song and continued their drinking.

"I am from Los Angeles," my father said. "From what part of the state do you come?"

A reminiscent look came into the old man's eye.

"From the northern part," he responded slowly. "As I say, it has been a long time since I was there. I have no reason to return. All my loved ones are gone."

He and my father ordered refreshments and as they sipped the old man said suddenly:

"In those days California was unsafe. Bandidos were ranging up and down the state."

My father stared fixedly at him. The coincidence of his having been thinking himself about Joaquín Murrieta as he rode towards the town impressed itself upon him greatly.

"Yes," went on the old man, "it was a very dangerous time. Joaquín Murrieta, Three-Fingered Jack, and all their evil companions were robbing and killing. Often it was just for revenge, getting even. It was unsafe for people to be abroad at night and often even in the daytime. Coaches were robbed, horsemen were shot, women attacked in their homes and the whole region was in terror."

My father could hardly believe his ears at this virtual continuation of his own recent thoughts.

"You seem to know a great deal about it, señor," he said courteously.

The old man hardly seemed to hear him. But then he started in again as if dragging up memories out of the long ago.

"The people living around San Miguel Mission were in the heart of the territory where Murrieta was carrying on his depredations. At San Miguel the residents kept in a constant state of readiness in case of a bandit raid. They had a certain number of cattle and horses and stores of grain in the mission for emergencies. The little adobe huts of the mission workers were scattered around in the fields and pastures for quite a distance.

"One day the long-feared warning came. A wounded messenger arrived saying the Murrieta band was on its way to the mission. Panic set in immediately. Women and children rushed towards the mission building, the men gathered up their best horses and rode quickly to the mission after posting scouts nearby to warn of the near approach of the outlaws. The gates of the mission were closed and the women and children huddled inside praying, while the men loaded the rusty old muskets which they had been able to find and held old swords and anything which they could use for a weapon. They intended to fight off the bandits as long as they could.

"Soon a messenger rushed in crying that the bandits were close by, leaving a trail of blood in the valley, robbing the homes of the mission workers, killing the cattle and stealing the horses. One of the women in the mission was carrying a tiny baby. She knew how ferocious the bandits were and feared that they would actually penetrate inside the mission walls.

"It so happened that in the patio of the mission there was a huge heavy bell sitting on the ground. It had never been hung. When it was sent from Spain after being cast from all the beautiful combination of metals which would make its tone beautiful, the people who made it neglected to send the clapper with it so it was of no use until the clapper arrived, and nobody knew when this would be. The mother with the suckling babe could see the smoke rising from burning homes and could hear the screams of a few unfortunate who had been caught by the bandits.

"She was desperate to save her baby. She looked around frantically and saw the bell.

" 'Quick!' she cried to an Indian boy, 'Levante la campana! Lift the bell!' She laid the baby down momentarily. Then she and the Indian boy tilted the bell and she seized the child with one hand and thrust it underneath, placing a small rock so as to hold up one side of the bell a little for air space.

"With tears streaming down her face and sobs racking her body she seized a gun and took her place beside the men ready to defend the mission.

"The bandits after devastating the homes nearby concentrated their attack on the mission itself. They brought a huge battering ram, knocked in the door which was not intended to be used as a fortress anyway, and burst inside. They shot the men in cold blood, raped the women and then murdered them, and galloped away.

"In a few minutes the vigilantes who had been pursuing them arrived and found a scene of utter horror and death within the mission walls. The silent crucifix looked down only upon bodies which had been desecrated by the horrible bandits. The vigilantes pressed on immediately and pursued the bandits all night.

"Finally the vigilantes caught up with the desperados near the coast although Murrieta and Three-Fingered Jack were not with them. The vigilantes lassoed the bandits and dragged them screaming and kicking into the surf until they were drowned. It was not a complete punishment for their horrible crime but it gave some satisfaction to the members of the posse who had seen what had happened at San Miguel.

"Soon afterwards, Murrieta himself and Three-Fingered Jack with his long necklace of Chinamen's ears hanging around his neck were killed near Pacheco Pass by Captain Harry Love and his hard-riding rangers. Their heads were cut off and pickled in alcohol so they could be identified for the reward. It was a grisly sight when the heads were displayed in the bars of San Francisco.

"Joaquín Murrieta had paid for his crimes of vengeance at last.

"But his death could not erase the memory of the massacre at the Mission of San Miguel.

"That, Señor, was one of the most horrible moments in California history. I remind you of it because the sight of you in your California clothes has aroused old memories in my mind. I am still a Californian at heart."

My father who had sat fascinated by the story told in these strange surroundings amid the din and the drinking and the music was unsatisfied.

"But, Señor," he asked eagerly, "what became of the baby under the bell?"

The old Californian, now transplanted so far away to the wilds of Mexico dragged for a moment upon his brown cigarrillo, musing, his brooding eyes shaded by his hat brim.

After a long dramatic pause he finally spoke: "That baby is telling you the story."

3

Año · 1860

TERCERA

PARTE DEL LIBRO

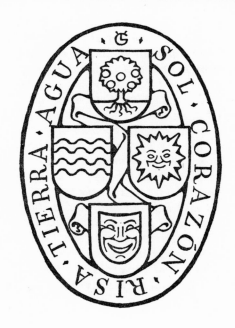

"THE WORLD'S A STAGE"

LEO CARRILLO

LONGING

I long for the smell of the sagebrush land,
For the tumble weed and the desert sand.
I think and I think and it gets my goat,
And a sort of a lump come into my throat.
I put out the lights—a New York hotel—
And I grope in the dark for the things I know well.
I go back to my days of punching cattle,
Kinda tired of people and their idle prattle
Of the things they'd do if they had the chance,
For their fiddlers play but they never dance.
I want to go back where there ain't no crowds,
Where my mountains kiss the hanging clouds,
Where the blue sky bends to a turquoise sea,
And the Joshua serves as my only tree,
Where the rattler coils in the cactus shade,
And you go to sleep to its serenade,
Where the heat's hell hot and you're short of breath,
And the raven trails and you flirt with death.
Well, you keep your streets and your buildings grand,
And I'll take my cactus and sagebrush land,
Where the blues and the pinks and the purples blend,
And I'll wait for God till He says the end.

CHAPTER 26

LURE OF THE WORLD

A COMPETITIVE spirit burned within me when I was sixteen. I yearned to go forth and conquer the world. It was true that there was some doubt in my mind as to just what I wanted to conquer and how I was to go about it. Still the urge was there to venture from home surroundings into a new realm and to find a place for myself somewhere.

In recent ocean swimming contests I had won world's championships. This whetted my appetite for achievement. I felt if I could win over other competitors in swimming it might be that in the great outside world there would be a chance for me, too.

Art still continued to be my chief interest. Ever since early days in school when I had been reprimanded for drawing cartoons and caricatures of my fellow pupils, the desire to express myself in this medium had remained. Strangely, though, it was an almost unnoticed talent which indirectly launched me on my first modest venture into the working world.

This was my ability to imitate. A friend of mine, Bert Bassett, was proud of the fact that his father was a conductor on the Southern Pacific Railroad line. Bert himself had gone all the way over to distant Arizona the year before to work with a surveying party in an engineering crew of the railroad.

It so happened that a number of Chinese were employed on railroad work in Santa Barbara. Bert asked me one day whether I would like to go up to Santa Barbara and get a job with the railroad and help to communicate with the Chinese. Bert's father had heard me do some of my imitations of the Chinese, which I had retained from my early childhood around the Plaza, and this had given him the idea.

My father and mother granted their permission for the journey because it was so close to home. Bert and I set off together riding on a train pass, which was a great thrill for me. We sat in the chair car with our mandolins and sang popular songs of the day. The train trip didn't last long, however, and when we arrived in Santa Barbara we were confronted with a problem. Where were we to live?

We soon discovered. We were assigned to a box car in the freight yard. This particular box car was dirty and littered. We carried our homemade sleeping bags over to it and decided it would require a real cleaning out. We left our sleeping bags and went to obtain brooms and mops so we could start on the job.

Then came an experience which shaped the thinking of my whole life.

Santa Barbara was a mecca for rich tourists. They came from the Eastern United States and even from abroad. As we went into the baggage room at the station I was confronted for the first time with the whole romantic appeal of the wide world—there before me were fancy leather suitcases and traveling bags with gaudy stickers from Japan, China, London, Paris, Rome, Madrid, all the places of which I had dreamed in my reading.

The sight of these reminders of the far corners of creation struck me with a terrific impact. Instinctively I remembered Peer Gynt in Ibsen's play as he lay on his back in the hills looking at the clouds and in them saw the King's Henchman who created an indelible memory.

I spoke out loud as I looked at the fancy luggage and the stickers and said, "I'll be there someday too!" It was a promise to myself. From that moment I began to have a goal of achieving success so that I might go forth and see the wonders which beckoned to me and which seemed at the moment so far away.

That night I went to the baggage car and retrieved my sleeping bag and slept in the baggage room, by the exciting luggage. For a long time I lay awake thinking of the trips I would take in the future, pasting stickers on my fancy trunks and suitcases in all the romantic ports and cities of the world.

Then I dropped off to sleep, and dreamed of Hong Kong and Bombay and Bangkok and Constantinople as I traveled leisurely around the world, loaded with luggage.

More prosaic matters immediately interfered with my dream.

We had to fix up our dirty box car. The next morning, back in Santa Barbara instead of Bombay, we swept it out, papered it with newspapers so that we always had something to read, and plenty of pin-up girls from the Sunday supplement, built bunks out of old two-by-fours and slats to fit our sleeping bags. We installed a Syblie stove, a cornucopia of sheet steel four feet high set on dirt on the wood floor of the car, and belching smoke through a crooked stove-pipe. It created a glowing fire which we welcomed because it was chilly in the evenings and mornings.

Our other utilities consisted of a tin can on a box for washing and nails driven into the side of the car for towels. We built steps up to the floor level of the car. We had access to the water car and cook cars which were operated by Chinese.

I held classes every night teaching some of the engineers Chinese, and some of the Chinese English. The meals created by the Chinese cooks were marvelous even if they did have to work in cramped quarters and devote most of their attention to the old caboose where "the brass" lived.

In Santa Barbara, I made many friends. The name "Carrillo" was well known there, dating back for a century and a half or so, and I was invited to the homes of many of the old families who had known my father or grandfather.

It also was my good fortune to become acquainted with a young newspaperman who wore a Derby hat and was interested in everything. His name was Tom Storke. He was extremely kind to me at a time when I was a stranger in the community. We began a friendship which lasted a lifetime. Later, he became the famous publisher of the Santa Barbara *News-Press* and a United States Senator.

But to me he remained just "Tom" in his jaunty Derby looking for a story, and nearly always finding it.

We worked from daylight to dark cutting brush so the surveying instruments could have an unobstructed view for the surveying. We went out in line wagons drawn by horses through areas which are now solidly built up with fine homes.

We were opening up land which once belonged to my ancestors in an area where my father had many fond memories because of having grown up in Santa Barbara. The boss who came occasionally to look at the progress of the work was George W. Boschke, who had built the sea wall at Galveston,

Texas and later was Chief Engineer of the Southern Pacific. He had a great sense of humor.

One Sunday Mr. Boschke asked me whether I would be interested in an engineering job. I thanked him and told him that I would be interested but that my chief ambition was to be an artist and that I made drawings all the time. Then I added, "I have a brother who is an engineer." Mr. Boschke seemed interested.

"Where is he?" he asked.

"He's working for Santa Monica," I told him.

"Oh, he's not an engineer, he's a surveyor," Mr. Boschke responded.

I didn't like this very much so I bragged on my brother Jack. This tickled Mr. Boschke's sense of humor.

"If he's so good why isn't he on the railroad?" he inquired.

"He would make a fine railroad engineer," I responded valiantly.

Actually Jack had started out at $2 a day driving stakes and carrying instruments for the rod men and had worked up to be City Engineer of Santa Monica through this experience.

As a result of my conversation with Mr. Boschke, Jack was offered a job on the railroad and took it and soon was able to sign his name "E. J. Carrillo, Assistant Engineer, Southern Pacific Railroad Company."

From this humble start he went on to become the world famous engineer in New York, builder of Idlewild Airport and many other magnificent creations in the metropolis before his retirement.

When Jack went to work for the railroad it gave me a jolt. I knew that he was interested in engineering work and fitted to go on to great achievements in that field.

But what about myself? Was I doing the right thing in cutting brush and carrying stakes and instruments for the surveyors? Might I be neglecting my real opportunities in the art world where my inclinations really lay?

These things ran through my mind as I lay in my crude bunk in the baggage car and tried to decide what I should do with my future. In the meantime, though, I kept on working at Santa Barbara and trying to do a good job in my daily routine.

At that moment I might well have said of my prospect in life: "Quién sabe?"

THE BECKONING STAGE

A RAILROAD job wasn't so bad when it was in California but when the Southern Pacific moved our engineer party over to the wilds of Nevada, I began to long for my beloved Santa Barbara coastland. I knew a young fellow named Ernest French and he and I agreed that railroad work was something which was all right to make a little money but not as a career.

"This desert has got its limitations," mourned French as he looked around at the bare sterile hills. "Let's get out in the big world where we have some real opportunities."

By doing our own washing, knitting our own socks, and getting our board and bunk as part of boxcar life, we were somehow or other $400 richer, partly because there wasn't any income tax. The $400 seemed like a tremendous sum and enough to let us lead the kind of life we wanted, so we decided to go to San Francisco. That was the way the Southern Pacific lost a couple of potential executives.

This was in the period when the city by the Golden Gate was the mecca of the literary and artistic people of the West Coast and, in many instances, from all over the world. Its reputation rivaled that of New York, New Orleans, and as we liked to think, even Paris and London. French wanted to study law and I was determined to try something that was in my heart almost from infancy, an art career. I had continued with my sketches and cartoons ever since the days when I was a small boy in Santa Monica and had received some encouragement from my family and from the people whose pictures I had drawn.

French and I were able to get a railroad pass to the coast from our Nevada camp and with our $400 carefully hidden in money belts around our waists we embarked on the great adventure in San Francisco.

I shall never forget my first day there. Fascinated, I stood at Fourth and Market Streets looking at the sea of faces, the squirming herd of humans all scurrying along as if they were too confused to know where they were going. People, people, people! I always loved people and wanted to get close to them so I could understand them better.

Portsmouth Square provided as great a thrill. I could imagine Robert Louis Stevenson sitting on a bench there while he wrote of the South Seas.

Everything seemed cloaked in magic. I was looking for the blue beyond the blue and the hill beyond the hill.

French and I finally came back to earth long enough to realize that we had to have some place to live.

We found a room in the home of two little old ladies and agreed to pay them $3 a week rent. This included pancakes and coffee which were really delicious and made the seemingly high price of $3 more palatable.

French started his law studies and I looked around for a place to begin my art instruction. I found an art school on California Street over the California Market. At the time I signed up for the courses in life classes, painting, still-life drawing, and all the rest I was unaware of the greatest advantage which this particular studio afforded. In a few days I discovered what this was.

As I went to the school with my art materials under my arm one morning I saw on the step of the studio next door a man of medium height with a grizzled beard and moustache. He wore the full black tie of an artist and a black, rather slouch beaver hat. It was a bright morning and everyone seemed in a friendly mood so I nodded and spoke to him and he returned the greeting. At this time I had no idea who he was.

Later I saw him on several occasions and once when I was with another student I finally learned the importance of the man I had encountered so casually. He was the immortal William Keith, greatest California artist of the period. His facility with a palette knife was so great that you could almost believe the bark on the oak trees which he created was the actual thing in nature instead of something applied with paints. Keith scorned to use a brush and resorted exclusively to the palette knife, a technique which appealed to me greatly because of the realistic effect it provided. Gradually I became acquainted with Keith and found him to be a kindly and understanding critic of all young art students. He would generously spend time with us, criticizing this or that and offering suggestions for improvement. He was particularly kind to me and gave me encouragement to proceed with my art work. He put great stress on the need for basic training in the essentials before attempting really elaborate oil paintings.

Keith was a leading member of the Bohemian Club. Grateful as I was to him, I still didn't realize that he was one of the masters of the age. He was a great inspiration to me.

I also was encouraged by Richard Partington, my art teacher and brother of the great Gertrude Partington whose drawings of old San Francisco Chinatown with its Chinese inhabitants in the pigtails and loose clothes of the period were real historical documents.

All this time, although my art career seemed to be flourishing, my financial status was growing more and more desperate. The $400 which had seemed so large when French and I came to San Francisco by now had dwindled to a very small sum indeed. In fact, French, suffering from the same difficulties had been forced to move to other quarters. Pride kept me from asking help from my family because I was determined to be "on my own."

Necessity required that I economize as much as possible on everything so my meals were restricted to one Swedish restaurant which dealt in good food at extremely low prices. It was across the street from the California Theatre where the immortal David Warfield had started as an usher before launching into his great *Music Master* for David Belasco, and his Shakespearean roles. I could sit at the little table which I frequented in the Swedish restaurant and look through the window at the theatre.

It held a fascination for me because of faintly stirring ambitions I had to tell my dialect stories which constantly were being expanded as I prowled through Chinatown and the other sections of San Francisco inhabited by odd peoples from all over the world. I had begun to think of appearing on the stage. My unvarying diet at the restaurant was a breaded veal cutlet with all the trimmings, including coffee, for only 20 cents. I have never been able to look a veal cutlet in the face since.

Finally my money was so near exhausted that I knew I had to give up the $3 a week room even though I hated to lose the splendid pancakes and coffee which the little old ladies dished out in large quantities to satisfy my boyish appetite. My pride also prevented me from asking them for a cut in the room rate, and I believe that they never suspected how near I was to being a pauper.

My first thought was of the Y.M.C.A. when it became necessary for me to move because in Santa Monica I had been treated very nicely at the "Y" due to my swimming ability. In Santa Monica I was a champion at sixteen and had broken all ocean world's records for surf swimming at that time.

At any rate, the "Y" in San Francisco agreed to take me in on an athletic membership at a cut rate if I would devote myself to the swimming team. I swam half a mile every day to keep in condition although this had one drawback because it increased my appetite and I lacked the funds to buy as much food as I would have liked.

Times were bad and there was what I suppose we would call a depression today. In those days people just said that in San Francisco everything was so tough the pigeons were feeding the pedestrians.

The "Y" was close to San Francisco's famous Union Square, frequented by every sort of character one can imagine plus the pigeons which in this case despite the depression were still looking for handouts of corn and popcorn.

The strange human beings on the benches in Union Square appealed to my artistic talents and I was constantly making sketches of them.

One day in the Square I was sitting next to a real "character"—unkempt, with ragged clothes and piercing eyes. And he smelled. He could have been arrested for fragrancy instead of vagrancy. I noticed that he was staring at a statue in the park and that he seemed transfixed by the image represented. He was so engrossed and his expression was so remarkable that I immediately began making a sketch of him. He seemed oblivious of my activity. His eyes were fixed upon the statue with such intensity that it seemed a physical impossibility for him to quit gazing at it.

After I had finished, I showed him my little sketch in the hope he might make some comment on it, but he merely glanced at it, and without a word, resumed his staring at the statue.

"What is it all about? Who is that statue?" I asked.

Slowly he lowered his gaze.

"Why are you so interested?" he asked in a guttural voice.

His eyes turned once again to the statue overhead as he paused. Then he looked at me and spoke as if something from inside must have been talking to him. I shall never forget his answer:

"Boy, that is Victory! The symbol of Victory! The reason I'm here on this park bench looking like this is because I have never been victorious in anything."

Once again he began looking at the statue with a gaze of intense sadness as if it represented everything in life which he had been unable to attain.

His remark struck me so forcibly that it brought to my mind immediately something that the great William James had said, "Our minds are the playrooms of other people's thoughts."

This certainly was the case with me. I looked at this human derelict, dirty, hopeless, baffled, longing to make up in some impossible way the frustrations and defeats of a life in which victory had never played a part, and a sudden resolution came over me.

I decided that I must be a victor.

Also I had a great urge to get to the "Y" to swim away the contamination of the physical presence of this unkempt character, although spiritually I felt a great impetus towards victory in whatever I might undertake. In this way I felt gratitude to him but otherwise his very memory was unclean.

Elbert Hubbard, the philosopher, once told me, "If you want to renew your circulation and stimulate your mental activity rub hell out of yourself with a Turkish towel!"

After my swim I rubbed extra hard with the Turkish towel as if I really did need circulation to wipe away the thought of the poor creature I had just left. I kept thinking of being victorious. The statue became a part of my subconscious mind.

I dressed and started out for my key at the "Y" desk.

It was then that fate and Victory seemed to begin to team up for me. As I got my key the desk clerk also handed me a little note. It was from my uncle John T. Gaffey of San Pedro, a wealthy real estate owner who had always shown an interest in my career ever since I was a tiny child. Tío Juan had given me my first book, *Don Quixote*, which possibly explains why I like windmills and have them all over my ranch nowadays.

The note from Tío Juan said:

"Call at the San Francisco Examiner and ask for Mr. Dent Robert, the managing editor. He will receive you. A job is waiting."

This seemed such a miraculous piece of good fortune that I could hardly wait to get to the Examiner office. Mr. Robert received me kindly and told me about the job. It was rather a menial one in the art department and the "take home" pay was $10 a week. Small as the pay was, I was extremely happy to get it at that time because it represented my first major victory in my determination to make my own way and not appeal to my folks at home.

Of course at first I was doing only the simplest work in the art department, layouts and pastedowns although I tried a few local cartoons, too. It was routine but actually I almost forgot about the tediousness of some of the tasks because of my surroundings. Suddenly I was in the presence of newspapermen and artists whose names were nationally known, and it was a thrill for me just to see them and to feel that I was working with them even if in a very humble way. The immortal Robert Edgren, later one of the greatest sports writers in the nation; William Norton; Edward H. Hamilton, sport and editorial writer; and young Edmond Coblenz, who later became editor-in-chief of all the Hearst papers, were my confreres.

Coblenz learned of my language ability in Chinese, Japanese, Italian and Spanish, as well as English and he took me to the waterfront and to the colonies of different nationalities to assist in the gathering of stories through the use of my language skill. Some of the stories were risqué and off-color or too esoteric for publication. They merely represented the humorous slants of the Chinese, Japanese, or Italians as the case might be.

When Coblenz later wrote *We Covered the Waterfront* I was part of the "We."

I had an ability to mimic and to repeat the stories in a sort of pidgin form which was intelligible to people who spoke English but still retained some of the flavor of the foreign language and the thought of the people it represented.

Coblenz each night asked me to get out in the middle of the editorial floor and tell some of these stories which we had encountered during the day.

The staff members were amused by the performance and one severe-looking gentleman with pince-nez eye glasses actually laughed out loud. The other writers regarded him with astonishment. Somebody remarked it was the first time this particular man had ever been known to laugh at all in the editorial department. He was Ashton Stevens, the widely-known dramatic critic of *The Examiner* and the Chicago *Herald American*.

After breaking his long silence by laughing at my little act he became interested in me and suggested that I should try for some vaudeville outlet. All of the fellows in the editorial department joined in the urging and of course I was tempted. This was my first recognition since I had performed in the privacy of my own home in the presence of my numerous relatives, who, it is true, laughed at me but might have been considered a prejudiced audience.

Stevens told me that I had to put together a connected act with some continuity and coherence to it and then try it out in some fashion before I attempted to get any professional vaudeville engagement. This was all new ground to me, of course, and I was anxious to get advice and to follow it.

At that time in San Francisco there was a young insurance broker active in the financial district who was known for his efforts in behalf of amateur theatricals and everything of that nature. He was trying at this time to raise funds for a new club which since has proven one of the greatest in the United States, called the "Family Club of San Francisco."

This young producer who was trying to put together the amateur talent was known to us as Eddie Bowes. You may know him as "Major" Bowes, later the best known name in the United States in the field of amateur shows and producer of his own notable programs on radio and television. At that time, though, he was feeling his way in attempting to put together a program which would appeal to a San Francisco audience. Some of my newspaper friends suggested that he might give me a spot, and he agreed.

This really scared me. It had not been so bad to act for my family or even for the men I knew on the Examiner, but here I was going out to face a real audience for the first time. I was timid and frightened but still I saw a chance to move a step forward towards the vaudeville appearance which now loomed on the horizon as my next "victory." I still was thinking of the remark of the ragged old man in the park which had just preceded my first big break in getting the job on the Examiner.

So on the night of the performance I stiffened my knees and wiggled my toes, remembering what George May Marion, the great director of *Tugboat Annie* starring Marie Dressler, had told me: "If you can do that the situation is yours."

That dispelled my fear and nervousness to a degree. But I was under double tension because my spot on the program was the very first one. When the curtain went up I marched resolutely out onto the stage and went into my act. Pretty soon people in the audience began to laugh and clap, and I knew I had the crowd with me.

Also, Bowes was prompting me from the wings to do my imitations of a horse or a Chinese vegetable peddler or whatever it was and this helped me get over the hump.

From then on I lost all my nervousness and knew that I was approaching the goal I had set for myself after my encounter with the foul smelling bum in Union Square.

Greatest thing of all I did not recognize at that moment.

I was Major Bowes' first amateur.

ACCOLADE IN GREASEPAINT

Word of my success in my first theatrical venture circulated quickly around San Francisco, spread by my fellow newspaper workers and friends in the audience. The staff of *The Examiner* made me repeat every word and gesture of the act from Major Bowes' show on the editorial floor. They were more determined than ever that I should get a chance in real vaudeville. Ashton Stevens was kind enough to ask Phil Hastings, the press agent of the Orpheum Theatre, the goal of every amateur performer in the country, to listen to my stories and patter.

"No, I don't want to do it myself," Hastings replied, "but I will do something else. I will send around the greatest monologist in the world. If he likes the kid I will make a story out of it that he has discovered some new talent."

Sure enough, the monologist came up to the *Examiner* office. Some of the older men who knew him personally greeted him and I was introduced. Again I felt shy and self-conscious at trying to impress so great a performer. However, we went into a little 8 by 10 room and the monologist with a grin on his face and a smile in his Irish eye, with a face hungry for fun, sat on a pile of old newspapers and indicated he was ready to listen.

I went out of the room, closed the door and then re-entered as if I were going on stage. As I came through the door I bowed and said formally:

"Ladies and gentlemen—." But there were no ladies present. Anyway I went into my act and the monologist's smiling eyes grew even brighter and he broke into laughter. He laughed and laughed. I thought he was just being sympathetic and kind but I kept on anyway and soon realized that his laughter was genuine.

The monologist went back to the Orpheum management and said, "Give this kid a chance. He's got something different. Those Chinese, Japanese, Italian, and Mexican dialect stories of his amuse me no end. The shyness of his personality (he was scared to death!) is cute."

The result was that I received an offer to appear on the Orpheum stage at a Sunday matinee.

This so overwhelmed me that I took my savings, $80, to Bullock & Jones and bought a blue double-breasted coat, striped pants and white shoes. If you wore Bullock & Jones clothes you were in the swim.

When I went to the theater Pat Rooney, the vaudeville headliner, and his wife put on my make-up. I was ashamed because it was the first time I had ever had rouge on my face.

This time I was practically petrified with fear but I took my little bag of tricks, and with that persistent vision of Victory in the back of my mind, walked out on the stage that Sunday afternoon.

In the audience were gamblers, bartenders, stockbrokers, newspaper people, and livery stable owners; all the people who made up old San Francisco. Just as I walked out, a great tribute was paid to me even before I started my act.

From the back of the theater sailing majestically down the aisle in ostrich feathers and gossamer form-fitting dress came Doty Valencia, the most fashionable madam in all of San Francisco with her girls in their finery, too. They seated themselves in the second row where they always sat on Sunday afternoons when there was a special show. I knew then that I had been paid the supreme tribute with Doty's attendance, and I plunged into my act with new inspiration.

Looking back now and judging from the number of flowers handed to me at the conclusion of my act, flowers which came from my newspaper friends, the Press Club, the Olympic Club, Doty and the girls, and from just plain citizens of San Francisco I know that I must have been a success.

That night there were parties at all the hangouts of the newspaper crowd— Bug 'n' Louse, Fly Trap, Dirty Spoon and Sloppy Joe's.

Up in *The Examiner* editorial room Coblenz passed the hat, as was the custom then, so that the food bill could be paid for everybody and thus include the guys who were broke and couldn't have gone otherwise. Nobody knew how much each fellow put in, if anything.

Kolb & Dill who were playing across the street from the Orpheum; Barney Bernard, the developing vaudevillian; the quartet from Eddie Graney's Saloon —Sylvester, Jones, Pringle & Morrell—and Harry Fox all joined graciously in welcoming me to the ranks of the pros.

The Orpheum kept me on for three weeks.

The management moved me from the No. 2 spot to next-to-closing, the most important place on the bill.

By the time the three weeks was up I had gained additional confidence and felt that I knew a little something about what appealed to the wonderful, ordinary people who make up an audience in a vaudeville house. I was determined to carry on toward a new and greater victory in this field which actually seemed to offer more promise than anything I could produce in the art world.

I never ceased to be grateful to that kindly Irish monologist who sat there so patiently on the pile of old newspapers and listened to my act and then gave me the blessing which resulted in my first professional appearance. He was Walter C. Kelly. Kelly's brother was Jack Kelly, father of Princess Grace of Monaco. He was known throughout the world as the "Virginia Judge," a great teller of Negro stories and one of the finest Negro dialect characters the vaudeville stage ever saw.

After hearing me and giving me the boost with the Orpheum management, Kelly continued his tour of the United States as he was in great demand and a headliner everywhere. I went back to my art work at the end of my engagement.

The booking agent for the Orpheum, Robert D. Girard, had seen me during the run although he actually worked out of Los Angeles. To my great surprise and joy I received word that Girard had billed me at the Orpheum "back home" in Los Angeles.

My return was a triumph. "Little Leo, the railroad boy" had returned as a stage star—or so it seemed to my relatives. I found out from Girard that my cousins, nephews, aunts, uncles and even distant relatives had felt neglected and had gotten up a petition when they heard about my San Francisco success, requesting my appearance in Southern California.

At that, there were enough relatives to fill the theater, which they did. They came from miles around and I met kin-folk I didn't even know I had.

The only sour note was from an elderly aunt who said:

"Leo is fine but I don't like to see him with powder on his face."

Bolstered with this home town adulation I once more went back to my little cartoons and routine art work in San Francisco, wondering whether my "career" in the theater was over. I had liked the experience so much I wanted to go on. The feeling that I was lifting people out of their humdrum existences for a few minutes and giving them a laugh was the greatest thrill I ever had. Always there was a voice inside me, telling me to go on. Even at night I would wake up thinking of the "Victory" statue in the square, which had become a kind of guiding beacon in my life. I was determined somehow to go on— and stay on—the stage.

But the art job kept me eating, and I stuck with it.

One day a telegram came addressed to me. It was the first I ever received. With considerable awe I opened the yellow envelope. It was from Walter Kelly:

"Can you accept week's engagement, Haymarket Theater, Chicago, doing monologue? Please wire."

CHAPTER 29

SCALPS OF THE SIOUX

NATURALLY, I asked my father's permission to make the trip. This may appear a strange thing nowadays, but it was perfectly normal for me to seek his approval before taking such a great step in my life. Boys from old California families continued to request their fathers' opinion until they were well along in early manhood, and nearly always abided by it.

In my case, too, the trip was going to cost $40 by chair car from San Francisco to Chicago, an immense sum. I couldn't risk it lightly.

My father who had lived in the East while attending Holy Cross and knew conditions there considered the matter carefully and finally rendered his verdict. I could go, provided I took one major precaution.

I must wear the heaviest long underwear I could find.

"You've never even seen snow," my father reminded me. "Chicago is a city where the cold winds come sweeping in from Canada, and they just about freeze you. Take my blessing and two suits of woolens."

On the train I was too excited to mind the big cinders which blew in the unscreened windows from the old coal-burning engine or the hardness of the seat or the lack of other comforts. My mother had prepared me a large sack of tortillas, fried chicken, chilis, oranges and cookies which lasted me to the Illinois line. At a station restaurant, then in vogue, I splurged a quarter and enjoyed a hot meal consisting of two kinds of meat, mashed potatoes, cornbread, gravy, beans, corn, squash, three kinds of pie and white and chocolate cake.

I was positively misshapen from gluttony when I went into the men's toilet on the train to change into my long underwear, a feat in gymnastics in the tiny smelly cubicle with the old chair car rocking and swaying drunkenly on the rough roadbed. The underwear was bright red and must have weighed four pounds.

When I went back to my seat I began to simmer gently. It was hot outside under cloudless skies but my promise had been given, my father had spoken, and I felt sure it would be cold in Chicago.

Actually, the reverse was true. The closer we came to the city the hotter it got. The dog days of Indian Summer were in full sway. Heat shimmered on the ugly tenement buildings as we puffed toward the old La Salle Street Depot. Naked children were shooting water on one another from hoses. Hounds lay panting in any spot of shade they could find.

As for me, I felt as if I were in a Turkish bath. My red underwear already was sodden. It was too late now to take it off because we were close to the station and the dirty, weary train was slowing down for the final stop.

For the first time in my life, my faith in my father was shaken.

Red-faced and sweating, I lugged my suitcase off the chair car and got directions to the Haymarket Theater, the mecca of my dreams. It was a long way. It seemed longer than it was when I set forth. Naturally, I walked. The thought of taking a cab never entered my head. That was an extravagance for dudes.

As I trudged along, changing my suitcase from one hand to the other, I ceased to simmer. I boiled. Each block stretched out as a sizzling infinity. Sweat poured off me in such torrents I'm sure I lost seven or eight pounds on the journey.

Finally, in a sort of heat-daze, I saw the theater ahead of me.

Immediately my spirits revived. This was where I was going to start the road to fame.

Out in front was the usual printed broadside listing the acts in the order of their importance, the headliners being featured in big type at the top and the small fry being graded according to their insignificance in letters progressively smaller. Eagerly, I looked for my own name, starting about half way down because I really didn't expect feature billing yet. By the time I got to the bottom of the list the type was so small I had to lean forward and strain my eyes to see it.

My name wasn't there at all.

The very last item, in pygmy type, was simply "George Gardillo."

Absence of my name was such a shock and I was so hot and exhausted that I hardly had the nerve to go to the stage entrance but I finally approached timidly and gave my name and asked to be let in.

The bored doorman admitted me in after understandably-suspicious glances at my crimson face. He pointed to a dirty room backstage which I apparently was to share as a dressing room with a monkey act and a forlorn burro. The monkeys, too hot and depressed even to pick fleas, hardly bothered to give me a glance, but the burro wriggled his ears in friendly salute and I patted him as one comrade to another. I felt pretty much like a jackass myself in my underwear.

I was too timid to try to take the damn sopping thing off for fear somebody would come in and catch me and think I was crazy. So for a while I just sat and stewed and tried to figure out my act for the evening before going to meet the manager. It was my big chance and the longer I thought about it the more scared I became. The panting monkeys and the dejected donkey didn't do anything for my morale.

At last, after what must have been a couple of hours, and with a desperate effort to keep my respect for my father's wisdom intact despite my discomfort and embarrassment and the fact that I had begun to itch all over, I sidled out past the doorman into the outdoors.

It was snowing!

In the short interval I had been in the theater one of those unpredictable Chicago blizzards had swept in from the North Pole and was engulfing the entire city. The wind howled and bore the snowflakes and sleet along horizontally so you were pelted sideways as well as from above. The streets already were white and the snow was piling up at a rapid rate.

My wet underwear began to congeal. I thought I was going to freeze into a sort of walking icicle, unable to bend, and the horrible thought of having to be chiseled out of my red casing popped into my mind.

Simultaneously my respect for my father went up 100 points.

The best place for me seemed to be the theater. Back I went past the doorman who now seemed more soured than ever due to the change in the weather.

Screwing up my courage for the ordeal, I went past the desolate, empty, echoing vacant seats in search of the manager. He was in a cubbyhole up near the box office, staring morosely out through a smoke-blackened window pane at the driving snow.

"What you want?" he asked bitterly.

"I'm Leo Carrillo, the actor," I said with as much courage as possible.

"Actor?—Oh, are you the kid from Frisco who's going to do the monologue?"

"Yes, sir, but I couldn't find my name on the bill."

"I thought you were down at the bottom," he said without enthusiasm.

"No, there is some guy there named 'Gardillo'!"

The manager looked puzzled for a moment, then began to laugh.

"Oh I get it," he said. "There's a wrestler here named George Gardillo and I guess the printer thought it was him."

My morale sank even lower at having been cheated out of a place on the bill by a mistake even if the type was so tiny that you needed a magnifying glass.

The manager started looking out the window again, chewing on an unlighted soggy remnant of a cigar.

"Don't look like nobody's going to do nothin'," he said morosely. "How the hell you goin' to get an audience in this muck?"

I remained tactfully silent, but the appalling thought came to me that the miserable weather might be going to cheat me out of the few dollars I had counted on to sustain me in Chicago. The manager sat silent too, mauling the cigar.

"Mightn't it quit?" I asked hopefully after a while.

"Nuts!" he snapped, "it might go on for three days."

Savagely he slammed his fist down on a copy of the *Chicago Tribune*, then stared at a point close to where his hand had struck. He was looking at a headline.

"By God, I'll do it!" he said with sudden resolution, and reached for a dirty old telephone.

I saw then, by peering, that he had been looking at a headline which read:

SIOUX INDIANS CAMP HERE
IN COLORFUL CONVENTION

Then I heard him talking on the telephone to someone I presumed must be the theater owner.

"Let's get the whole goddam bunch of those Indians over here and fill up the joint," urged the manager. "We ain't goin' to have no paying customers anyway, and we might get some publicity with the Indian stunt."

He listened a minute and his face brightened.

"I'll get right on it," he promised, and hung up.

I went back to the monkeys and the donkey. I still had two faded tortillas and one chili, which I ate while my thoughts turned homeward to sunny California. The one thing I did not want to do at that moment was to go out and face an audience of Indians. But remembrance of the tradition of the theater came to me: "The show must go on!"

When the curtain went up for the matinee I was in the wings waiting my turn, scared and fidgety, not even wanting to look out in that cavernous cold theater. The snow had continued and drifts were piled up two feet deep outside. Yet we heard the creak of boards, the slamming of seats and sundry grunts as people of some sort filed into the place. The Sioux were gathering, evidently having disregarded the blizzard because of the prospect of a free show put on by the palefaces.

My act was sandwiched between the monkeys and the trained jackass.

I was trembling violently when the monkeys finished their feeble little performance, but somehow as I stepped out on the stage my nervousness vanished in that amazing transition which comes over you when you are actually "on." Almost without volition on my part I began my patter. The words came out but I scarcely was aware of them except to know that I was remembering my lines.

At first my eyes were blinded by the proscenium lights but in a moment, because the lights were so dim and ineffectual, I could see the faces of the audience.

Indians!

Row upon row of stolid Indians, hundreds and hundreds of stoic aborigines.

Some wore feathered headdresses. Nearly all were in buckskin suits decorated with beads. Many had their faces painted.

I went on and on telling some of my funniest jokes, stuff that had sent my San Francisco friends into convulsions. Each time, at the punch line, I paused, imperceptibly, for laughter.

Nothing came.

The Indians just sat there, like red statues, their faces utterly impassive, no facial muscle moving in the slightest degree. I might just as well have been preaching a funeral oration for Sitting Bull.

Faster and faster I went, not waiting any longer for response.

It seemed that thousands of red faces stared at me, mocking me, daring me to make them change expression.

Desperately I played my one remaining ace.

I switched to my Chinese stories, mixing in real Chinese words with the patter, calling on all my skill to break down this barrier of silence, recalling incidents straight out of my beloved San Francisco Chinatown.

The Indians remained impassive. Not so much as an eyelash moved.

But suddenly, in one of the boxes where I had not noticed them before, four white people began to clap. I was inspired. Recognition! A friend!

I plunged on into more Chinese stories.

The palefaces clapped some more. One of them, a big man with a tanned face, stood up and waved his arms and yelled "Bravo!", clapped louder than ever.

A tremor ran through the Indians. Their impassive eyes turned almost in unison toward the box.

One of the Indians said, "Ug!"

Then another said, "Ug!" and another.

An "Ug!" ovation began.

The sound mingled with the shouts and bravos and applause from the box.

An Indian, excited now beyond endurance by the contagious fervor, jumped up and began dancing in the aisle. Another waved a tomahawk. War whoops sounded. More dancers whirled into the aisles. The Indians bent, crouched, stamped. They punctuated their war whoops by clapping their hands to their mouths. One swung from a cut-glass chandelier, some flung their headdresses in the air.

In from the rear ran the manager, looking for a fire or a riot. A look of utter bewilderment came over his face.

He was viewing pandemonium.

I had stopped the show.

It was my finest hour.

Up in the box, the big man who had started it all was doing a war dance himself, whooping and waving, spurring the Indians on as if he were a cheerleader.

He leaned far over the edge of the box to call out another "Bravo!" and for the first time I saw his face clearly.

He was a San Franciscan for sure.

You may have have heard of him.

He was James J. Corbett, heavyweight champion of the world.

CHAPTER 30

A COWBOY SWINGS A LARIAT

AFTER the Sioux coup, in Chicago, with a lot of entertainment scalps hanging on my belt, I looked around for new theatrical worlds to conquer. Word of my triumph with the red men after they got stirred up by Jim Corbett spread around by word of mouth almost as fast as if it had been sent across the country by tom-tom telegraph or smoke signals.

In fact, it was wafted all the way out to Los Angeles where my friend, the paleface booking agent, Robert D. Girard, was so impressed with my unprecedented feat at the Haymarket Theater coming on top of my West Coast triumphs that he got busy in the really big time. Almost before I knew it I was signed up for six weeks in New York at Keith's and Proctor circuit opening at the Union Square Theater, which sounded like the realization of all my dreams.

Of course my pay in Chicago had not been equal to the sensation I created among the Indians the night of the snow storm, and I was faced with having to save every penny I could even to get to New York.

Coming out from San Francisco on the train I had been thrilled even to ride the cindery day coach, but now an opportunity for even greater luxury presented itself. On the bill with the monkeys, the trained jackass, and me at the Haymarket there had been an act labeled "Burton & Brooks, Topical Songs."

Burton was a six footer weighing about 230 pounds. In his stage act he made good use of his white hair and dignified appearance by decking himself out in a checked suit with a bright vest and a Panama hat so that he was the living image of a political ward heeler. His partner, Brooks, in startling contrast, was a little pint-sized one-armed Englishman who wore riding breeches, a riding coat, a cap on the top of his head and a monocle, and carried a riding crop.

In their topical songs one of the joyous little numbers was:
"More Work for the Undertaker,
"Another Little Job for the Casketmaker."
Unfortunately, this song came true for them both before long.

Right at this time, though, a break in their schedule gave me an opportunity to get a cheap trip to New York in a style to which I was totally unaccustomed. Burton, the big partner, was staying in Chicago for a few days to visit some relatives, but Corny Brooks wanted to go on to New York where their next appearance was to be. Little Corny Brooks told me that if we shared an upper berth it would cost us hardly more than a chair car and we could get a little rest on the ride. I had never slept in a berth in my life and it sounded like a great adventure to be in a Pullman car with the swells.

We took sandwiches with us and ate them on the Pullman although some of the people who were going to the diner looked at us with rather disdainful glances.

When it came time to go to bed I was fascinated by the deftness and agility of the porter in making up the berths. The upper one looked mighty narrow and it was. The only thing that saved us was the fact of Corny having only one arm, which gave us a little more room. If he had been normal we would have been squeezed to death.

The snow storm had ceased when we left Chicago, but when we woke up in the morning on arrival in Jersey City, a swirling blizzard was going on outside. It seemed to be my luck as a greenhorn to have bad weather accompany me.

We managed to get across the Hudson River on the ferry to Manhattan, but the snow was piling so high that no streetcars were operating and we had to take a horse-drawn hansom cab.

The snow drifts were 8 to 10 feet high on each side of the little canyon which had been dug out so the cabs could get through. As we went along the cold was so great that the steam from the horses' noses made us almost believe that we were being pulled by a steam engine instead of a poor dilapidated cab animal.

We headed for the Union Square Hotel because Corny said he had reservations there. When we carried in our two little straw suitcases, though, the clerk looked at us scornfully and said there were no reservations available, that the blizzard had caused so many people to be stranded the hotel was full.

There we were in the strange big city in the middle of a blizzard with no place to sleep. Some kindly man in the lobby took pity on our forlorn looks and said, "Why don't you go around the corner to the little hotel in Irving Place? You can usually get a room there."

We battled our way through the sleet and, sure enough, were able to get a chilly little room from the proprietor who was much more human than the supercilious clerk of the Union Square Hotel.

I had a few days before my opening performance and Corny told me of a new thing called a subway. I wanted to see some of the big city about which I had dreamed so long and I went and got into the subway for a nickel.

I was down there for two hours but I didn't see a bit of scenery. Nothing but one damn tunnel after another.

Then came my big moment. I went over to the Union Square Theater, feeling even more excited, if that was possible, than I had in San Francisco or Chicago.

Not a soul knew me in New York. There was nobody I could rely on for a friendly hand or any interest in what I did. This was a big contrast to San Francisco and Los Angeles where I had enough proud and loyal relatives to fill up almost any theater by themselves, or even Chicago where somebody friendly like Jim Corbett turned the tide with the Indians.

I arrived for rehearsal at nine o'clock in the morning of opening day. Immediately I was swallowed up in the rush and hubbub of vaudeville acts, baggage, scenery, barelegged girls, snatches of music, singers and the loud and raucous timing of the show in which minutes were cut out like appendices, only with a broadax.

I stood transfixed in the wings.

The stage manager whose name was Abe Jacobs was a little fellow with a cap on the side of his head, a dingy sweater, a cigar in the corner of his mouth, his shoes out at the heel, and a voice like Uncle Tom calling the bloodhounds. He didn't talk, he barked. Timidly I went up to him and asked, "Where do I dress?"

Abe screamed—and I found out later he always screamed—"Dress on the top floor, with that cowboy."

"Thank you, Mr. Jacobs," I replied. "I'm from the West myself."

"Don't tell me," screamed Abe, "tell it to the cowboy up on top."

Later I found, of course, that this was the most undesirable of all the dressing rooms and was reserved for the lowliest hangers on at the bottom of the theatrical ladder. At the moment, though, it was all a great adventure as I climbed up the iron staircase and found the little cluttered room high in the wings.

I took out my other suit, my other shirt, and my makeup from my little kit and was just preparing to change when a knock came at the door.

A cowboy entered. He wore a narrow-brimmed Stetson on the back of his head and his hair hung down like bangs on his forehead. He was smiling shyly, a smile which was a part of his personality. He wore levis, a cheap cowboy shirt, and boots and was carrying a pair of leather chaps and fumbling with a handful of lasso.

"I'm the cowboy that's dressing with you," he drawled as he put on his chaps.

I took one glance at him and liked him immediately. We became amigos from that moment.

He was nervously handling the rope and seemed at a loss for words. Then he blurted, "I want you to see my act."

"I can't help it," I told him. "I'm following you."

"I guess we're the best because they want to see us first," he remarked with the first show of pride I had seen.

I couldn't tell whether he was serious or not, but I went along with the gag.

"They must want to see us more than anybody," I told him, "because we're on three times and the rest of these guys only twice."

He had told me he had come up to the dressing room to dress but apparently the outfit he had on was the one he was going to use on the stage because he had no handbag with him and nothing but the rope for a prop.

"I'm the Cherokee Kid," he told me, sitting down on a stool. "I've been with the 101 Ranch. The only thing that worries me about this city business is my horse. He's down in the alley with a bale of hay and Buck McKee is taking care of him, but I still worry about him not being able to see any trees or grass."

Just then Abe's voice, screaming as always and this time rattling the rafters, smote our ears as he bawled, "Overture!"

"That means you're going to be on in a minute," I told the cowboy.

His hands gripped the rope with a new resolution and he started down the precarious stairway to begin his performance. I went down to stand in the wings to see what on earth he was going to do. His horse had been led in and the Cherokee Kid mounted and began twirling his rope.

As the overture ended he rode out on the stage and went into an act where he twirled little and big loops while riding the horse around. The horse was just an ordinary range critter from some ranch somewhere, looking almost as much out of place on the stage as a tumbleweed.

But he understood his new job and helped his rider as much as he could.

The audience evidently wasn't much impressed because it sat in silence. Finally the announcer went out and said that the Cherokee Kid would do the "big loop" with the 60-foot rope.

Cherokee started twirling the giant loop but something went wrong and he missed the trick and the rope fell flat on the stage in a big circle. Even from where I stood I could see the poor guy trembling and thinking that he had flubbed his job the first time out. In this nervousness, trying to recoil the rope, he dropped his hat in the middle of the circle made by the fallen rope.

Sheepishly he spoke his first words then in a southern drawl.

Peeking out from under the brim of his hat, he blurted:

"I guess I'm just a politician—my hat's in the ring."

The audience laughed and clapped because it was election time in New York and the impromptu remark touched a topical note.

Cherokee retrieved his rope and retreated from the stage. He was sweating and nervous as he went by me and I could tell he was discouragd.

But I had no time to worry further about him at the moment because it was my turn and I went out with my patter and jokes, and once again got a good response.

When I went upstairs I was all elated at this new success—another step on my goal to Victory—and I burst in the dressing room all full of fire and ginger. Cherokee was sitting there on the stool in a disconsolate attitude as if the end of the world was about to come.

"I guess they don't like me," he mourned, "they laughed at me."

"Hell," I said, "they weren't laughing at you. They were laughing with you. This is election time and you said just the right thing."

He looked puzzled for a moment and then brightened up.

"Well, I guess that's so. I saw it in the papers. All I know is what I see in the papers."

"Where ya roomin'?" he asked.

"I've been thinking about the Somerset Hotel," I told him. "I hear it's cheap and must have something to do with the theater because it sounds like there are acrobats over there."

"Could I tag along?" he asked.

"Sure," I replied. "It'll be cheaper that way."

He took care of his horse and we went over to the Somerset Hotel and got a double room for $1 a day—50 cents apiece.

As we went up the stairs, lugging our own cheap suitcases, I asked, "Say, what's your real name, Cherokee? I didn't see it when you registered."

He shifted his suitcase to the other hand and said simply, "Will Rogers."

LIGHTS ON BROADWAY

How I love the Chinese, Mexicans, Italians, and Japanese!

It was the use of their dialects in my stories which launched me on my career in vaudeville. By indirection, too, they also led me into the legitimate theater after my apprenticeship on the "two-a-day" circuit.

In San Francisco I leaned particularly on Chinese, Mexican, and Japanese material for California audiences. My visits to the colonies of these various racial groups and my association with the people in their eating places, at their work, at their places of amusement, all gave me an insight into their national characteristics and their sense of humor. By taking these and stream-lining them into anecdotes and stories for vaudeville I conveyed the "feel," I think, of all these people and their outlook on life.

While in San Francisco I also got a smattering of the Italian language and a bit of association with the Italian people. But it was not until I went to New York where there was such an enormous number of Italians that I actually began to understand these people and their inner characteristics in the same way I had understood the Chinese, Mexican, and Japanese.

The volatility and emotionalism of the Italians lent itself particularly to mimicry and satire on the stage. Here in New York I learned to speak Italian fluently. Of course I never used the Italians for ridicule but always only as amusement, so they could join in the laughs as well as other people. This was what I had tried to do with all the races, for that matter, because I felt unless

I entered fully into their feelings and made them a part of the act, so to speak, I might offend. And I was determined never to hurt the feelings of anybody merely to get a laugh out of an audience.

So the Italians in New York intrigued me everywhere I went. I stopped to talk to laborers in ditches, to dishwashers, to waiters, in fact to Italians wherever I found them. They responded always to my approach and it was never more than a few minutes before we were laughing back and forth and really getting acquainted.

After awhile, out of all this, I formed a genuine attachment and respect for the Italians, even those of the so-called lower classes and got along wonderfully with them wherever I happened to be. I began to introduce into my act some little stories with an Italian flavor and found that New York audiences liked them. They were simple little yarns but somehow they seemed to have a universal appeal.

I used to tell about Tony who was digging a ditch and had an Irish boss. An Irish priest came along and the priest said to Tony, rather patronizingly, "I see you have an Irish boss; how do you like him?"

"He'sa good," replied Tony. Then he added, "Father, how do you like your Italian boss, the Pope?"

Those were the days when people liked little anecdotes and dialect jokes. Perhaps it was an unsophisticated era, maybe it was an age of innocent merriment. We didn't have to have stories about sex, Hollywood show-offs, or integration, or make dirty remarks about other people. Off-color jokes meant the cancellation of your vaudeville engagement.

A great deal depended, of course, in the case of a mimic like myself, in catching the gestures and phraseology of the particular racial group with which we were dealing. If we did that and told the stories good naturedly and with proper timing and punch lines we could have 'em rolling in the aisles.

Another little Italian story I used to tell in later years was about the return of Charles Lindbergh after his epochal first solo flight over the ocean to Paris. He came back on a ship and there was a great crowd at the dock to greet him. Tony Bachigaluppi, we will call him, took his six kids down to the dock to see Lindbergh. There was all the excitement of a great American show. Kids everywhere were wanting to do what Lindbergh had done so Tony thought his gang ought to have the opportunity like everybody else.

As the ship docked Tony said to his kids, "Look, look. Great American boy fly ocean. Fly ship by himself. Now he come home."

The people were cheering and pushing and there was a tremendous mob on the dock. Tony was trying to keep his kids from getting squashed and he kept yelling "No pusha, no pusha!" Then, as I told the story on the stage, Tony said, "All of a sudden I hear people yelling 'Man overboard, man overboard!!' And I hear a big splash.

"And I look around, and damn, itsa me!"

Of course, all this time, I kept perfecting my Chinese and Mexican stories, too, and they were all a part of the repertoire along with the Italian ones.

I received an offer to go to Los Angeles and put on my act there and of course this was a triumphant return for the hometown boy. I went back with all the enthusiasm of anyone who returns to his native region after having made a success elsewhere, all fired up to show the old neighbors what I could do.

At that time the great Oliver Morosco, the impresario and producer who used the slogan to show the excellence of everything he did, "A Typical Morosco Cast," was in his heyday in Los Angeles. The Morosco Theater was the place where many famous plays were introduced. Matinee idols from the New York stage welcomed the opportunity to appear with Morosco. Word of my homecoming appearance was emblazoned in the newspapers and was discussed among theatrical people in Los Angeles and naturally came to the attention of Morosco himself.

He visited my show and afterwards asked me to come to see him. I called on him and he told me, "Sometime I will find a part for you in a real play—you can go places in the legit." This thrilled me, of course, and I told him that when the time came all he would have to do would be to whistle for me.

I went on my rounds on the Orpheum and Keith circuits after that, playing all over the country.

One day in Philadelphia, at the Seneca Hotel where most of the theatrical people stayed, I met the two great comedians, Weber and Fields.

Joe Weber told me, "Hey, Leo, Oliver Morosco is going to put on a play called *Upstairs and Down*. Why don't you ask him for a part?"

I went right down to the Western Union and wired Morosco that I would be home in a few months for a vacation and asked him to keep me in mind for a part. In a few hours I got a telegram back from Morosco in Los Angeles telling me to call when I got out there. I did so as soon as we reached the coast. He offered to put me in *Upstairs and Down* as "Louis Latour," the French valet.

After casting and rehearsals we opened at the Cort Theater in New York.

As is always the case, we waited with tremendous excitement and apprehension to see what the newspaper critics would say about it. When we got hold of the late editions nearly everybody felt like jumping off a bridge. The newspapers unanimously called the play a failure. We all went to bed exhausted and disappointed that night feeling that the show would be bound to close ofter such a panning.

But Morosco had other ideas. He called the long-faced cast together in the morning and when we were all on the bare gloomy stage he stood in front of us and said:

"I don't believe the newspapers. I'm dumping another $5,000 into ads claiming a big success. The main reason I'm doing this and the reason I really think we can be a success is because of the part that Leo plays as Louis Latour."

Morosco did start a big newspaper advertising campaign immediately.

He came to me and said, "Leo, cut loose and do anything you want on stage. It's the kind of thing that will save the show."

I did exactly that. We salvaged *Upstairs and Down* and it ran 44 weeks to sell-out audiences. Morosco always was kind enough to say that my part was the main factor in its salvation. I was having fun!

The great Frederick and Fannie Hatton, who had written *Upstairs and Down*, were attracted by my performance in this role of Latour which they had created. They had done *The Great Lover*, *Years of Discretion*, and many other major stage hits and they knew the theater as few people did.

They told Morosco I should have a play of my own in which to star. He agreed. This was one of the great moments of my life because I respected the Hattons and Morosco very much, and their belief in me was an inspiration which I have never forgotten.

This was at a time after the first World War had broken out in Europe but before the United States had been drawn into the conflict. It was a period of strange calm. The world may have been troubled but Broadway seemed unaware of it. The stage lights glittered brighter than ever, new productions were being put on all the time, stars were being born, and many Americans seemed more interested in what happened on Broadway than they did about the events in the trenches in France.

Mrs. Hatton actually thought of the key idea of the play which emerged. She was particularly impressed by my imitations of Italians and from this came her inspiration.

She thought that a play built around an Italian modiste in an atelier which was the gathering place of young fluff and of society matrons for clothes, gossip, love trysts and everything which accompanies the goings-on in an atelier, would provide the basis for a play. The part the Hattons envisioned for me was that of a character modeled after Phillip Magnone, the famous designer of women's apparel. At the time he was furnishing Hickson and Bendel with advanced styles and his name was as well-known in that day as that of Christian Dior was in recent years.

The part appealed to me, of course, because it would permit me to indulge in all the antics and comic gestures and racial characteristics which I had gathered in my long study of the Italians. I was avidly interested as every scene emerged under the magic touch of the Hattons. They had a flair for the little touches which lift a play from mere mediocrity into something great. They consulted frequently with me and together we worked out some of the bits of action and business which later were to prove so successful.

In one scene I was to come on stage as the bustling, gesticulating, artistic designer and there, in the presence of the audience, create an evening gown on a model who walked on in the scantiest of scanties and then left radiantly arrayed in a fashionable gown of the latest model.

During all the scenes there was a running fire of social gossip which we were determined was to be topical, and appealing to all classes of people.

As a name it was finally decided that *Lombardi, Ltd.* best expressed in a simple and provocative fashion what we wanted.

Among the actors chosen for the cast was my lifelong friend Warner Baxter, who played an American-born Italian who couldn't speak a word of Italian. I think he was almost as enthusiastic as I was about the possibilities as we went through all the intricate preparations and rehearsals for the show. We had to maintain a mood throughout, and Oliver Morosco showed his genius in assembling a cast so perfectly balanced that each person in it contributed a special talent. It was so gauged to public taste that we felt confident it was bound to be successful.

We played eight weeks in Los Angeles and I improvised the third act at the outset because there had been no time to learn the lines.

When we came to New York the play was recast with Janet Dunbar playing Nora, the forewoman in the atelier; Marian Abbott portraying Molly, the seamstress; and Grace Valentine doing the part of the Baby Vampire.

We were a smash from the first night.

I named the gown in the big scene "The Sunshine after the Rain." This part of the show in itself attracted a lot of attention, naturally, and this was carried into the emotional aspects of the third act. My line that there was "a heart in every fold of the gown" stirred the audience tremendously.

By contrast, in the second act there were 250 belly laughs.

On opening night I received 29 curtain calls.

The whole thing became a theater classic.

Morosco said to me that my Christmas present was the sign on the Morosco Theater marquee with my name in big electric lights. I had made Broadway as a star: LEO CARRILLO in LOMBARDI, LTD.

Life seemed to stretch ahead of me to the far horizon in this one role.

Lombardi did run for two years on Broadway to absolute capacity. Altogether it played four years over the United States. We went on tour for a year in Australia, New Zealand and Tasmania, then came back for repeat performances in the United States.

All during this time we had to change the styles to suit the trend of the times. Even the scanty underwear of the model on whom I perfected the evening dress became scantier and scantier as the years went by.

One day when the show was at the height of its success a very polite and precise little Italian man came to see me.

He bowed formally and started out on a little speech:

"Mr. Carrillo, because you have do so much in *Lombardi*, my boss send me to talka to you. He understands Bosca champagne people giving you bigga banquet for what you do for Italians. They givva my boss banquet on Tuesday, you on Friday. My boss send me ask you if all right"—he searched for a word and couldn't find it, and then stammered—"can we push 'em together and mix 'em all up?"

I was puzzled at first.

"Who is your boss?" I demanded.

"I'm secretary to someone love you very much—Enrico Caruso."

That made it all right with me. We took the banquets and "push 'em together." Caruso was starring at the Metropolitan and I at the Morosco.

The banquet was held in a huge vaulted room of the Bosca Company where we were surrounded by two million bottles of champagne, which we unsuccessfully sought to eliminate that night.

I must say that Caruso and I had considerable help in this project, including that of George M. Cohan, Raymond Hitchcock, William Collier and many others. But there were still a few bottles left at the end of the evening.

Caruso and I became so inspired that we reverted to our respective original vocational loves, and spent the evening making sketches of the guests. The only trouble was some of them looked as if they had bottles for bodies.

My dear friends the Hattons later exhausted their fountain of theatrical values and as age came upon them they went into retirement. Morosco produced, as many remember, some of the greatest successes of the Broadway stage, *Bird of Paradise*, *Peg o' My Heart*, *So Long Lettie*, and many others.

He developed such stars as Lewis Stone, Walter Catlett, Bert Lytell, Laurette Taylor of *Peg o' My Heart*; Herb Carthel, Charles Winninger, Maude Fulton and Charlotte Greenwood.

He always was my staunch friend.

Later, when I returned to California and devoted myself almost entirely to film productions, I lost touch with him in the stress of my work.

One morning in my home at Santa Monica I was shocked to see in a headline that Morosco had been killed by a streetcar. His fortune was gone and he had, unknown to many of his old friends, been reduced to extremity.

When they picked up the old man and took him to the morgue, the producer of *Lombardi, Ltd.* had only 20 cents in his pocket.

CHAPTER 32

LOVE IN A MUD PUDDLE

My one lifelong love-affair always is with me, and always will be.

It all happened, I guess, because I went to New York. I was depending upon myself and trying to economize in every way by taking modest surroundings. It was lonely. The little room in which I lived on 43rd Street for $6 a month included one "luxury"—a little gas jet stove. It was a room where I could hear the music of the night—the sound of musical comedies that were playing over in the New Amsterdam Theater or the Lyric. I remember one, in particular, was the great piece called "Tammany":

> "*Tammany, Tammany, the big chief sits in his tepee,*
> *Cheering braves to victory!*
> *Tammany, Tammany, wampum, swampum, get the wampum!*
> *Tammany!*"

That was the strain of the music.

When I sat on the porch of this old stone house on 43rd Street I began to try to figure myself out, what I was going to do and how far I was going to go. These surroundings were familiar but were they my real world?—the little place where I used to eat called Minks, next to Child's; and Child's itself next to the Victoria Theater; the saloon on the corner named Dowling's, which was the rendezvous of all the actors who liked that sort of thing.

I was playing the Procter Theater on 23rd Street and going over pretty well with my little stories.

Never can I forget my associates there.

Corny? I guess so, but dear to my memory.

On the bill were the Three Rubes. One was supposed to be deaf and his companions had to holler into a cow's horn to make him hear. I think the deaf guy was the first "Master of Ceremonies" I ever heard of in my life. He would get up and say, "Well, ladies and gentlemen, next song is going to be sung by Rufus over here entitled *Sleep in the Depot, Complaint by the Guitar.* All right!" And one of the other fellows would sing this song.

Another actor on that bill was a Negro named Irving Jones, who sang a very strange song for New York as you can imagine—*Saint Patrick's Day Is No Day for a Man with a Face Like Mine.* These things became indelibly imprinted in my mind.

Another one was Willard Sims, who did a paper-hanger act. You never saw such a mess in your life as this man trying to put paper on his own wall with a great big bucket of glue and rolls of paper that he got tangled up in. The dialogue was very, very funny to me then.

And on that bill was a young man named Leo Carrillo.

I emerged on the stage with a white suit I had bought, very immaculately dressed, made-up, to start my monologue. My opening there was very successful.

There's where it all happened.

I walked out on the stage and I think it was the first time I ever understood the word "swoon." I heard somebody sigh, and it was a young lady. She was sitting in a box with her sister and the manager of the theater, Harry Leonhardt. They seemed very much amused at my little offering. Mr. Leonhardt came back to my dressing room when I had finished and said:

"Leo, you did a very good act and I'm very pleased. I'm the manager of the theater but we haven't met yet. I have been sitting with some friends of mine in a box and they expressed the desire to meet you. Would you meet them?"

I said, "I would be very glad. I don't know anybody here and I would be very glad to meet them."

"We'll be standing in front of the theater when you've finished dressing," he told me.

I took the make-up off my face, got into my other clothes, went out into the front of the theater and there were Mr. Leonhardt and the two ladies. They were young girls. One worked for Doubleday, Page & Company at that time in the publishing department, and the other one had a secretarial job.

Mr. Leonhardt introduced me to these girls and one of them was the most beautiful girl I ever saw in my life.

It had been raining earlier in the evening but I was so excited over meeting this lovely, lovely girl whose name was Edith I didn't realize I was standing in the middle of a mud puddle almost to the top of my shoes.

We got to talking and Edith said, "We ought to invite Leo up."

The girls were half-sisters. One was Jennie Demarest and the other—the one at whom I was gazing—was Edith Hazelbarth. They were both Shakespeares on the maternal side. Their grandmother was a Shakespeare. They lived in Nyack, New York, and Edith's stepfather, Demarest, was a politician in Rockland County.

It definitely was not politics which was appealing to me, though, when I began "calling" in Nyack. Interesting guests were arriving at the house nearly all the time but they, for the most part, were merely passing shadows. My eyes were for Edith alone.

One politician of the group did become my lifelong friend even though I was not particularly aware of him at first.

His name was Jim Farley, later the political mentor of Franklin Delano Roosevelt.

Every chance I got, I visited Edith. Remembering that sigh in the theater when I first came on stage that night, it seemed possible that she might reciprocate the instantaneous love which surged up in me for her. And so it proved.

We were married before long.

I was inspired to seek greater achievements on the stage. The strong and sustaining love of this beautiful girl, who always remained young and beautiful in my sight, made it possible for me to go on from one stepping stone to the other in my quest for stardom. Without her, I never could have attained the goal.

We lived at first in a little house on Long Island, then bought a larger site as things went well with me and built our own lovely home.

She motivated my career. She encouraged me whenever disappointments came, cheered me on when success arrived. We traveled, went boating, collected antiques and fine glass, met the most wonderful people in the world.

Then our daughter Antoinette came to us. From the first her soul was moulded in the image of my Edith's. Antoinette gave our lives new purpose. We were traveling a bright path, illuminated by the glittering lights in which my name appeared on the theater marquees of the nation.

Love and stardom both were mine.

CHAPTER 33

FRIENDS, ROAMINGS, AND COUNTRYMEN

My name was in lights. Entertainment was my career. But something else meant a great deal to me, too. This was the discovery of the great American success story wherever I went. Both in vaudeville and in the legitimate plays in which I starred we made tours to many cities of the United States, and later abroad. On these trips in this country I encountered amazing examples of poor boys who, like myself, had yearned for "Victory" as represented by the statue in San Francisco that had inspired me.

It didn't seem to make much difference what part of the country they came from. The same spirit of individuality, of ambition, of willingness to work had marked them all.

In Dayton, Ohio, I met Charles Kettering, a young man who invented an electrical device to open cash registers and then went on to invent the automobile self-starter. Result: General Motors!

In Chicago I was inspired by the enthusiasm and knowledge of the great Albert Harris who knew more about Arabian horses than anyone else in the world and helped to popularize these wonderful animals with their royal lineage dating back to the days of the Prophet Mohammed.

Over in Toledo was Royce Martin, the man responsible for every electric auto light on automobiles in this country.

Some of the friends I made had had to overcome not the handicap of poverty, but of riches. Young W. Averell Harriman, son of the great E. H.

Harriman, President of the Union Pacific Railroad, went on to enter into political affairs and to become the Governor of the great State of New York. He had worked as a young man on the same railroad job I did in Tejiguas Canyon near Santa Barbara.

Everywhere I went I began to look for the men whose success stories typified the opportunities offered every American. It became one of my great pleasures as I traveled all over the country.

New plays were coming my way. Booth Tarkington wrote *Magnolia* for me, the story of the cowardly scion of a plantation family along the Mississippi River. This weakling is shamed in front of his sweetheart by a rival and slinks away. Later, he comes back as "the notorious Cunnel Blake" and of course is a swashbuckling, fighting lover who sets out to retrieve his lost prestige.

I starred in this play all over the country and I think the review which of all others in my career stands out most in my memory was in connection with this play.

The great John Corbin in the New York *Times* wrote of me in this fashion:

"There were those in the audience whom he reminded rather of Richard Mansfield. There was not the least evidence of the mannerisms that are all too easily and too often mimicked; but the actor's mood and method were those of Mansfield at his best. In the quieter moments there was a living eloquence in his eye, an amiable humor in his lips; in the moments of dominant rage, Mr. Carrillo was as erect as a poised sword, as cool and dangerous. It was the best work of a very able young actor."

Another favorite role of mine was in *The Bad Man*. Naturally, too, I made personal appearances and once in a while even succumbed to the lure of a vaudeville appearance because this always had a special spot in my heart after my early experiences in San Francisco, Chicago, and New York.

In my little talks at personal appearances I sometimes started out in Spanish dialect until people thought I didn't know much English. Then I changed my accent and in the best tones I could command I would say something like this:

"In order to dispel any hallucinations under which you may be laboring, I would like to qualify my previous remarks to tell you that all of my characterizations are devised analytically to project themselves effectively for the edification of my audiences, and by now you have probably come to the conclusion I speak the King's English occasionally!"

All this time I was making friends along Broadway and among actors and people connected with the theater and also among writers and artists. I became a member of the Lambs' Club. I spent many happy hours there with Booth Tarkington and other literary immortals. It also was my privilege to visit the Salmagundi Club, the oldest art club in the United States. There I encountered one of my early friends from Los Angeles and Santa Monica, Clyde (Vic) Forsythe, the cartoonist of the New York *World* whose wife, Cotta, I had known when she was a little girl in Santa Monica. He and Irvin S. Cobb and other immortals of these early newspaper days were working together at the time. It was a great treat to me to encounter anybody from California and I particularly admired Clyde because of his ability in art work. He was a lot better than I was.

Then, too he had the biggest heart I ever knew. He was always trying to help somebody. Later on in his career he took a young man named Norman Rockwell to the *Saturday Evening Post* and got him started there so that Rockwell became the most famous magazine cover artist in America. That was the kind of thing that gave Clyde more pleasure than anything else. He was a big success almost from the start in New York and worked both for *The World* and later for William Randolph Hearst.

When I was getting started in vaudeville I decided that I wanted a stage set with a typical California and western desert scene for my background. I went to Clyde and told him what I needed. He was working long hours on *The World* and going out to draw pictures of trials such as the one of Harry K. Thaw for killing Stanford White over the affections of the beautiful Evelyn Thaw, but he was ready to pitch in right away to help a fellow Californian. He drew such remarkably life-like sketches of the West that they were transformed into my first major prop on the New York stage.

I have always been one of the greatest admirers of Clyde Forsythe who, when he came back to California as I did, became one of the greatest of the western desert painters. He did magnificent oil paintings of Will Rogers and his landscapes have become famous all over the United States.

He wrote his autograph on the desert sands and his signature in the brilliant blue of his skies in his desert paintings.

I have always felt privileged to know so grand a soul who found his inspiration in nature and was able to convey his message to the rest of America.

During this time my seemingly predestined fate to have the Chinese people figure prominently in my life came to the fore again. My personal valet was Ling, one of the most loyal, jolly, companionable persons I have ever encountered. Ling had been with a famous Chinese magician who played all of the great theaters of the United States. Ling learned so many of his master's tricks that he went out on his own with an animal act including chickens, ducks, rabbits, squirrels, and all sorts of trained creatures. Business got bad, though, and he was in financial trouble with many hungry animals around him. He neatly solved his problem.

He ate up his act and came with me as my valet.

Will Rogers, Cobb, Ed Borein, and Fred Stone remained among my closest associates and we met as often as we could and sometimes discussed the possibility of living in California. I suppose some kind providence was looking down on us and planning a happy reunion in a region which always remained dear in my memory although the time for fulfillment of this destiny had not yet arrived.

CHAPTER 34

THE MINSTREL'S TALE

IN their heyday, the minstrel shows were just about the most popular entertainment in the world.

They were typically American, blending the wonderful humor and songs
of the Negro and the puns and gags of the Yankee character and philosophy.
The most famous and best-beloved minstrel of his time was Willis Sweatnam,
a man I was proud to call my friend.

He had his black wig and his black make-up, a big mouth and the huge
striped necktie maybe a foot across under his chin, and a tambourine or
bones—he was an "end man." An end man was important; he was usually the
star of the show. Havelley and his Minstrels with Sweatnam as the chief
attraction were then the most famous of all minstrels. Dockstetter, Primrose &
West, and Dumont of Philadelphia, were popular but Havelley was the one
most acclaimed throughout the world.

This Willis Sweatnam attained international fame.

He was a great lover of dogs. Always he was fascinated by any kind of
dog. Perhaps he used to hunt when he was a young man.

As he made a success on the stage, he built a cottage over in Vinewood,
New Jersey, and lived very happily with Mrs. Sweatnam, and their pet dogs.

Finally as the years went by, Mrs. Sweatnam passed away. The two dogs,
Nero and Rover, also died and Sweatnam buried them on the grounds at the
little country place.

We had a little spot in the Lambs' Club for Sweatnam, who was an old man, and retired, by the time I knew him. We called it "Sweatnam Corner," and people used to enjoy talking to him because he would reminisce and go over his life.

One evening he started to tell me the story of his dogs and of going back to their burial spot under the honeysuckle which had spread all over the ground, where only debris and pieces of rotting timber remained from the house which had fallen down. He said he went over and stood there and looked and everything in his life came back, the death of his wife and his love for his dogs, and a little tear trickled down his cheeks.

Mr. Sweatnam knew I owned a police dog named "General Pershing," which had the distinction of riding with my blessed wife who was with the Motor Corps of America in World War I, in the great Victory parade in New York. He saw me bring this dog into the Lambs' Club one night and check him in the cloakroom. As I walked into the grill over in the corner sat Mr. Sweatnam, and he motioned for me to come and sit down by him.

And he said, "Mr. Carrillo, I was just looking at that beautiful dog of yours in the cloakroom and I want to tell you, sir, I been reading about those dogs and how they train 'em to find enemy soldiers."

He went on to talk about my dog and began telling me about his dogs in New Jersey.

At that moment I noticed his pockets were bulging. I didn't ask him just then what he had in those pockets, but I should mention that he was no longer the great Willis Sweatnam of his heyday but a man who had won and lost. The curtain had lowered on his career. He didn't know he was the subject of charity at the Lambs' Club and that four hundred to five hundred members were contributing 10 cents apiece every week for the "Willis Sweatnam Fund" to give him pin money and to pay his bills and room rent. Apparently he thought the money came from what was left over out of the fortune he had made at one time.

He was a hypochondriac, always having a belly ache or indigestion, but he would sit and talk to you and while he was talking he would order ice cream and corned beef and cabbage. Then he would start to belch and almost bark and say with his slight speech impediment, "—I d-d-don't feel very good, a-a-, 've had indigestion all day long, a-a- waiter, waiter, just a little bit more of that ice cream please. I just had some corned beef and cabbage—and Mr.

Carrillo, I just want to tell you I go out all the time by myself I love animals so—"

"What have you got in your pockets, Bill?" I asked.

He said, "Well, in this pocket I've got sugar. I steal it from the Club right here. Over here I've got meat that I go around and pick up off the plates and wrap it up and put it in my pocket."

I said, "Well, what do you do with it?"

"Oh, I go over on Sixth Avenue where the cab horses are over at Jack's Restaurant, and I walk along and I hand them sugar, and they all know me and they whinny. I go up the alley and the cats are there and I feed the cats. I do that maybe a couple of times a week and I get a great, great deal of comfort out of it."

He paused a moment and then went on, "Well, I've got to tell you something because you asked me about dogs. I had a little dog named Peggy, that came after my other dogs passed on. I took little Peggy—she didn't look unlike that picture you see on the phonograph, the dog 'Listening to His Master's Voice.' And that little dog used to sit in my dressing room with me, and slept in a trunk. I took that little dog all over the world. She was never denied space in the Pullman Palace car—didn't have any airplanes then. I took her in the steamers right in my stateroom.

"I took her to London with me and I want to tell you, Mr. Carrillo, I never enjoyed such a great triumph. I did a command performance for the King and Queen and I was on the stage taking my bows and they were applauding and I could hear the sound of my little dog over all the applause because she was barking in the dressing room, barking and barking. She evidently knew what was going on and the acclamation I was getting from the people of London. Any reason why I shouldn't love my little dog?"

And his eyes were wet as he looked at me.

I said, "Go ahead, Bill, tell me the story."

"Well," he went on, "we had this great triumph in London, and then we went all over Europe and around the world, with little Peggy 'applauding' in her own way from the dressing room, by barking, in all the cities where we appeared. It got so I listened for her almost as much as I did for the audience.

"Then we came to the great city of San Francisco, by the Golden Gate.

"I tell you, Mr. Carrillo, we were royally received there, too. The Governor and his lady came to hear us, and all the famous people of San Francisco crowded into the theater.

"Let's see, that was 35 years ago. I'm eighty-seven now.

"One foggy night during our San Francisco appearance something happened to my little Peggy. She got sick. After the show I nursed her, she had a fever all night and I nursed her all during the next day too. But the following night I guess God wanted her, and He took her from me.

"I just sat in my dressing room looking at my little dog that had traveled all over the world with me, Mr. Carrillo, and I don't remember going on the stage that night because there was no response in my dressing room when the audience was applauding.

"It was very foggy the night Peggy died. When the show was over I took my little dog, wrapped her in a blanket and walked out into the fog and night. I wanted to find a place, a vacant lot somewhere to bury her and I wanted it near some street where I could make a note of it and remember and maybe someday I would come back again.

"I walked and walked in the fog, with Peggy in my arms for the last time. My grief was very great, Mr. Carrillo.

"It was hard at first to tell exactly where I was, but it was up towards Twin Peaks. By peering at the street signs under the yellow lights in the fog I located myself finally, and then walked out into a vacant lot.

"So I buried her and said goodbye, hoping I could come back some day; because I knew the exact spot.

"And sure enough, not long ago, I was able to go back out to San Francisco at the invitation of some friends.

"I took a walk up the same streets that I had made a note of and I looked in this corner where I had buried little Peggy. When I had put her there it was in the midst of a lot of tin cans and debris and all that sort of thing that you find on a vacant lot.

"But that vacant lot wasn't there anymore. Instead, there was a nice black iron fence with gold tips, and lovely walks, and flowers blooming.

"Mr. Carrillo, I just stood there and I couldn't believe the transformation of that old lot into the garden I saw before me.

"If I tell you something will you believe it?

"Exactly where I had buried little Peggy, at a spot nobody else knew about, was a sign in gold and the sign read: 'No Dogs Allowed.'

"And I smiled and went to bed and dreamt of my little old Peggy."

CHAPTER 35

SIREN CALL OF FILMLAND

ALL of us legitimate actors turned up our noses a bit at the new entertainment medium—the motion picture—which seemed to be associated with player pianos and little hole-in-the-wall film houses where "the flickers" were shown.

A tremendous gulf existed between the "sure enough" actors and the people who ran around on the edge of roofs, dangled from ropes, were tied on railroad tracks and otherwise contributed to the new cinematic "art."

This attitude persisted for a number of years. Then, along in the late 1920's, there came a thing which we understood to be called the "talkies." Even this addition of a sound track to the conventional moving pictures failed to impress us greatly—except in one respect.

That was money.

I was used to being paid as a star by this time but, even so, it was an era in which the fabulous salaries of today, where the government gets most of the money, were unheard of. So it was an offer of participation in one of the first four-reel "talkies" that weaned me away from the legitimate stage for at least one day. A new concern called "Vitaphone" was making these four experimental films with a sound track to see what public reaction would be.

Sam Warner and his brothers were in charge of the proceedings. They built a floor over the seats of the old Manhattan Opera House on 34th Street as a studio. The lights and cameras were installed and then they called in the talent.

The four attractions which were signed up for the first little short films were Gigli of the Metropolitan Opera Company, a black-faced comedian named Al Jolson, the Howard Brothers who sang, and myself.

My fee was to be $2,750 for the day.

But there was a slight difficulty. Sam Warner said to me, "We haven't got much money so would you take your pay in stock at 25 cents a share?"

"No," I replied, "I'd rather have the money because I am planning to go back to California one of these days and I want to invest out there."

Al Jolson was more reasonable. He took the stock. It went up to $400 a share soon afterwards when he did *The Jazz Singer*, the first major talkie. I guessed wrong that time!

After this first venture into the new realm of Klieg lights, directors, sound equipment, and film acting I went back to the legitimate theater. I wasn't too impressed with the "talkies."

But fate was conspiring against me—and how glad I am that it was!

Always in the back of my mind was the tender memory of California. Even after my happy marriage and my success on the stage there always was a nostalgic yearning for the great mountains, the wide Pacific, the old ranchos, the crumbling adobes, and all the romantic associations of my youth.

We were living in a lovely home on Long Island. Everything was going well with me on the stage. Still this little voice kept whispering that perhaps California held something for us, too.

Then, after the success of *The Jazz Singer*, with sound, there was a great upsurge in film-making. The first little experiment in which I participated had shown that I was suited for cinematic roles because I seemed to photograph well. Still, there was not any artistic appeal for me in the new medium. To stand before a camera and to speak lines, without the stimulus of an audience, merely into hidden microphones provided no real inspiration for me.

Then there came such attractive financial offers from Hollywood that it seemed almost impossible to resist. I talked it over with my wife and we decided that I should at least attempt it and see how we felt about it after giving it a fair trial. So I prepared to go out to the West Coast and embark on a film career which at that moment might have lasted for one week or a few days and been over with as far as I was concerned. Still I wanted to see how it would feel to make the kind of money which was offered.

MGM was planning some pictures and wanted me to participate.

The happiest of my early associations in Hollywood was with Wallace Beery. We made *Viva Villa, Twenty Mule Team, Barnacle Bill,* and others. This wonderful man had such a marvelous personality, he was so warm, generous and sincere, that the privilege of working with him was one of the highlights of my life.

So it was too with Clark Gable. He was a down-to-earth human being whose kindly qualities in many instances were hidden from the public because he would not permit them to be publicized. I know that he always excused himself on the weekends from parties and junkets and went out with his father, carrying a boat on top of the car and the two of them camping out in the open with their sleeping bags. I always felt he was one of the greatest individuals I encountered in the realm of make-up and pretense where so many of the people were fawning or insincere, and it was impossible to count on genuine friendship.

I also had the inspiration of the great voice of a great lady, Grace Moore, in the film *Love Me Forever.*

People of this caliber, though, were too few and far between. Their contribution to the industry is written indelibly on its pages. It is so unfortunate that there are not more like them to provide their high type of performances in filmland.

I appeared in more films than I can count, but there never was the thrill for me in this kind of acting that I received from facing a "live" audience. The emotional waves that flow between a stage actor and the people making up the audience are far beyond anything which can be conjured up on celluloid. My first love always was and always will be the legitimate stage.

But even beyond the films there was another medium—television. Later on, I took part in television shows too. This also lacked some of the ingredients that I found so stimulating in stage performances. At any rate, in the films there were no commercials between the reels—at least not very often—and in television the intrusion of the commercials always was disturbing to me.

Both my film career and my television portrayals are too recent really to compare with the golden memories I carry of the legitimate stage; still both the films and television had their compensations.

These consisted mostly of the reaction of children to the parts which in some instances were aimed particularly at them.

My role as "Pancho" in the *Cisco Kid* series apparently struck a responsive chord in the hearts of children all over the world. Everywhere I have gone on my trips I have been greeted with welcoming cries of "Hey, Pancho" in whatever language happened to be spoken in that particular country. I remember down in Argentina the kids followed me around the streets, some of them practicing their English in discussions about Pancho and the horses ridden by the Cisco Kid and myself.

In fact, one bright-faced little kid with shining eyes and dark hair came up to me and said in Spanish:

"Pancho, I love you and I love the Cisco Kid and I love your horses. But I sure wish you wouldn't keep riding around that same rock. Us kids all recognize it now. Can't you get a new one?"

These associations with children have been the really rewarding features of both my film and television careers.

The films aggravated me in many respects, particularly on account of the synthetic cowboys which they featured.

Most of these were incubated on Madison Avenue in New York and sat in a saddle as if it were a chafing dish. Many of them have never known how to handle a horse and there has been, in my opinion, extreme cruelty to the animals because of the inexpertness of the riders. Those of us who were brought up in the saddle are repelled by the actions of so-called "cowboys" in both films and television. I speak rather bitterly of this because I love horses and I love to see them treated properly.

But there was one great reward for me in the early portion of my film career besides my association with Wallace Beery and the other small groups whom I considered to be the genuine people in Hollywood. This was the monetary return.

It permitted me after a while to make a lifelong dream come true, but only following a brief, strange interlude while I was traveling towards the land of sunsets and new hopes—my native California.

SONG IN THE WILDERNESS

FAR off across the desert in the land that God forgot, heat lightning of the summer season was ripping the blackness of the night as we sped along. Above us, though, the stars shone with that unusual brilliance of the high deserts of New Mexico. The great sparkling expanse of the heavens seemed to reach down to pronounce a benediction upon the infinitesimal speck known as the earth whirling its way through space.

Inside the Santa Fe Super Chief, as we rolled so smoothly along the glistening rails, everything was comfort and elegance. I was on my way home to California, traveling this time in a beautifully-decorated train compartment. It was impossible for me not to think of the contrast of my first trip so many years before from San Francisco to Chicago in the little smelly, dirty chair car when the cinders came flying through the unscreened windows and we took it in stride.

I was gazing out into the night lost in my thoughts of this long-contemplated return home to the arms of my family when the train slowed down and gradually came to a stop. I knew we were nowhere near any town and I was unable to understand what had happened. In a few minutes the conductor came through the car explaining that we had developed a hot box on one of the wheels and that it would be necessary to remain here for an hour or two. The night was so beautiful that when I walked out into the space between cars and looked at the stars, it seemed that one could almost pluck them from the heavens with a fishing pole. I decided to go on a little stroll. The scent of the sage brush dilated my nostrils with its fragrance. People were standing in groups along the tracks discussing the delay and also enjoying the vast expanse before them. The lightning continued to flash far away in great fiery sheets across the sky but it was so distant we heard no thunder. Nearby, lightning bugs tried bravely to outdo the celestial display.

Slowly I walked a little way into the deserted countryside, breathing deeply of the bracing air and wondering whether we could have found a more desolate spot on the whole North American Continent in which to stop.

The stars were so beautiful I was not minding the delay at all.

Suddenly I heard a sound which at first I could not believe to be actual. I thought it must be a kind of night mirage of my mind—a manifestation of the memories conjured up by my homecoming. But I listened and knew that this was a reality. Out there somewhere just ahead of me I was hearing the strains of the cradle song which my mother had sung to me when I was a baby. Accompanying the voice was a guitar. It was *La Golondrina*, the song of the swallow, a tender melody which had lingered in my emotions all my life as intertwined with the image of my blessed mother.

There was absolutely no habitation anywhere, but I did see, as I now looked more closely, the tiny glimmer of a campfire beside some brush and rocks ahead. I moved closer and began to whistle so that anyone noticing my presence would know I meant no harm.

In a moment I came to the small campfire and saw a man with a guitar seated beside it. He was dressed scantily because it was a hot night. He continued to strum the guitar as I stood there in the firelight and watched and listened to him.

Around me, I now became aware, were many goats. This was a goatherd.

The coincidence of his having been playing the cradle song seemed almost incredible. The goatherd smiled and nodded to me as he finished the last few strains of the beautiful haunting melody. To me the sight of him there in the firelight beneath the great winking desert stars gave me a greater thrill than any show I had ever witnessed in a cabaret or on the stage. This was nature's own theater and the vaulted sky was a proscenium larger than any mortal man could comprehend.

Finally I spoke.

"Where do you live?" I asked in Spanish.

"Where my flock takes me," he answered simply. The fact that I had spoken to him in Spanish seemed to move him deeply.

"Who are you?" he asked.

"A traveler," I told him. "The train has been compelled to stop here a little while."

He looked at me and the lighted windows of the Pullmans and began to talk again.

"You might think it was lonely out here," he said tentatively, "but it really is not. This is a life I love. I have my tortillas made from the masa de maíz, a few red chilis, and an occasional wild fowl or rabbit. I have my fire at night and the sunshine by day. It is a happy life. I think my goats like it too. We like simple things. But this particular spot I love. I come here every night and sing my songs. Then the train comes by and the blaze of lights is as if God were dragging a flaming golden ribbon across el desierto which I love so much."

Then becoming practical, he said, "Señor, I have just been eating a piece of carne seca, the dried meat which is part of my sustenance in this wild land. Would you do me the honor to share a piece of carne seca with me?"

"I would be honored," I told him.

He handed me a piece of the leathery goat meat which had been dried in the sun of the high New Mexico plateau. From the train at this moment there came a warning whistle. I knew we would be leaving in a little while.

"I am pleased you have told me of your life," I said. "It coincides with my own thoughts. A man finds in the stars and in the sunshine the realities. I wish you well, amigo, and thank you for sharing your meal with me. Muchísimas gracias!"

"De nada," he replied.

"If you must go," he added hastily, "Take a piece of the carne seca with you."

"I appreciate your courtesy," I replied, still in Spanish, "I will be pleased to do so."

Near me on the desert I saw in the dim light an old piece of newspaper. I picked it up and my new friend wrapped the carne seca in it and handed it to me with a light bow. I bowed in return, raised my hand, said "Adiós" and started back to the train. After I had gone a few steps I heard once again the music of the guitar and then the voice of the lonely wanderer in the wasteland singing gently the strains of *La Golondrina*.

As I came into the brightness of the train lights and climbed the steps, I paused a moment to look out into this immense lonely land where the chance meeting had transported me back to my childhood. Then I happened to glance at the little package of carne seca wrapped in the newspaper in my hand. On the New York newspaper was printed an advertisement in large type saying, *Lombardi, Ltd*. Starring Leo Carrillo."

This was the rendezvous with memory God had arranged for me in the land that God forgot, and that I shall never forget.

CUARTA
PARTE DEL LIBRO

&

REINCARNATION OF
THE CABALLERO

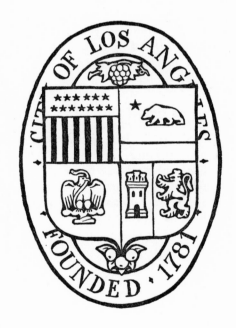

LEO CARRILLO

&

PURPLE HILLS

Purple hills where I was born
I think of you sometimes forlorn—
I long for you my purple hills.
My heart looks back and gently thrills
To your canyons deep that I adore,
Where arroyos creep to the ocean shore.
'Neath spreading oak and sycamore,
Your graceful slopes I used to roam,
Sierras of my boyhood home,
Set against the sunset sky,
Where the blazing rays bid the days goodbye,
And the setting sun of amber hue
Sinks into that ocean blue,
And the ripples of its sun-kissed shore
Sing to me forevermore.
Take me back where I can sleep
In the silent hush of your canyons deep.
Where my fathers roamed in the days gone by,
Take me back to live and die.

CHAPTER 37

HOME AT LAST

It was good to be back! Soon after I took up residence again in Southern California, I became convinced it was the place where I wanted to spend the rest of my days. I was commuting back and forth to New York between motion pictures to see my wife because we had not wanted to give up our lovely home on Long Island until we were sure what we wished to do.

While I was in California it was as if some yeast of memory were fermenting in me, bringing up the past and building images which I wanted to re-create. I recalled picking watercress in the little stream which came from the pools called the "Tears of Santa Monica." I remembered hunting hummingbird nests in the giant sycamores along the stream and finding two tiny eggs like little jewels in their nests. I could visualize the golden orioles building their nests which hung down like a sock and the golden owls in the hollows of the trees blinking their eyes at us as we played. All this continued to create in me a wish for a home of my own in a proper setting where the spirit of old California could permeate the patios and the rooms and I could feel genuinely at home and not an alien, as I did sometimes in New York and in the other cities where my stage career took me.

I went down one day to look at the little stream which came from the "Tears of Santa Monica." The whole area was one solid bramble patch but I could hear water gurgling amid the stickers and I knew that with some work the stream could be retrieved and made a wonderful asset. I made inquiries about the lot which was on Channel Drive and was able to buy it for a very nominal sum. Then I put a crew to work clearing it of the brambles. It was on the exact site where my brothers and sisters and I had played as children and waded in the pools and chased polliwogs and minnows.

When the lot was cleared I enlisted the aid of my sisters and between us we got up a barbecue for a number of film people and other friends out in the open on the site of what I hoped was going to be my home. At this time I did not tell my wife my full plans because I was so anxious to surprise her. In fact, just before I went on a tour of Australia, I bought another lot 600 feet deep with 1000 feet frontage so that all together I had close to ten acres along the stream and at the foot of the beautiful bluff. I still didn't know exactly what I was going to do with it but I felt the property had great potentials.

When I came back from my tour I looked over the property again. Some farmers up on Amalfi Drive had a big pile of dirt and I arranged for some of it to be brought in so I would have fine top soil on the lots. My hope was to build an adobe house. But I encountered bureaucracy and restrictions, and found out it was virtually impossible to build an adobe house because of the safety requirements which were imposed by the authorities.

Just at this moment I encountered a man who told me about an old kiln which was used for making tile and was to be torn down. The kiln was constructed of baked adobe bricks. I thought to myself, "If I can't have regular adobe, the next best thing would be baked adobe because it is the same thing with just a little cooking."

I went over to the kiln and made a deal. For $200 the immense lot of tile was delivered to my yard almost before you could say "Jack Robinson." It had all the beautiful characteristics of adobe with a mellow red tone from the baking. The bricks were 14 inches and 4 inches thick and the heat of the kiln had twisted them so that they were extremely picturesque; I hired an old Swede to make arches for me and told him that I wanted them to be uneven and to have the corners knocked off so they would have the appearance of age.

"We don't do that in the old country," the Swede told me.

"But this is the new country," I told him. "Go ahead and do it the way I say."

Then I arranged to have a long rambling house made of the adobe tiles, with fireplaces in every room, beamed ceilings, and all the other characteristics which I remembered in the beautiful old California houses of many years before. I planted avocados and flowers and pretty soon the place began to take form and shape. All this time I was keeping the surprise for Edith and when I would see her on my trips to New York she would ask me rather quizzically, "Where are you spending all this money?"

Finally the great day came when Edith was coming out to the Coast. I arranged with some of the MGM boys to bring over some of their lights and put them in the trees where they wouldn't be observed under cover of darkness. Edith and our daughter Antoinette were coming in on the Grace Line with Clara, our maid, and our dog and were to arrive at San Pedro early in the evening.

I arranged with the highway patrol to meet them and to escort them with sirens and a lot of fanfare to the site of my new house, the existence of which my wife knew nothing about. I waited at the house to make sure that everything was in order with the lights. After what seemed like a long wait I heard sirens approaching and the little cavalcade drew up. I ran to greet Edith and Antoinette, and they got out of the car and stood there in the dark apparently completely bewildered. We were surrounded by trees. There was no vestige of a light and they apparently felt that they were going to have to get sleeping bags or go to a hotel.

Then I gave the signal and pressed a button and the flood lights came on in one great mass of brilliance, and illuminated the long house with its beautiful portico and the arches and all the plantings which had been carried out according to my instructions.

My wife and Antoinette blinked and looked in astonishment at this home which apparently had sprung out of nothing as if Aladdin's Lamp had been touched and the Genie had produced it to order.

My wife gulped, rubbed her eyes, looked again, and then her first remark was:

"Where is the ladies' room?"

We were home!

In my home and in my little office amid the orange, avocado and palm trees I have gathered many sentimental treasures during the years. There are gold keys to cities all over the world, the pictures of friends I have made during the years, the faro dealing box of Wyatt Earp, the muskets and pistols of the era of my great-great-grandfather in California, Indian artifacts and baskets, all sorts of things which have contributed to the upbuilding of California and the West. They are my storehouse of memory.

All sorts of images are conjured up as I sit in my office looking at these mementoes or sometimes as I stand on my verandah in the evening and listen to the tinkle of the little stream and look back for a moment in the past which has such glorious lessons for us all.

I remember one of the highlights of my life. My mother drove a little pole buggy from the ranch where we were visiting in Culver City to my aunt's home in Santa Monica. It seemed like a long journey. At my aunt's we picked apples and pears in the orchard and they were piled in all their freshness and profusion in the back of the buggy.

Drowsily I snuggled amid the fruit and looked at the stars winking down at me as we started home. The fragrance of the fruit was so enticing that it has remained with me all my life and still dilates my nostrils with delight when I close my eyes and think about it.

I seem to see José Chapman, the ex-pirate of the Hippolyte Bouchard expedition as he builds the first important sailing vessel in California, the *Guadalupe* constructed at Mission San Gabriel.

Little legends of the naming of landmarks in Southern California come to mind. They tell the story that when Don Juan Bandini, one of my kinsmen, owned the vast area surrounding a big lake a stranger might come along and say to one of the natives, "What lake is that?" And the reply in Spanish would be:

"El Lago del Señor."

Later, the Americans, hearing this phrase picked up the latter part of it and called the lake "Elsinore."

To my mind comes the image of magnificent old José de la Luz who, at ninety-two, was the last of the vaqueros for the Muchado family which figured so prominently in my early life. De la Luz was a trainer for Charlie Howard, the famous owner of Seabiscuit, the immortal race horse. To me de la Luz was one of the glorious figures of California, a connecting link between the vaqueros of the early days and of our own era. He taught me much in the art of horsemanship.

Memories come to me also of my famous Aunt Arcadia Bandini Stearns de Baker about whom I once wrote a little poem:

"Dos polpalomitos centados en un árbol laurel
Qué bonita Doña Arcadia y qué feo Don Abel."

These fancies come to me at all hours and brighten my reveries. I can look on my walls and see physical reminders of the past in the faces and poses of my friends, the pictures of my horses, and the possessions of famous Californians. They all have a message for me, they all add to my comfort and my delight in the past of this great state.

CHAPTER 38

"WALK ON YOUR LAND"

IN every Californian there is a great desire for the wide open spaces if he comes from families who were born in them, as I was. All the time I was in New York, living in pigeon holes and hotels, I thought quite often about that song *Don't Fence Me In*. Then I would wonder: Where would I like to go? What would I like to have?

And I said I would like to have rolling hills, some cattle, twisting sycamores, doves, owls, coyotes, quail, a few deer and, of course, horses.

I well remembered the advice my father gave me when I was a youth:

"Walk on your land! Plant your feet on ground you own! Never be satisfied with mere money or stocks or bonds. Possess a part of the earth!"

So, even after I built my home in Santa Monica, with all the fun involved in getting the right materials and creating a romantic California atmosphere, there was a yearning in me which was not yet satisfied.

Sometimes I felt cramped. Too many people were crowded too close together around me.

One night a group of sportsmen was sitting around the fireplace in a duck club in Lancaster, California.

Senator Pittman was there, Irvin S. Cobb, and Sterling Hebbard who was a dealer in real estate for R. A. Rowan and Co., and the Rowan boys. Everybody got to telling about his choice of a hideaway. Some liked the desert, some liked the High Sierra, some liked different parts of California.

I said I wanted a climate that was mild where I could see the ocean, and be in it in 10 or 15 minutes. I went on and described this terrestrial paradise— the coo of the dove, the call of the quail, the moo of the cow summoning her little baby who perhaps was in danger of the coyotes that were howling about. I romanced it all over the place.

Then I added I would like to get an old adobe which was forgotten, but not too late to save, and rebuild it and put it back where it was one hundred years ago.

My description was so complete it evidently left its mark on the mind of several of my listeners, and Sterling Hebbard who dealt in ranches kept thinking about it. Finally, one day, he stumbled onto a place and called me on the telephone and said:

"Say, Leo, remember that description you gave of what you would like to have in the form of a ranch? Maybe I've found it. Can you come out with me one day this week?"

We drove down back of Carlsbad, on El Camino Real. It was spring.

The hills were covered with wild flowers. A few dairy cattle were grazing at the site Sterling pointed out. The house was abandoned, but it was adobe and I thought it could be saved. I looked from the top of the hill down at the view, the rolling hills and the little valley and I said, "If there is enough water there for domestic purposes I would like to buy it. See what the deal is."

He got me the deal in a day or so and I gave him a deposit and bought it.

I obtained from Mr. Charles Kelley 1700 acres in the first purchase for $17 an acre, and later bought about 3000 acres more very reasonably too. This land now is worth $3500 or $4000 an acre partly because there is plenty of water on it. I have retained a little more than 3000 acres.

Then I would come down on the weekends and look around and go back to Santa Monica again. In the meantime I was mulling it over in my mind, "What am I going to do with what I've got?" So I put up a tent down alongside of the creek and took an old Negro cook named Willie and we came down and we cooked outside in the rocks and enjoyed the fun of figuring out the whole thing.

One day I was sitting at the side of the little hill looking at the old adobe house and again I said, "What can I do?" I had looked at it for several weeks and, lo and behold, a man and his three sons drove up in an old ramshackle car. The father got out, approached me with his hat in his hand and said, "We're from New Mexico, and I'm a carpenter and adobe builder, my son's a plasterer, my other son's assistant carpenter and a mason, works in stone, and we haven't anything to do and we would like to rebuild this place for you. We could make the adobes right here."

Well, I worked out a deal with him and I was very fortunate because I hired the four of them at $3 a day apiece and I kept them three years—$12 a day for all of them!

All of the materials for the repairs we ripped off the old house. It was two-story adobe. We took off the top and made it a one-story rambling adobe and added an L-shaped wing.

I don't know the size of the rooms because I stepped off and put a stake at the corner and squared it off and said, "Put a room here, put a room there, put an arch over here, and we'll take these old bedrooms that are still standing and clean 'em up and make a living room out of the two front bedrooms. Then the old dining room we'll turn into a kitchen."

We did it.

These men—these wanderers—did a magnificent job. Their carpentry work was perfect, the stone work was artistic, the plastering excellent, all done on small chicken wire.

I was working on a picture at the time with Zasu Pitts. At that moment, I was sort of stuck as to where I was going to get some real California tile for the roof. They didn't have many around here in this part of the state at the time; at any rate I couldn't find any. One day Zasu Pitts mentioned to me, "You know, Leo, I am tearing down my Spanish house and building a modern home and I'm up to my hips in old Spanish tile. Do you know anybody that wants it?"

What a shot out of heaven that was!

I said, "Yes, I know somebody."

She said, "Tell them to get it off of that damn place of mine."

I said, "It'll be off!"

That afternoon I got hold of two trucks and by the time she got home all the tile was loaded and on the way down to the ranch. That's the tile that's on the house now.

It's a very picturesque house—flagstone patios, weeping willows at one side and weeping pepper trees which were called "Los Perus" in Peru where they came from originally. Incidentally, the first one was brought by my great-great-grandfather to the Mission of San Luis Rey and the little birds have propagated the growth of these trees all over this part of the country. There is one enormous tree that stands by my kitchen. I guess it is one hundred years old, and the trunk is five or six feet at the bottom and it stands up about 60 or 70 feet and spreads over the whole patio. The pepper trees are not very clean, except at certain times of the year, but they are beautiful when the red berries come out.

All these little adventures in fixing up the place excited my imagination.

My blessed Edith, my wife, was crazy about antiques and somebody told her the way to furnish a California house was with the same furniture they brought around by Clipper ship which was early Victorian, New England and Boston furniture. So she scouted around and we have lovely four-postered beds in our bedrooms and rosewood beds, handed down by an ancestor, in other bedrooms. My bedroom is more of a horseman's room with all the souvenirs and little things that I have put together and saved.

The living room contains two fireplaces, one at either end, and on the walls are the paintings of my forbears by Barberry, the great painter who painted all of the grandees in Santa Barbara along about 1830 and 1840. There are paintings which really are museum pieces along the walls. One is my grandfather, the other is my great-grandfather, and my great-grandmother. I have other small portraits of my grandmother on the paternal side and my own mother and my father which makes a complete array of ancestors on my wall.

Oftentimes I go down to the ranch and hold lovely conversations with them in my mind and wonder what they're thinking of my efforts to perpetuate a little monument in their memory.

I planned before I lost my dear wife that this would be our haven of rest when we got away from everything. I guess God needed her and took her but gave me our daughter Antoinette. She and I are enjoying it tremendously and at the moment we are very happy because we are fortunate enough to have disposed of a little piece of land which makes it possible for us to enjoy this to the hilt for the rest of our lives.

When we look out the window, the hedge and the approach of my driveways is one great planting of hybrid cactus that Luther Burbank invented. It's a very lovely, beautiful, atmospheric planting.

Then I have the whole side hill covered with lemon trees, oranges, and grapefruit. The barns are back by the side of the hill.

At the highest points of the ranch you can see the ocean and in clear weather San Clemente and Santa Catalina Islands.

The ranch has plenty of grazing. I keep as many as 600 head of cattle and horses.

I built the caretaker's house down below and at the entrance of the main driveway.

There's only one trouble.

They are crowding me all around with great subdivisions and gentlemen's estates and an airport about seven or eight minutes from the front gate. It makes it convenient in many ways but the old isolation, the lazy mornings when nobody was around, the feeling of being off by yourself, all of these are vanishing.

But I'm not giving up.

This is still my retreat.

And the sun and the moon and the stars and the sea are as beautiful and tranquil as ever.

CHAPTER 39

A VAQUERO VANISHES

IT was at this period I began to be aware of Fate linking up the various stages of my career, from the earliest days to the present. It was as if Providence were directing me in events and associations which were to have a profound influence on the shaping of my life. How else can you explain such things? . . .

Whirring quail wings always have stirred my blood, ever since I was able to lift a gun.

They led me indirectly into one of the greatest friendships of my life.

On my tenth birthday, my father got me a shotgun, it being a common practice in those days to trust small boys with firearms when game was abundant in the Santa Monica mountains near our home. My father was running a livery stable in Santa Monica at the time. He was going to send some of the men up to the famous Rindge Ranch owned by Frederick Hastings Rindge for his horses which had been pastured there. I asked if I could go along. This was for a special reason which I kept to myself.

Mr. Rindge had given me permission to hunt quail on his place although most hunters were barred by big signs, and the ranch hands ejected any intruders. This remarkable man, Mr. Rindge, had been kind to me in many ways. He had made his fortune in woolen mills in Boston before coming to California and acquiring the historic Malibu ranch where "The Owl Woman" once had lived in her cave. He felt naturally that Boston was the center of culture and that any real education must be gained within its environs and at Harvard University.

He had even offered to send me to Cambridge Manual Training School which he had founded and then on to Harvard for art study because of the interest I showed in sketching.

This tempted me, of course, but my family felt a great pride. They said no because it would have seemed to be demeaning themselves to someone when they were not able to pay for such a luxury for me.

Then, too, my Catholic parents reminded me Mr. Rindge was a Baptist!

On the day the men were going to the ranch for the horses, I was not thinking of either art or religion because I was so delighted that my father gave me permission to tag along with my shotgun.

I don't remember too much about the shooting that day but one incident stands forth vividly in my memory.

After my hunting I made a beeline for the bunk house because it was there that I could associate with real cowboys who handled the large number of cattle on the far-flung Rindge Ranch of 30,000 acres. The range boss was Francisco Ruiz who was actualy bluish-black in color with a white beard, a startling centaur. He rode a horse as if he literally were a projection of it, seeming to share in its every movement and to anticipate anything that it might do so that he was never unsettled in the saddle, a real "jinete."

I admired Ruiz for his horsemanship and for his great skill at lassoing wild steers but I was a little afraid of him too because of his formidable appearance.

On this particular day I sat waiting in the bunk house for a chance to talk horses and cattle with some of the cowboys.

On a table I saw some drawings. Since my own inclination was so strongly towards art it was only natural for me to go examine the drawings. Even to my young untrained eye they appeared spirited and full of a feeling of reality. I was leafing through the collection which showed bucking horses, roping of steers, branding, and all the other exciting events of a cattle ranch when I heard whistling outside. The bunk house door opened and in came a fellow I knew only as Ed. He did odd jobs around the place and took care of the sheep and goats but was not considered a regular vaquero.

As he came through the door Ed noticed that I was looking at the drawings and he stopped whistling and said cheerfully, "Any good?"

I nodded enthusiastically and told him that I thought his drawings really represented ranch scenes better than any I had ever seen.

"Why don't you send some to a magazine or something?" I asked.

Just at this moment Ruiz came in and heard our discussion.

"What good ees thees pictures?" Ruiz demanded. "If you study hard you be good cowboy, make $40 a month instead of $25 like you do now foolin' round with all thees seely pictures." He looked disgustedly at Ed, who only shook his head good-naturedly and started whistling again.

I don't know for sure what finally influenced Ed but a little later he took the advice of Ruiz rather than me. This possibly is understandable because nobody could expect a ten-year-old boy to be much of an art critic and there certainly was a great lure in the $40 a month as a vaquero when it meant $15 more than Ed was getting in his present more menial job.

Anyway, Ed started out to become a vaquero.

The first thing the ranch foreman did was to provide him with a half-wild horse on which he was supposed to stay under any circumstances. When, on top of having to ride the maverick horse, he was supposed to rope young steers and drag them in for branding in all sorts of rough country you can understand that Ed was going to earn his extra 15 bucks a month.

It wasn't long after the day I had seen Ed's sketches that I went back to the ranch again on a quail hunt. It chanced that the annual spring roundup was on and I could see the smoke from the branding fires in several locations. It was quite cold and I headed for one of the fires.

Almost immediately I saw Ed who was wearing a long black scarf around his neck.

He was just taking off after a young steer and his horse was going at a great clip. Ed was trying to look nonchalant and stay in the saddle while whirling the reata for the throw at the steer. He was a pretty good roper but he was not a good enough rider to permit his full talents to be exercised in throwing the rope. The reata was looped once around the saddle horn so as to permit a give and take when the rope had settled over the neck of one of the animals.

Finally Ed threw the rope and made a good catch on the steer. The trouble was that as he leaned forward for the throw his scarf was caught on the rope between the end of the reata and the saddle. The steer of course immediately took off faster than ever when he felt the rope around his neck and he ran so hard that the scarf yanked Ed's head down toward the saddle horn, pulling so tightly on the portion knotted about his neck that he began to strangle. His face turned red and then blue as he was choked while the steer continued its mad jumps, continually tightening the reata and thereby pulling Ed's head lower and lower. He finally was barely managing to hang in the saddle and he appeared in imminent danger of being choked to death.

"Can't you help him?" I yelled in my boyish voice to Ruiz who was watching the whole performance without a flicker of emotion on his face. He was really enjoying the situation.

"Let the damn gringo learn something," Ruiz snarled contemptuously, turning away as if the incident were over with.

Fortunately, at this moment Ed's horse ran under a sycamore tree and with his final strength Ed grabbed a limb and was jerked off the horse, the scarf ripping from around his neck. He hung for a moment from the limb and then dropped to the ground, flat on his culo. I ran to his side and found him gasping for air. In a few moments he was recovered enough to mount again and complete his work in the roundup.

Not long afterwards he left the ranch, throwing over his princely $40 a month and not even asking for the $25 a month job back again.

With him he took his many drawings of the cattle and horses and the brandings and the roundup. I often wondered what became of him.

CHAPTER 40

REUNION IN MANHATTAN

My life later became entwined with the theaters on Broadway. New York rather than Santa Monica was my home most of the time. In the great canyons of Manhattan I yearned for the out-of-doors which I had known as a boy and continually was on the lookout for anything which might remind me of those past days.

One of the compensations for living in New York, besides my success on the stage, was the companionship of men who became my life-long friends. One of these was Fred Stone of the famous team of Montgomery and Stone. At this time Fred was appearing in *The Red Mill*, one of his great hits on Broadway. He was a western enthusiast and particularly so in the realm of pictures dealing with Southwestern subjects, such as the cattle ranges and the wild country of California, Arizona, and New Mexico.

Will Rogers was making a lot of money by now and spending a good deal on western art. He used to show me these painting and drawings, and some of them I liked particularly well. But I never happened to notice the name of the artist, although the pictures looked vaguely familiar.

One night I was in Fred Stone's dressing room during the run of *The Red Mill* and after the show while he was taking off his make-up he began to tell me about a painting he had seen that day over on Fifth Avenue. It was of a horse sun-fishing. The price was $3,000. I asked him who painted it because he was so tremendously enthusiastic about the reality of the scene and the splendid way in which the artist has portrayed the bucking horse high in the air. Fred said he didn't know the artist.

Fred was so enthusiastic about the painting that the next day I strolled down Fifth Avenue to take a look at it myself. The moment it came into view it awakened recollections within me as if a bell suddenly had rung. I was transported back to the little bunk house on the Malibu Ranch with the drawings on the table and Ed, the prospective vaquero, coming in the door whistling so gayly. I knew this painting and the pictures in Will Rogers collection, which I had admired, were by the same artist. I went forward eagerly and pressed my nose against the glass so as to see the signature on the oil painting of the sun-fishing horse. It was "Ed Borein."

I don't even know myself whether I had ever heard Borein's last name. But there could be no mistake about the technique and the fidelity of action in this spirited scene. It was the Ed of the bunk house who had done it.

I went back to see Fred Stone because he had told me that he had obtained the address of the artist.

"Where is he, Fred?" I demanded. "In Santa Monica? Texas? Montana? or where?"

Fred laughed.

"You don't have to go that far," he said. He reached in his pocket and pulled out a scrap of paper with an address and handed it to me. It was at 42nd and Broadway, only a few blocks away.

I had a little while before going out for my own appearance in *Lombardi Ltd.* which then was having its long run on Broadway and I headed immediately for the address which Fred had given me. When I arrived at 42nd and Broadway I saw that the number indicated a building squeezed in next to the Knickerbocker Hotel. The card showed that Ed lived on the third floor. I went up to the rather unpretentious front of the building where a closed door faced me and saw that there were strings dangling down through the floors above. On one of these was a sign marked "Third Floor." I rang the bell on the end of this string and there was a click and the door opened. In I went.

Instantaneously, I was almost asphyxiated by the pleasant odor of California frijoles cooking, a smell which I certainly didn't expect to find in the stone jungle of New York.

As I glanced up in the half light of the stairwell I could see the silhouette of a big hat and an artist's palette as a man leaned over the railing.

"Come on up," he yelled.

I went up the stairs and sure enough there was Ed of the bunk house—
now Ed Borein, the famous New York painter whose productions were
bringing $3,000 apiece on Fifth Avenue.

"Why the hell didn't you let me know you were here?" I demanded as Ed
enfolded me in a big bear hug and beat me on the back.

"Oh, I've been reading about you in the theater but I was too shy to come
bother a big stage star," he replied.

"I haven't seen you since the old bunk house at the Malibu Ranch,
remember?"

"Of course," he responded. "You're the one that got me started on this
business. That day you told me it was good stuff and to keep it up and I tried
to be a cowboy and get that big money of $40 a month has always stuck in
my mind. You were just a kid but you seemed to know what you were
talking about and I never forgot it."

We were so busy talking as we went into his studio that at first I did not
even notice there were other people there.

Then I saw a fresh-faced man with skin that looked as if his mother had
just washed him with kitchen soap. He was busy modeling an Indian girl who
stood in native costume on a little raised stand in one corner. The man wore
brand new Levis, a red kerchief, and new boots.

"What is that?" I asked, pointing to the sculpture of the Indian girl. The
fresh faced man turned to me and drawled, "Prairie chicken."

Ed Borein introduced me and I gasped to learn he was Charles M. (Charlie)
Russell, the great western historian of painting and sculpture.

"What are you doing in New York, Mr. Russell?" I asked. "I thought
Montana was your bailiwick."

"Nancy brought me here," drawled Charlie as he continued deftly modeling the Indian girl. "She's over on Fifth Avenue selling 'em while I turn 'em
out over here. I don't know how to get over there, to tell you the truth. I get
lost every time."

"Don't you like it here?" I asked.

"I wouldn't like it if I stayed here fifty years," he said with great vehemence.
"All I want to do is to get back to Montana."

"What's the matter with it?" I persisted. "I've gotten so I like it pretty well
although I like California too."

"Listen," responded Russell, "the more I see of the men in New York the
more I think Darwin was right. In fifty years the only thing that will be left

of these guys is a thumb for pushing a button. If they were in a herd of buffalo with a butcher knife they would starve to death."

The odor of the frijoles in the studio was so enticing that I must have looked hungry because Ed looked at me quizzically and asked, "How would you like some good old-fashioned California food?"

"Just try me!" I told him.

Even Russell was affected by the wonderful aroma of the red beans which evidently were nearing a point of perfection.

In a few minutes Ed brought out a great bowl of old-fashioned frijoles mashed with hot lard so that the whole creamy mass was a delectable potion for my palate which had longed for just such a meal.

We visited a long time and I learned of Borein's wanderings and his success in New York which came when the really discerning people began to appreciate his drawings.

It was hard for me to tear myself away to go appear in the play that night but we all promised to get together again immediately.

We had many get-togethers, in the studio and elsewhere. Out of this happy situation grew an incident which Ed Borein never forgot the rest of his life. Some of us actors decided to get up a Wild West show for charity. The scene of our activities was in an arena at Freeport, Long Island close to the actors' colony where it was easy for us to get together and dream up our stunts in our free time. Fred Stone, Victor Moore, Frank Tinney, Ed Borein, and myself formed the nucleus of the equestrian portion of the act and in addition we had a clown band and all sorts of freak attractions.

My job was to round up the stock for the Wild West performance and I was content with any old horse or any old cow. When we got our stock assembled in the old corral it looked like part of a ranch although some of the animals were mighty ratty.

Once we got a big fat bull from a dairy. He was so fat and round that it was impossible to clinch your heels under him to hold on in the bareback bull riding. Will Rogers was routining the riders on this part of the show and he would accept volunteers from the audience, drug store cowboys, anybody who wanted to have a go at the "wild" bull. He would put a rope around the bull's belly which was like tying a string around a big rubber ball, and then invite the riders to go ahead. The bull always threw them in the grandstand and the spectators never knew when an unfortunate cowboy was going to land in their laps.

Will Rogers had a trick up his sleeve in all this. When the other fellows were all through and had been tossed either into the audience or onto the ground, and the bull was so damn pooped he couldn't throw a bubble off his back, Will would go up bravely, get on with his big wide disarming smile and ride him all over the place. He liked the bull and the bull liked him. I guess it was just like Will used to say, "I never saw a man I didn't like." The bull must have known this motto.

Our biggest success was an act we called "The Horse-Thief," which was presented with the nostalgic music of *Home on the Range* played very slowly. The idea was that there was a campfire and a couple of cowboys going to sleep. Frank Tinney was one of the cowboys and I was the other. After we had dozed off with our heads on our saddles the sneaking horse thief was seen coming in from the edge of the arena. In pantomime, he looked carefully at us to make sure we were asleep and then stole the horse and slipped away.

We cowboys were supposed to have been awakened by the departing thief and we jumped up and grabbed our ropes and went after him on the remaining horses. Fred Stone, as the Sheriff, who must have been warned somehow by radar and appeared on the scene almost instantaneously, led our chase of the horse thief. This chase was much to the edification of the clam diggers of Long Island and the rest of the people in the audience who had never seen a Western scene in their lives. Neither had anybody in the cast, for that matter, except Borein, Will Rogers, and myself.

Anyway, one night we were putting on a particularly realistic interpretation of the "Horse Thief" with all the action imaginable because we were spurred on by some enthusiastic people in the audience who apparently thought we were the greatest western actors in the world. Fred Stone roped Borein, yanked him off his horse and then dragged him all over the arena with such reality that when I ran up supposedly to seize the horse thief and tell him that he was going to be hanged, Borein looked up at me as he rubbed his backside and in a hoarse stage whisper said, "What the hell was he trying to do, kill me?"

"Why, Ed," I said innocently as I helped him get up, "you know we wouldn't do a thing like that. Anyway, even if you have made a lot of money with your pictures, it seems like everytime I see you whether it's on the Malibu or out here you're flat on your culo!"

CHAPTER 41

THE RANCHEROS VISITADORES

WHEN I arrived back in California I discovered that we had been taken over by the gringos.

I have used the word "gringo" many times in this book. Perhaps I should explain more fully what I mean. I know that there are many explanations, some of them fanciful as to how the word "gringo" came into existence in the first place. Some say it was the result of Mexican soldiers, during the Mexican War in 1846-1848, hearing the Yankees in their trenches sing the new song, *Green Grow the Lilacs*. To the Mexicans this sounded like "Gringos," and the story is that out of this corruption of the phrase came the term applied to the detested Yanquis themselves. Whether this or some other story is true is of no matter.

The sense in which I use "gringo" is for those alleged Californians who make no effort to understand the background or history of the state and who either distrust or are ignorant of Spanish-Mexican culture and tradition. "Gringo" to me is almost a synonym for ignoramus.

We have here the finest blending possible of the splendid Spanish civilizations and our Anglo-Saxon heritage of a love of liberty and inspired political evolution. We should make the most of those.

So, as I say, when I returned to my native state I was appalled to see how the newcomers had trampled upon the traditions which had been so dear in my youth.

As contrasted with the ignorance of the gringos there is a term in Spanish which is extremely expressive when applied to those who do understand the two civilizations. It is an expression in common use. We say a person is "simpático" if he is in sympathy and close accord with those of us who have tried to maintain the ideals and heritage of both our civilizations.

"The California Spirit" is hard to define. Yet it reaches out and takes hold of the heart and emotions of people of various backgrounds. It is the wonderful comradeship created by this spirit which made possible one of the most remarkable revivals of the early California days in our whole history.

On my arrival here I found there was a mass exodus from New York going on. My closest friends there, who had become sick of the clang and clatter of traffic and the unending hordes of people swarming through the streets of New York, had begun to come to California to seek not only beautiful physical surroundings but spiritual and mental solace as well.

It was remarkable how many of these were here or on the way. Ed Borein was living in Santa Barbara. Jimmy Swinnerton had returned and was doing paintings of the desert as well as his cartoons. Will Rogers was building a vast estate where he could rope calves and ride his horses in the hills of Santa Monica close to my own home. Clyde Forsythe, the great cartoonist, who now was engaged in serious desert painting, had returned to the Los Angeles area close to where he had been born in the town of Orange. Irvin S. Cobb, despite his loyalty to Paducah and Kentucky in general, moved out here and had a house on San Vicente Boulevard, close to me. Frank Tenney Johnson, the great artist of the West, shared a studio in Alhambra with Clyde Forsythe. Fred Stone was here and with him were many others who simply had been unable to endure the rigors of the East any longer. They longed for something finer and deeper in life.

This small group and others, both native Californians and newcomers, who had felt the charm and inner spirit of this great western state were joining in similar efforts.

Ed Borein was the leading spirit in the most vital and spectacular of these movements. He remembered the old days on the Malibu Ranch when he yearned to be a real vaquero and yet also was torn by the pull of his ambition towards an artist's life. Now that he was a smashing success and had won worldwide fame for his art based upon cattle and horses and the life of the ranchos, he wished to express his gratitude to the pastoral past of California which had inspired him. So he talked to friends in Santa Barbara and elsewhere, and from these discussions grew an idea.

It was a combination of two old California customs, at opposite ends of the season, as it were. The "pastores" which included a procession and visits to keep alive the spirit of the Christmastime was continued with one of the great spectacular events of California—the rodeo, or spring roundup of the cattle.

In Los Pastores, the group on horseback rides up to a rancho and stops respectfully outside. The dueña of the house receives them. A spokesman dismounts, hat in hand, and approaches her. He kneels, kisses the hem of her skirt, and she blesses him with a rosary.

The rancheros cheer, leap off their horses, tie them to the hitching posts, and gather at the rancho for a fiesta. It was—and could be again—a beautiful custom.

The spring roundup, of course, was not only for the serious purpose of gathering the cattle and sorting out those belonging to different owners and branding new calves, but also the signal for fun and celebration. It was a roundup combined with a fiesta. What Californian could miss such an opportunity in the springtime?

So Borein and others decided that if a group of horsemen were to get together at Santa Barbara and start out on a tour of the ranchos it would provide a perfect opportunity to revitalize and recreate the true California spirit.

Borein was not alone in wishing to revive the ancient customs.

For some time, in fact, throughout all of Southern California, various individuals with the desire to perpetuate the romance of the early days had been busy. Harry Carr, the great columnist of the *Los Angeles Times*, wrote unceasingly in his efforts to interest newcomers and apathetic Californians in the heritage which was theirs. He fought to save old adobe houses from being torn down, to revive the historic moments in the state's past, to glorify the deeds of its heroes.

A little woman, Mrs. A. S. C. Forbes, started a movement to mark El Camino Real with bells. This was so successful that all along the historic route beautiful standards with their bells were erected to remind everyone who whizzed by in an automobile about the days of priests and soldiers and the rancheros with their horses and crude conveyances.

Men like Bill Magee of San Juan Capistrano and Pala, the manager of the Santa Margarita Rancho, Frank Miller of the Mission Inn in Riverside, Lindley

Bynum of the Huntington Library, Sheriff Eugene W. Biscailuz, and a few others worked all the time to bring to life once more the early days with their drama and color.

But Borein's idea was something you could get your teeth into. It was specific. It attracted attention from the start. I was enthusiastic about it and agreed to try to interest Will Rogers, Irvin S. Cobb, Clark Gable, and other friends of mine.

It was decided to hold the trek of about five days in May, at a time when the countryside would be at its best and the weather probably would be fine. We were to camp out as we went along from one ranch to another and have campfires in the evening, and meals in the open, with everyone sleeping in a bed roll and doing most of his own horse wrangling.

For the first trek, bronzed old-timers came in from all over California to join in this outing. We had Alonzo Crabb, the husband of a granddaughter of Joseph Chapman, one of the "pirates" captured when Capt. Hippolyte Bouchard raided the coast, Sam Stanwood of Santa Barbara's old Spanish Days, Dwight Murphy, Ray Skofield, Jack Mitchell, United States Marshal Bob Clark of Los Angeles, Sheriff Emmett Shay of San Bernardino County, Elmer Awl, later President of the Santa Barbara "Old Spanish Days," Frank Tenney Johnson, Clyde Forsythe, Joe De Yong, the artist, Capt. William Banning of the famous Banning family which used to haul freight from San Pedro to Los Angeles, Sheriff Biscailuz, W. Parker Lyon, owner of the Pony Express Museum at Arcadia, and a couple of hundred others.

As the riders assembled and started up the trail towards their first night's camp I exclaimed involuntarily, "We are going to have lots of fun, but, down below it all, there is a heartbeat!"

That was the spirit in which Borein started the whole thing. He felt the old West, the spirit of old California, in his heart and he had to express it. This was his way.

Sure, there were jokes told and a lot of horse play and a little drinking but ever present was the realization that for a few perfect days the cares of the bustling modern world were shaken off and we were returning once more into the era when men were able to enjoy simple pleasures in the outdoors.

It is easy for me to conjure up out of my memory some of the typical scenes on the ranchero ride. The horses of every hue and color with beautiful saddles and the riders attired in red, blue, green, yellow and purple shirts spread out in long lines along the crest of the green hills and by the tranquil streams. Conversation flowed easily and naturally. The sun shone down brightly. Cattle grazed on the hillside just as they had done for one hundred and fifty years, and we felt we were literally being transported into another age.

The start of the journey was in the true tradition.

Priests at Santa Barbara Mission on the hill overlooking the Pacific blessed the riders as they prepared to head into the mountains. Families were gathered around as the simple ceremony took place, as if the Visitadores were going on some long exploration trip into the wilderness.

Then the signal to start was given, and there was the creaking of leather and the clatter of hoofs as the cavalcade turned eastward for its first day's trek.

Many a groan came from the greenhorn riders as the sun grew hot and tender bodies, unused to the saddle, began to feel the stress and strain of the distance traveled.

But by the time evening came and the program of fun started everybody was ready to join in, even though some walked a little carefully to protect their strained muscles.

It wasn't too late when everybody turned in and went quickly to sleep as a result of the day in the outdoors.

Some sportive soul started turning over cots of the rancheros about 4:30 A.M. As a result there was a court a little later and the culprit didn't have a chance. He was thrown into the Santa Ynez River, clothes and all. Justice still prevails, as Joe De Yong, the famous cowboy artist, who was one of the victims, opined.

The outing attracted the old-time kind of western officer.

Marshal Bob Clark, who originally hailed from up Ventura way, helped preserve order. So did Sheriff Emmett Shay of San Bernardino County, who followed in the footsteps and the job of his illustrious father. Shay was telling about one of the toughest hombres he ever met. He went to the fellow's house way up in the mountains to question him. He couldn't find anybody except a woman.

"Oh, Jim's under the house," she said.

"Hey, what are you doing under there," yelled the Sheriff, trying to peer into the inky blackness.

"Aw, a blankety-blank so-and-so of a rattlesnake came under here," replied a gruff muffled voice, "and I'm feeling around trying to find the so-and-so."

Leo Ecord of San Fernando took part in so many events in the rodeo that when it came time for the beer race he was plumb tuckered out. He raced up to one end of the field and tried to drink the beer but his stomach was too tired. He couldn't get it down. . . .

Undertaker Hal Reynolds of Pasadena was accused of advertising his business because he was wearing a coal-black sweater.

For five days then the men from all parts of the United States camped, rode, ate and frolicked together on the journey into the oak flecked hills of the historic San Marcos Pass and Santa Ynez River country.

They rode in a body to John J. Mitchell's Rancho Juan y Lolita, bronzed men in large hats. They sang the songs of the rancheros as they trotted along the ways where Franciscan padres had trod with sandaled feet more than a century ago.

Luckless celebrants were thrown into the old iron-barred wagon that served as a hoosegow. Exuberant giants wrestled in the sawdust of the bar floors. Booted feet thundered in tune to the tinkling old piano played by Dick Alter.

And then to the music of bronze mission bells, just as they had started, they prepared to say adiós.

This time it was at the tranquil old Mission Santa Ynez.

As the rolling notes of the bell echoed out across the oak-covered hills the rancheros, resplendent in red, yellow, green and blue silk shirts and riding togs, brought to a dramatic finale their journey in the early-day wonderland.

Impatient horses with their riders in gleaming silver saddles champed in the courtyard of the mission for the final ceremonies. Bareheaded gray-robed student priests chanted the chants of one hundred years ago. A señorita in a yellow dress sang *Cielito Lindo*.

And the 5,000 spectators who had gathered from all over Southern California cheered the riders who came clattering over from Juan y Lolita Ranch six miles away.

The crowd had waited for hours in the lane and around the mission.

The little boys in the high bell tower began to pull the ropes as they saw the first riders approaching.

The bells boomed and boomed.

At the head of the brilliantly garbed column rode El Presidente Jack Mitchell. With him were Dwight Murphy and Ray Skofield, hosts at the ranches visited by the outdoor group on the trek.

John Boles and I were alongside Elmer Awl, major-domo of the Visitadores.

Irvin Cobb was there.

El Presidente Sam Stanwood of Santa Barbara's Old Spanish Day was driving a buckboard in which sat Dr. Frank Barham, owner of near-by Rancho Los Alamos.

Stage coaches and wagons filled with more Visitadores rolled along behind the horsemen. The riders wheeled and formed a hollow circle in front of the mission as the crowd cheered.

Marion Parks Partridge extended greetings of the Native Daughters of the Golden West.

Mrs. Crabb was introduced as the honorary mother of the Visitadores.

Florence Dodson Schonemann, another descendant of famous Californians, was presented.

Señora Raoul Ramirez of San Gabriel sang *Estrellita*.

And all the time the sun beamed down hot and the horses clanked their bits. A slight haze was settling over the oak hills.

John Boles and Lanny Ross sang.

Father Aybrian O'Leary of Santa Ynez Mission extended his greetings and blessings.

The crowd sang *La Golondrina* as the cavalcade started to move away.

Rancheros Visitadores had come to the end of the trail for another year.

Farewell handshakes began.

From green pastures to mountain heights, from mission bells to grazing cattle, from campfires to sweaty saddles. It was all part of the journey into yesteryear.

Ed Borein was satisfied. He had captured a moment out of the past; it had inspired all those who participated. He wanted to see this trip go on. It has. And I know that Ed is happy over the institution he started. If he is drawing pictures up there in the great corral, I know that one will be of the rancheros along a green ridge looking down at the placid waters of a California stream and saying to one another:

"Vaya con Dios!"

CHAPTER 42

QUEST FOR A PALOMINO

Many times as I have ridden horseback in great processions such as "Old Spanish Days" in Santa Barbara and "The Rose Parade" in Pasadena, it has seemed to me that my great-great-grandfather, José Raimundo Carrillo, should be riding there beside me.

He saw a horse miracle occur in California.

On that first day of July, 1769, when Father Serra and Don Gaspar de Portola arrived at the site of San Diego, there was not a single horse in the entire area that we now know as California. For two hundred and fifty years horses had been used in Mexico but not a single one had penetrated across the arid deserts to this part of the Pacific Coast. Here there stretched millions of acres of lush pasture lands ideal for grazing and yet only wild creatures could be seen.

José Raimundo was a great horseman himself. He sprang into the saddle with that easy motion of the born vaquero and at once became, as it were, a living portion of the spirited creature that he rode.

Something of that period of daring horsemanship must have come down the generations to me. From the moment I could toddle or speak I loved horses. It is impossible for me to remember when I could not ride. At first I clung to my father as I sat behind him but soon I was riding alone, using only a hackamore as was customary among the early Californians.

My memories of those days remain very vivid. I recall with particular clarity the process by which I learned the lore of horses.

The tiny foal lay on the green grass, and the sun shone bright overhead. Beside him stood the mare, his dam. The foal was still wet and glistening. After a few moments he tried to stand on his wobbly legs. At first he was unable to do so, then gradually he teetered to a position on all four feet, and collapsed again. Once more he tried.

"See him!" exclaimed my Tío. "He has spirit!"

I watched fascinatedly. This was the youngest foal I had ever seen.

My Tío stretched out his arm and swung it in a wide circle indicating the vast rancho on which we stood. It was a land of meadows and ciénegas dotted with live oaks and a line of sycamores by a distant stream. Far off my purple mountains were etched against the sky.

"This shall be a great horse," said my Tío solemnly. I nodded, child that I was, hardly understanding anything except the beauty of the newly-born creature here before my eyes.

It was watching the growth and development of this foal, a dark chestnut, which initiated me into the secrets of the training of a California horse, an art which had been practiced for centuries here, in Mexico, and in Spain.

It was an art of exactitude and patience—"Paciencia, poco a poco."

Many speak of the "cruelty" of the Spanish race to horses. Nothing could be further from the truth. This gross libel usually is based upon the nature of the equipment which is used on a mature horse after he has been meticulously trained over a period of years so that the seeming "cruelty" is in reality only ornamentation, and sometimes is misinterpreted by the uninformed. I speak with some heat on this subject because it was my privilege to watch the training of Gimnasta. That was the name my Tío gave the little foal that day in the meadow because of his activity and gymnastics in trying to get to his feet so quickly. During the next few years I felt almost as if I owned that little horse because at every stage of his training my kindly Tío would tell me what was going to happen and then let me watch the successive steps in the training.

It was a beautiful thing to watch, the gentleness and the care lavished upon this little horse—this caballito—which in turn seemed to understand that something special was expected of him.

Long before a saddle was put on him he became used to the feel of a rawhide hackamore. These hackamores were made of braided material from rawhide, like a reata, with a rawhide button about an inch and a half in diameter on it and mecate or rienda, hair rope, for reins.

After the little horse was trained in this fashion, he was introduced to a saddle without anyone in it and led around for a long period. After that a light rider was put in the saddle.

The first reins were made from the braided tail of a horse, and the prickly ends, when they touched the neck of Gimnasta, gave him to understand that he must respond in the direction the rider wished to guide him. After he became proficient in this technique the reins were changed. This time they were lighter and more delicate and made from the hair of the mane of a horse so that the guidance was a much more subtle arrangement.

After an exercise boy had put him through his paces for a long time in this fashion, one of my Tío's daughters was brought out to do the finishing job. She always rode side-saddle, as was required for modesty in those days, and her riding habit covered her legs down to the toe of her riding boots. Her hands were so delicate that Gimnasta soon came to follow directions almost without an observer being able to tell that the reins had been moved at all. He would gallop forward, stop, and slide, turn left or right, whirl, all with such precision and finish that I thrilled at the wonderful accomplishment which had gone on before my eyes.

I think the charge of cruelty in regard to handling of horses directed against people of Spanish descent was caused largely by the so-called spade bit and the huge spurs which were worn in the early days. The truth is that the spade bit with its long shank and reels is to make noise for the entertainment of the onlooker and perhaps even for the horse himself as he goes along with his rider.

The handling of a spade bit is a delicate procedure. A good horseman would never pull on such a bit because it would cause a severe injury to the horse's mouth, breaking down the bars in the roof of the mouth and causing him to become a so-called "steel jaw." In that case a horse would not respond to any kind of a bit.

The whole idea was that after the careful early training, the horse instinctively would respond to the slightest touch of the reins, making the use of a bit unnecessary except in the most unusual circumstances. The training was called, as I have said, "poco a poco"—little by little.

Just as the spade bit was more for show than for use, so were the large spurs with their long rods. These were used largely in the mountains when hunting for cattle and they were used to spur the horse only in cases of extreme danger from a grizzly bear or a mountain lion when a quick leap by the animal was necessary to save the rider from death or mangling. In my observation of the training of Gimnasta, I learned many of the arts of good horsemen.

All during this period I gleaned the secrets of magnificent leather work. I watched the saddle makers as they patiently shaped the beautiful saddles fringed with silver. I learned the technique used in making the rawhide reins with swivels.

For the cowboys there were the tapaderas, or stirrup covers, perhaps 18 inches long to be used in chaparral and cactus country. These also were decorated with figures in the leather or sometimes with silver. These tapaderas also were used as flaps to urge the horse along by striking him under the belly.

Also for the cowboys were the armas or the large rawhide wings, likewise a protection from cactus. The stirrups ordinarily were hewed out of an oak tree and then carved to fit the foot. I have two preserved from the very earliest days of California which belonged to Captain Gaspar de Portola himself.

The quirts always were carried on the right wrist of a caballero but he so respected his horse that the quirt was rarely used except in moments of danger when the spurs also were applied.

The most impressive thing to me always was the fashioning of the rawhide for reatas. The rawhide was stretched out on the ground and then the expert in the making of reatas would cut it round and round in strips so that the entire hide was used and cut into one long piece. Then this was woven— almost like "knitting"—in four, six, eight, or sometimes even twelve strands into a rope as smooth to the touch as one woven from fibre.

The remarkable talent of these reata weavers has rarely been equaled on this continent for sheer manual dexterity and adept use of the hands. It actually became a folk art to create a proper reata. The finished reatas, of course, were used as a rope for lassoing cattle, usually with the head and heel being caught at the same time due to the amazing skill of the vaqueros, so that the animal would be stretched out lengthwise convenient for the branders at roundup time.

The registered brand of a ranchero was his seal, as sacred as his signature, and it was just as dangerous to forge a brand as it would have been to forge a man's name upon a note.

I have mentioned the fact that women often did the finishing training of horses but even then they were so modest that they wore a riding habit which covered them down to the toe of the riding boot. Even so seated and so encumbered, many women were marvelous riders and able to impart that delicacy of response from the horse which most men were unable to attain.

The first book I ever read was *Don Quixote* but the second was the immortal account of the conquest of Mexico by that incredible old soldier, Bernal Diaz, the companion of Cortez. As soon as I could make out the letters I was poring over the pages of Bernal Diaz's account of the trip from Cuba to the site of the present Vera Cruz in Mexico. Diaz had a particular fondness for the horses which were brought along on that voyage by Cortez.

With love and respect, the old soldier described each one of the sixteen horses and mares on the voyage. This "cavalry" was the salvation of the Spaniards in their battle with the Indians of Mexico who had never seen such creatures before. It was in this year of 1519 that the first horses were landed on the North American Continent.

Bernal Diaz in his descriptions evidently had favorites among the horses and mares. He describes one owned by Alonzo Hernandez Puerto Carrero as "a gray mare, a very good charger which Cortez bought for him with his gold buttons." It was true that horses were so valuable in Cuba it was almost impossible to obtain them. They were listed along with slaves as being "worth their weight in gold."

Captain Cortez himself owned "a dark chestnut horse" but this died at San Juan de Ulua. As if fate were making up for the loss a chestnut mare, owned by Juan Sadeno of Havana, foaled while on board ship on the way to Mexico. So the Spaniards were able to muster sixteen of their "cavalry" at the moments when they were needed so badly.

From the exact descriptions of the colors and other qualities of the horses by Bernal Diaz it is easy to tell that they were Arabians and Barbs. The Arabians came literally from the land of Arabia or that part of Asia, while the Barbs were a coarser-grained horse of somewhat different color from North Africa.

The Arabian, which has one less lumbar vertebra than the other horses giving it an extremely short back, is capable of carrying incredible amounts of weight in comparison with its own weight. For this reason, and for their intelligence, as they had been for centuries, Arabian mares were considered the finest war horses in the history of the world. A small Arabian could carry a large man with all the armor and weapons needed in those days and still travel immense distances and "live off the land." These horses did not have to be pampered in any way.

The Barbs also were spirited and long-enduring horses who proved their bravery in the battles of Mexico.

The Indians thought the horse and rider were only one animal. Indians were killed by the hundreds when they tried to oppose these strange beasts. The Indians were extremely brave and in many cases refused to retreat even after having suffered terrible losses. The Spaniards used artillery and the cavalry with great effect.

After one battle, at the start of the conquest of Mexico, some of the horses as well as the men were wounded. Fires were built and the fat from some of the dead Indians was heated up and this was used as medicine on the wounds of the horses. The wounded Spaniards had no medicine at all and some merely used cloths to bind up their wounds and others resorted to the fat of the Indian as if they, too, were horses.

In the conquest of Mexico and the looting of the gold from the temples of the Aztecs the horses played a great part. The Arabians and Barbs flourished in Mexico and gradually spread throughout the country during the next two and a half centuries.

Still, as I say, not one had penetrated to the distant land known as California. So when my great-great-grandfather came here he was astonished, as were all of the priests and soldiers, to note the absence of livestock of any kind throughout the land.

The amazing thing in the next few years was how rapidly the horses and cattle multiplied. It was one of the greatest increases ever noted in any one place in all history. Before too long the hills and valleys were dotted with bands of wild horses and innumerable cattle.

This was the "horse miracle" of which I spoke.

For a few years none of these had any particular value. A man was at liberty to take a horse anywhere he found it and to kill a beef animal, cut off a few pounds for a meal, and leave the rest of the body where it lay. Then the great Boston clipper ships began to come around the Horn, asking for cattle hides to be used in the leather trade of New England. Suddenly cattle, at least, took on a certain value. The hides were used as money, having a value of about two dollars apiece. The meat still wasn't worth anything at all. It remained perfectly permissible for a traveler to kill a cow or a bull and to eat some of the meat just so he left the hide where the owner would find it.

Now, though, the great bands of horses who had multiplied so tremendously began to suffer because the cattle had come to have a value. The horses in the drier years ate up the pasturage which was needed by the cattle. So the horses became, in a sense, "outlaws" and "robbers"—as far as feed was concerned.

The rancheros who desired as many cattle as possible to obtain the wealth in hides used many means to get rid of the unwanted horses. On the old Rancho Santa Margarita, which later became the prize in a great legal battle between Juan Forster and Pío Pico, the last Mexican Governor of California, a way was found to get rid of the horses. The vaqueros would spread out into a long line and start the wild horses running ahead of them. Gradually the vaqueros would close in closer and closer on the horses, keeping them headed in one direction. Suddenly the wild horses would realize that they were trapped between the hated men and a great cliff which lay ahead. Hundreds of them voluntarily plunged over the cliff to their death rather than submit to capture. In this way the pasture of the Santa Margarita was kept for the droves of cattle.

I speak of the Santa Margarita because this vast rancho, now the home of Marine Camp Joseph C. Pendleton and near the site of my own present ranch, was the scene of part of the events I want to describe.

My great-great-grandfather, as I say, saw the arrival of the first horses in California and their multiplication here. He was born two and a half centuries too late to participate in the introduction of horses to this continent by Cortez. But the blood of the Conquistadores burned in the veins of José Raimundo Carrillo and this was what caused him to come to California. He lived in Loreto almost 1000 miles down the Baja California Peninsula from the present Alta California line.

It was in Loreto that Father Serra and Captain Portola mustered their forces after they had been recruited in Sonora and Sinaloa across the Sea of Cortez or the Gulf of California. José Raimundo joined the leather-jacket soldiers who were to march to Alta California for the colonization there, and to protect the priests as they sought to convert the heathen Indians.

Somehow or other those soldiers and priests must have succeeded fairly well because, by the time I was born, the Indians were either dead, converted or drunk. At least they were not much of a factor anymore in California where the Spanish race and later the Anglo-Saxons from across the continent had moved in and pushed the poor red man into oblivion.

As I grew up in Los Angeles and Santa Monica and hunted on the great Malibu ranch and the other ranches I associated with vaqueros and American cowboys. From them I learned the lore of horses and how to judge them for conformation and for color. Of all the horses I saw there was one kind which appealed to my heart more than any others.

It was the palomino.

This magnificent horse is not a breed, as you know, but a color. It is the color of burnished gold, with white mane and tail.

These horses are told of in legend and story from the very earliest of days in medieval Spain. In the era of Queen Isabella and King Ferdinand, just as Columbus was setting out to find a New World, the great Palomina family of Spain indulged itself in a luxury. The family had made a fortune with wines—sherry and port—which because of their color and excellence spread all over Europe. The Palominas envied other royal families of Europe such as the Hapsburgs of Austria who indulged themselves in famous pure white horses. So the Palomina family decided it would develop a line of golden-colored horses with white manes and tails. These they called palominos.

The horses were obtained by careful breeding of certain colors so as to obtain the desired combination of genes to produce the true palomino. The Palominas wanted a "horse to match their name"—and they got it.

It was a process of experiment, of elimination. A sorrel mare with flaxen mane and tail when bred to a sorrel stud might foal a palomino. Gradually the Palomina family learned the technique of breeding this color true, and their palomino horses became the most famous and the most desired of any in Europe.

Naturally this inclination toward breeding of palominos was carried over to the islands of the Caribbean, and then to Mexico and then on into Alta California itself.

The story is told that there was a Juan Palomina in Sonoma who, remembering the story of his family's development of the palomino horse, offered a great prize to his vaqueros if they would find him a palomino horse. The vaqueros combed the ranches everywhere they went and finally a lucky one found a palomino. It was brought to the home of Juan Palomina and, so far as is known, became the first recognized palomino in Alta California.

After my boyhood and the opportunities which I had to express my love of horses in riding and hunting and jumping and engaging in the rough horse games of the day, I went to San Francisco and then east to New York for my stage career. Necessarily, my days of horsemanship were limited. Still I carried in my heart the love which had been instilled there when I was a child.

One day, I hoped, my dream of "the perfect palomino" might begin to come true.

CHAPTER 43

HAIL CONQUISTADOR

We were camping at the beautiful ranch of Dwight Murphy in the San Marcos Pass country back of Santa Barbara. The annual ride of the Rancheros Visitadores was under way. The Murphy ranch was one of the popular stops because all of the men on the ride, no matter what kind of horse they owned, wanted to see the specimens of palominos owned by Murphy.

We all knew it was Murphy's desire to produce the most perfect palomino ever foaled in this country. With his immense wealth he was able to acquire the finest stock. The resulting assortment of palominos which ranged his pasture lands and were lavishly stabled at his ranch headquarters caused all of us to wonder how one man could have amassed so marvelous a collection of horseflesh.

One morning, very early, before the rest of the Rancheros were awake I went down to the stables and slipped inside. It was just getting light outside and it was still very dim in the interior; but I knew where the stall of the great stallion, Rey de los Reyes, was located. I walked over there and stood looking in the half light at this golden creature, seemingly conjured up out of the dream of some horseman rather than really existing.

I put my arm around the horse's neck and fondled him. He was of a gentle disposition and we already were friends from previous occasions when I had visited the ranch. I was so engrossed in my admiration of the horse as the light gradually increased in the stable that I was unaware anyone else had entered.

Suddenly at my elbow I heard Murphy's voice saying, "You are a softy about this one, aren't you?"

"Can you blame me?" I asked. "This is just about as fine a horse as I can imagine."

"You think so?" asked Murphy quizzically.

I wasn't sure exactly what he was getting at and we started talking about the lineage of Rey de los Reyes. He was the son of the famous Swedish King of the Santa Margarita Ranch, who in turn was a son of the notable Del Rey, and Del Rey was the son of the immortal Rey de Santa Anita owned by Lucky Baldwin in Arcadia. Horses just don't have any more noble blood than that. It is as if you were descended from Crusaders and royal families and the signers of the Declaration of Independence all rolled into one.

We chatted for a few minutes and then Murphy said to me, "Have you been out in the pasture?"

"No," I replied. "I haven't had time yet."

"Come along after breakfast," he said, "and I will show you something special."

Sure enough, after we had eaten our outdoor breakfast, Murphy motioned to me and we got our horses and rode out into one of the pastures.

"What are you going to show me?" I asked, no longer able to conceal my curiosity.

"Just wait a minute," he told me. We went through a clump of oaks and came out into a little glen. There stood a beautiful Arabian mare with four white socks.

Then I gasped.

Just getting to his feet beside the mare was a yearling stud colt. In the early morning sunlight his coat glinted like burnished gold. His mane and tail were like flax. His great intelligent eyes, derived both from his dam and his sire, looked with friendly interest at us. His small ears twitched as if in greeting.

"That's the most beautiful thing I ever saw!" I exclaimed involuntarily.

"Everybody thinks so," agreed Murphy. "Rey de los Reyes is his sire. Clark Gable has tried to buy him, Robert Taylor has offered me more than I'd like to tell you, and a lot of others have been after me."

I could not take my eyes away from the colt whose conformation and coloring were so perfect that I truly believe he represented Dwight Murphy's dream of the finest palomino in the world.

"How would you like to have him?" Murphy asked simply.

I shook my head.

"I'd never be able to afford a horse like that," I told him.

"I'm not offering to sell him," Murphy added, "I'm giving him to you."

I looked at him in stupefaction.

"Give him to me!" I stammered. "You can't mean a thing like that—"

"But I do! You're the only man in California—and I guess in the United States—who deserves a horse like that. You've got the blood of old California in you and this horse has the best blood of old California and Mexico and Spain and Arabia in him. I don't know of a better combination than the two of you would make."

I looked at the little horse again. He was absolute perfection. It was impossible for me to speak. I realized that Murphy was indulging one of the most ancient of California customs—the giving freely of a prize possession to someone you felt deserved it or could use it better than yourself.

All I could do was to shake hands silently with him in mute token of my appreciation. I was beyond words.

In such fashion did I come to own "Conquistador."

It was natural for me to give the name Conquistador to this perfect horse. All my life I had maintained a nebulous dream of a Palomino with the sheen of gold and the white mane and tail of such color and texture that it would be unequaled anywhere. Now that this magnificent creature was before me in the flesh I was awed.

All the lore and details I had learned during my childhood and in later life about the training and care of horses stood me in good stead. It seemed appropriate that only the finest training in the world should be given to this finest horse so I obtained the services of the best trainers that I could find and devoted as much time as was possible myself to the little colt. He continued to grow in perfect proportions, bearing out the promise of his yearling days.

By the time he was old enough to ride we had lavished upon him every attention it is possible to give to a horse. He was sweet-tempered and loving at all times and this made our task easier.

The first time I rode him in a parade there were continuous gasps of surprise and admiration and bursts of applause all along the line of march. Conquistador had conquered!

At one point a man rushed out and cried: "I'll give you $25,000 for him this minute!"

"You can add another cipher and still couldn't have him," I replied.

It is true that no amount of money could have tempted me to part with this horse which had been given to me through the open-hearted generosity of Dwight Murphy. I not only felt an obligation to Murphy to keep the horse for myself but I had formed such an attachment for him that it would have been impossible for me to sell him, anymore than I could have sold any other member of my family.

Soon after I acquired Conquistador I was invited to go to the Bohemian Grove in San Francisco, that gathering of notable men where one of the rituals is the burning of "Care" so that all worries and perplexities and frustrations are put aside for a little while in the glow of comradeship and good food and wine.

Herbert Hoover gave one of his famous off-the-record speeches, and we all were having a wonderful time. The magazine *Collier's* had just come out with the story of my desire to own the best palomino in the world and the fact that I couldn't afford it, and then the story of how Dwight Murphy presented me with Conquistador.

One day a moon-faced man in old blue jeans came up to me and started talking about the story in the copy of *Collier's* he was carrying. I had not met this particular man and was a little taken aback when he slapped the copy of the magazine and said: "No so-and-so has ever outdone me. If Dwight can give you a horse, I'm going to give you a car to match the horse."

I thought he was kidding me, so I looked at his jeans and asked, "Where do you work?"

He gave a sheepish smile, ducked his moon-face, wiped his nose and said quietly:

"For Chrysler—I'm the president."

He wasn't kidding, after all. He was K. T. Keller, Chairman of the Board of the Chrysler Corporation.

Keller was one of the most enthusiastic men I ever met. He entered into the idea of creating a special car to match Conquistador with all the enthusiasm of developing a new model automobile. You would have thought he was going to make a million dollars out of the idea instead of presenting me with an automobile.

The special job was done with great care. Finally the car was finished back in Detroit. It was lined with specially tanned Hereford hide, it had a cow's head on the radiator, and a horn that bellowed like a steer and was strictly a car to make any ranchman happy.

The only problem was the color. Keller was a perfectionist. He wanted the car to match Conquistador's color in every respect. This was a tough job. If you have ever studied the burnished gold of a palomino and the silvery white color of the mane and tail you will know how difficult it would be to match it. Keller was sending telegrams back and forth between California, where he was staying, and Detroit to try and work out the color combination. Each sample that was sent him failed to satisfy. Finally he appealed to my wife.

"Edith," he said, "can't you help us out in this crisis? How are we ever going to get that car the color of Conquistador?"

My wife thought a minute and then nodded her head as if she had received a sudden inspiration.

"Wait a minute," she said. "I'll be right back."

She went into the house. In a moment she came back with a small piece of cloth in her hand.

"I just cut this off of one of our daughter Antoinette's shirts," she said. "It was dyed especially to match the color of Conquistador. Why don't you have your people back in Detroit try it?"

Keller sent the piece of cloth to Detroit by airmail.

Then samples of how the car would look with the paint on pieces of metal were sent to him. Keller personally took it out to compare with the glossy coat of Conquistador.

"We got it!" he exclaimed in delight.

I guess it was the first time in history that the color of a car, to match a horse, had been decided from a woman's shirt tail.

T

CHAPTER 44

FATE WITH A CHINESE ACCENT

ONE afternoon, not long ago, I was standing on a street corner in new China-town in Los Angeles. It was sunny and warm. The odor of frying shrimp and egg foo yung coming from the Chinese restaurants caused my nose to twitch. It made me a little sad to compare this Chinatown in a new location with the one I remembered around the Plaza in my childhood. Recollections came flooding back on me as I stood there sunning myself and thinking about the days of my childhood. A warm gush of memories overwhelmed me. I could see and hear once again the Cantonese I had loved as a tiny boy.

Then I noticed sitting close to me in a rocking chair, in a patch of shade, a little old Chinese man. He looked rather ragged. Out of the corner of his eye he was observing me in that Oriental fashion which is so hard to detect but which I remembered of old.

It made me want to share the nostalgic feeling which had come over me.

"Holama!" I said tentatively in Chinese.

The old man looked at me and nodded his head in friendly salutation but showed no surprise.

A sudden impulse came to me, born of the images which had been filling my mind.

"What do you do?" I asked. "How would you like a nice home and a place to stay for the rest of your life?"

He rocked slowly.

"Who you— You likee ketchum cook, houseboy?"

I nodded, rather astonished at his quick response even though I knew Chinese were capable of making an appraisal very swiftly.

"I need somebody," I told him, and he nodded again as if this had been a preordained meeting and everything was virtually arranged already.

I had to pursue the obvious, of course.

"When could you go?" I inquired.

He held up his and and with a gesture indicated that I should wait for a moment. He got up and disappeared down a small alleyway between two buildings and I wondered for a moment whether he thought I was crazy in the head, and was making his getaway.

In a moment, though, he came back with a small wicker basket.

"This mine. Ready go," he informed me.

"Is that all?" I asked in astonishment.

"That all I need," he said.

Then he stopped for a moment. "Where we going?"

"Santa Monica," I told him.

"Me know Santa Monica—me likee work for you," he declared with finality.

So we went and got in the car.

I was still feeling as if the whole matter were unreal and that I would discover in a moment that the little Chinese was completely a figment of my imagination. But he settled himself firmly in the front seat beside me with his wicker basket on his knee and looked alertly at the sights as we drove along in the afternoon sunshine. We went out towards Santa Monica and finally came to West Los Angeles and the Veterans Facility at Sawtelle.

I noticed as I glanced sideways at my companion that his Oriental orbs were lighting up in delighted surprise as we passed this particular region.

"Me know all about this place," he informed me.

"You do?"

"Yes, me come here when nineteen year old from China. Me work for very rich lady at Santa Monica by ocean, over yonder."

He was looking at the area around us with admiration and recollection in his eyes. I could tell that the terrain was familiar to him despite the great changes which had come over it since it was part of the great Ranchos San Vicente, Rodeo de las Aguas, and San José de Buenos Aires.

Gone were the spreading meadowlands and pastures. Apartment houses, the Soldiers' Home, a great university and palatial homes had taken the place of the browsing sheep and horses, the wild birds on the ciénegas, and the wildflowers.

He undoubtedly was remembering the strange sight of the great plain dotted with the grazing animals and here and there the tiny shelters of the sheepherders who slept in little cubicles like piano boxes on legs in the primitive surroundings. He no doubt recalled how they drank their wine from the little flasks made of the bladders of the animals, squirting the sour wine into their mouths as they tended their flocks.

Although this was only a memory the hills still ranged themselves in majestic rows on each side, just as they had many years before, and reminiscence grew full-bloom in the mind of my companion.

"She very great lady," he said softly. "Ride out here in fine buggy—lively horses."

The realization came to me suddenly that he was talking about Mrs. Arcadia Bandini DeBaker, my great-aunt who owned a large house on Ocean Avenue in Santa Monica.

"Did you cook down at the house in Santa Monica?" I asked with sudden interest.

"Sure, me cookum her house there. Lots of relation, lots of little kids. Come kitchen, ask for pie."

The realization of the truth overwhelmed me. I had been one of those little kids who had "come kitchen, ask for pie."

"Are you Leong Chung?" I asked.

"Sure," he replied nonchalantly. "I know you all the time. That way I come cook, be houseboy for you. Pretty old boy now, eighty year."

He chuckled softly, and we drove on.

Chung took over control of our household with complete assurance. He was apt and deft. He became an amiable dictator. Everything was under his control as he calmly directed our lives in the channels they should go. He was a master cook, completely at home in taking charge of wardrobes and linen and in every way fulfilling the obligations which he seemed to feel he owed us.

We talked a great deal as the opportunity presented itself. He spoke perfect pidgin English, probably better than my own when I imitated Chinese on the stage, but he preferred to converse in the Cantonese which I well remembered from my childhood.

Chung was eighty when he came to me, already having had more than fifty years in the service of some branch of our family. On his eighty-fifth birthday anniversary we reversed procedures and had a cake for him with an inscription in Chinese on it. I know he was touched but he took the whole matter in stride and never let us know how much he appreciated our thinking of him in this fashion.

Every once in a while he would get mad at me and stalk away to seek my daughter Antoinette.

"Me work just for you, Missy Tony," he would splutter, and he would shun me with great disdain until his anger had cooled and we would start our long conversations again.

Not once did the onset of age seem to dim his vigor or his assurance in serving us. He behaved in such a manner that we all seemed to be participating in a normal ritual rather than having any master and servant relationship whatsoever. It was a touching experience for me to see this old man in the fulness of age carry out so faithfully in actuality the idealistic concept which I, as a child, had formed of the Chinese race.

He loved to joke.

Between us there existed a running and exaggerated "feud" about our respective religions, burial customs, and belief in a hereafter. This part was strictly a man's realm. He never indulged in levity of this kind with my wife or daughter. But with me he would converse in the most outlandish fashion until we both were laughing at his philosophic and religious barbs, which I always fired back at him. The serious thing about it all was his almost fanatical wish to have his bones returned to the land of his ancestors, in keeping with immemorial Chinese custom.

So it went for years. At intervals, Leong Chung would take time off to visit obscure relations in Los Angeles or San Francisco Chinatowns, and perhaps with the aid of the poppy talk about the cherished wish of a journey to his homeland, China, which he never took.

When he was ninety he returned to us very ill after one of these trips.

In his bed he looked smaller and more wizened than we had ever seen him. His delicate hands, so pale that they were the color of old ivory, appeared almost translucent, his face was pinched and drawn. He lapsed occasionally into a semi-coma, then roused again.

During one of the stronger moments, he looked up at me as I bent solicitously over him and said quite clearly, "Holama, siloko,— Hello, little boy."

I knew he was thinking back to the long ago when I had "come kitchen, ask for pie."

"I'm all grown up now," I told him, gently.

"You do what I ask, siloko?" he inquired.

"What do you mean?"

"Me want chicken, duck, pig put on my grave," he said seriously, referring back to our oft-repeated conversations on funeral customs when we were joking with one another.

"Oh, let's quit thinking about that," I said, trying to cheer him up. "Anyway, why not some nice flowers?"

"No want flowers. Want cooked chicken, duck, pig."

"But when would you eat them?" I asked, playing straight man in our accustomed repartee.

He roused further, and responded as always.

"Same time you come up, smell flowers," he chuckled, and died.

The smile lingered on his lips as if he were thinking of hot suckling pig with a celestial apple in its mouth.

CHAPTER 45

FAR PLACES OF THE EARTH

SOMETIMES I have been called "The Modern Conquistador."

But I have never used a weapon. It has been friendship. I have tried to conquer with kindness and understanding, never with force and bravado.

In this role, I have traveled literally all over the globe, trying to spread the spirit of American idealism and decency as opposed to the brute force and cruelty of the dictatorships.

My recent appointment as "Ambassador to the World" by the Governor of California of course was unofficial, yet it signified recognition of what I have been trying to do.

Particularly in Latin American countries, I have sought to convey the essential inner feelings of Americanos del Norte. The fact that I came from California, where two civilizations, Spanish and Anglo-Saxon, have been blended into the most remarkably progressive human society in the history of the world, was an asset. An even greater one has been my ability to speak idiomatic Spanish, one of the tongues I have used since I spoke my first word at my mother's knee. How we ever could send non-Spanish-speaking envoys to Latin American countries, as we have done many times, is beyond my comprehension.

My journeys always have had a special zest for me, dating back to that night in the old baggage depot in Santa Barbara when I slept among the suitcases and the travel stickers and longed to see the great world. This has come true for me in many countries. Every one has been a delightful experience. People everywhere seem to respond to kindness and to the common bond of human sympathy. I have been greeted by crowds in Lisbon, Madrid, Istanbul, Rio de Janeiro, Buenos Aires, and innumerable other places.

All of them knew American film and stage and television stars and greeted them with an enthusiasm rarely seen in this country.

I have gone all over the world with Conrad Hilton to the opening of his hotels such as the great Hilton Castelana in Madrid.

The experience of my first trip to Spain naturally was a great dramatic highlight for me. I felt that I was returning home in a sense when I first set foot upon the soil of Castile where my ancestors had lived for many centuries.

When I spoke in our mutually native tongue, Spanish, to the people around me their faces lit up and their eyes sparkled and smiles came to their lips because of this common bond of language. I have felt that if I can assist the United States in overcoming some of the difficulties which it has encountered with Spanish-speaking nations it is my duty to do so.

I have traveled for the forthcoming New York World's Fair to many places in South America.

It was on one of these trips in La Paz, Bolivia, that I received one of the great shocks of my life. As our plane circled down almost into the canyon where lies the airport of La Paz at 17,000 feet altitude we could see thousands of Indians with little derbies like Homburg hats waiting to see our descent. As I stepped from the plane I saw the local newspapers with the news of the death of my great friend Clark Gable.

The shock of his passing and the effect of the altitude was such that it was necessary for me to be given oxygen as a restorative. Then, in what I felt must be respect for the tradition of the theater, I went out to greet all the people who had come to the airport and who later gathered in the streets around my hotel. I could not have been shown more honor if I had been an official minister plenipotentiary from the United States Government itself.

My great joy on these trips has been to talk with the little people of each country, to try to get beneath the surface and the mere superficialities of our relationships and to establish a feeling of comradeship and genuine friendliness. It is my sincere conviction that only in this way can we overcome the insidious efforts of world Communism to dominate the two American Continents and to undermine the United States. In this spirit I have always been ready to go anywhere at any time to assist in creating better Latin-American relations because it is a natural instinct on my part to do so.

One thing I have encountered everywhere is an intense interest in the background and the personality of California as a region of the globe. Many people in Latin America, in Europe, in Africa, in Asia, regard us as the modern Utopia towards which all men yearn so they may join in the building of the kind of civilization which is being created here.

It is natural that I share in this feeling. The efforts of my forbears to build up California even before the world was aware of its great potentialities has inspired me through the years. I feel it is my duty not only to my state and to my country but to my ancestors to carry the message of California and the spirit of America del Norte wherever I go.

So, whether it be interviewing Generalissimo Franco in Madrid or sitting with an ancient gaucho at a rodeo in Buenos Aires, I have tried to maintain this missionary spirit. It is not difficult for me. My zeal has been inborn and genuine. It has, I hope, conveyed itself to thousands of persons in many countries.

If, in this way, I have contributed my part to what we call in general terms "world understanding" it is enough for me. My satisfaction lies in accomplishment rather than in any personal aggrandizement.

It is easy for me to preach the doctrine of California. It is part of my blood and soul. I speak of it with reverence and affection because it is so deeply ingrained within me. The trips which I have taken have been more than trips. They have been a realization of that boyhood dream of seeing the far places of the world and at the same time conveying a message which I hope may help mankind in its struggle against the evil forces of Communism and dictatorship.

If any Californian can contribute to that end he has done something to aid his country.

CHAPTER 46

REBIRTH AT THE PLAZA

I RODE in so many parades and made so many speeches and public appearances that some of my friends began to urge me to run for public office in California. They pointed to the record of the Carrillos as having served the state, and the Spanish and Mexican Province before that, in many capacities. A number of people suggested that I run for governor, and said that they would give me enthusiastic support.

It is true that I was anxious to serve California in any way possible but the rough and tumble, pell-mell arena of politics did not appeal to me.

My feeling was that I could serve my state better in a different way. I had always been interested in the preservation of natural resources, beauty spots, historic sites, and notable buildings in California. These, I felt, were so important in our romantic and colorful history that they should be perpetuated and conserved for future generations, so they would never be used for any purpose except the benefit of the citizens and the education of children.

I persistently declined, therefore, to run for governor or any other elective office. In fact, I strenuously supported Earl Warren for governor in my first active participation in a political campaign. Warren was elected overwhelmingly and this gave me great pleasure because I was certain he was going to make a fine Governor, as he did, going on later to become Chief Justice of the Supreme Court of the United States.

It was during his administration that an opening occurred on the State

Beaches and Parks Commission. I was urged to accept the post, and it seemed more in keeping with the ideals I maintained for California. I did become a member and remained on the Commission for 14 years.

During that time it was my pleasure to see the setting aside of a tremendous number of areas in California either as state beach parks or state monuments. All of these stimulated the interest of newcomers to California in the history of the state and also assisted in promoting recreation for children as the metropolitan areas became more crowded.

These things gave me real satisfaction. I felt that I was carrying out to the best of my ability the wishes which would have been expressed to me by my ancestors if they had been able to communicate with me in this modern day. Their virile footsteps had sounded in many of the very areas which now my vote on the Beaches and Park Commission helped to set aside forever for the people of California.

Some of the most important projects were slow, or even controversial.

We had great difficulty, for instance, in arousing public interest to the point where we could establish the now-famous State and County Arboretum at Arcadia. This was located on a portion of the old E. J. (Lucky) Baldwin estate and included the famous Hugo Reid adobe dwelling, the picturesque Queen Anne cottage built by Lucky Baldwin, and the Baldwin coach barn, typical of the fine structures built in those days for horses and carriages.

The Arboretum, under the management of Dr. William Stewart, has gained such great popularity since it was opened to the public that the crowds are increasing all the time and the people are able to see not only the historic structures but plants from all over the world in a setting of rare beauty. The Hugo Reid adobe has been rebuilt and refurnished through the efforts of a fine group of patriotic citizens who devoted years of effort to the project. It now is surrounded by an adobe wall with an outdoor oven and all of the elements of that period to give modern visitors an idea of how a California establishment looked in the early part of the nineteenth century.

The preservation of historic sites had been rather neglected for many years and we made a sincere effort on the Commission to correct this and to lend our help to a rebirth of interest in such projects.

A remarkable instance of individual courage and accomplishment had been going on in the region of the Los Angeles Plaza.

Mrs. Christine Sterling, with the help of Publisher Harry Chandler of the *Los Angeles Times* and, later, of his sons Norman and Philip Chandler had succeeded in rescuing the famous Francisco Avila Adobe which I mentioned in connection with the early ranchos. This historic building, which had been the headquarters of Commodore Robert Stockton in the early part of 1847 when Los Angeles was occupied just before the end of the Mexican War in California, was going to pieces and faced utter annihilation from vandalism and the weather.

Mrs. Sterling became interested in the whole area and strove so mightily that she enlisted the aid of Mr. Chandler and the *Times* and John Steven McGroarty, the poet laureate of California, who wrote articles about Mrs. Sterling's project. From these efforts came Olvera Street, the re-creation of a typical little Mexican street, and the restoration under Mrs. Sterling's direction of the Avila Adobe itself. It now is recognized as one of the great landmarks in southern California, and Olvera Street is visited by more tourists than any other single attraction in Los Angeles, due in part to its strategic location across from the Union Station and near the interchange of the many freeways.

Through Mrs. Sterling's efforts a group was organized in an attempt to preserve other landmarks in the Plaza.

This of course was something dear to my heart because the old Pico House Hotel was on the site of my Great Uncle José Antonio Carrillo's home across from the little Mission Church. Alongside the Pico house were the old Merced Theater and the first Masonic Hall in Los Angeles, and back of them were an old fire station and some of the little business buildings typical of one hundred or more years ago.

An intense campaign was launched by the group known as El Pueblo de Los Angeles, headed first by Harry Chandler and then by Judge MacIntyre Faries, to save these historic structures. Great difficulties were encountered because they were privately owned and it was almost impossible to get people together in any sort of a concerted program.

At a meeting of the group I was invited to express my views. I made the suggestion that the whole Plaza of Los Angeles be turned into a State Park.

This was a new idea. It immediately received enthusiastic response, however. I agreed to present the matter to the California Beaches and Parks Commission and to lend my personal influence to obtain the objective. It took several years before we were able to obtain the necessary action in the legislature and the cooperation of the state, the county, and the city. But finally we did it. As a result the entire Plaza region is designated as a State Monument.

Only a block or two from the spot where I had been born this memorial to the birthplace of the pueblo became consecrated to posterity.

As funds became available the little fire station was recreated as it was in the olden days and the Pico House, the Merced Theater, Masonic Hall, and the other structures underwent strengthening so they could be used again for the entertainment and enlightenment of visitors. A kiosko, or bandstand, was erected in the Plaza exactly on the spot where the musicians on the day of my birth had been playing during the fiesta.

It was a sentimental triumph for me, I must admit.

Around this area there clustered for me many tender memories. I could remember traveling in my little home-made wagon with the wooden wheels to see the Chinese merchants. To my ears there came the soft sound of Spanish syllables out of the long ago as the Zanjero talked to the men and women who came to the water ditch with their buckets and pails to obtain the daily supply of water. I could remember the fantan games and the domino gambling of the Chinese, and could hear again the cry of the vegetable peddlers.

It solaced my soul to see that the birthplace of the Pueblo was to be preserved forever as a memorial to the brave souls who had come there in the first place and taken part, amid many hardships, in the establishment of El Pueblo de Nuestra Señora La Reina de Los Angeles de Porciuncula.

CHAPTER 47

THE GRAND PROCESSION

ALWAYS the grand procession passes by the Cross on my hill at the Rancho of the Spanish Daggers.

As the tender fingers of the dawn first caress the green hilltop in the springtime, the Cross is suffused with a crimson hue as if the sun itself were painting with holy blood the memory of the past. For this Cross stands high above "El Camino Real"—the Royal Road of the California Pilgrimage—where saints and soldiers, young couples in love, and old men with tottering feet have walked in days of old.

Some of the grand procession of which I speak is visible. Some is invisible.

It is compounded of the past, the present, and the future. It is a blending of civilizations, a merger of eras, a memorial to yesterday and a heralding of tomorrow.

The tall Cross on the hill at my rancho marks the resting place of my greatly-beloved Palomino horse, Conquistador. I do not consider it strange that I thus hallow the grave of a horse.

That blood of Conquistador came pure and unstained from equine royalty of medieval times. His ancient sires and dams of Arabian lineage carried the knighthood of Spain into the conquest of the New World, as his very name implies. In his veins flowed the splendid brave blood of war mares and chargers, who faced the enemy with as great courage as the redoubtable warriors who bestrode their backs.

273

Further, I loved this horse greatly. He typified, for me, all the magic yester-years of California when caballeros rode like centaurs amid these same rounded hills and the neighing of their stallions drowned the voice of the wind itself. He represented another day, a pastoral time when there was leisure enough for a friendly word, as comrades met, and the sound of guitars and violins and castanets heralded fiestas, and the tantalizing odor of broiling kid over encino coals called the hungry to feasts in the shade.

I know in my heart that this time, as a living reality, is gone forever.

Yet, here along El Camino Real, I feel sometimes that it has returned. Once more the señoritas and the caballeros appear upon the horizon, music sounds, and I am able to picture these romantic scenes as if they were occurring again.

Perhaps, in a way they do recur. Who can deny me my fancy?

Here on my ranch, there is a pastoral peace. On my doorstep is a message of welcome:

"Su casa, amigo!"

I mean that. My house is yours, friend. Here amid the mellow adobe walls and the orange and palm trees I cherish thoughts of long ago mingled with plans for the future. The red tiles of my roof nurture dreams.

Mine is no swan song. I look avidly to the future.

Overhead I hear the roar of jet engines on airplanes, even if in retrospect I lend my ear to the creak of carretas, the sound of hoofbeats, and the gentle song of a Spanish troubadour.

Life goes on here in the way it should.

When the sun does light up the Cross on the hill at earliest dawn, it soon makes visible the earthy, wonderful, varied, everyday things with which human existence is endowed. I am susceptible to these sights, sounds and smells.

Up there on the emerald hillside as I come out in the morning I can see a white-face Hereford cow heavy with calf. She stands placidly as the first beams touch the red of her sides. She is waiting in the springtime for a new life to be created from her body.

She had gone some distance away from the main herd so as to be alone to bring forth the calf, although later she will be so convivial that she and her sister bovines will take turns herding several calves in order to allow some leisure time for each other—nature's first "baby sitters."

On the opposite hill the heifers and the horses graze as the sunlight illumines the landscape more and more. The plumes of Los Coyotes glisten in the morning light too. They are the Spanish dagger plants that give the ranch its name, and the roots of which we like so much when roasted.

The adobe ranch houses are sheltered amid their trees. The peppers, or "El Perus" as they were originally called when brought here from South America, the oranges, grapefruit, lemons, all combine to scent the air with a clean fresh odor. The sun shines on the red-tiled roofs which have withstood rains, winds, and all the onsets of nature until they are polished by age.

A huge white-washed adobe barn is set into the hillside so that the hay trucks coming down can unload the hay directly into the loft instead of having to lift it up. We are practical here on Rancho Los Coyotes as well as sentimental. The grain fields are coming up, the shoots of the barley bursting with new life as they reach for the comforting sun.

On the hills, too, are great fields of tomatoes being raised for the markets of Los Angeles and San Francisco in this mild climate where frost is so infrequent as to be a phenomenon. Off on the hills to one side can be seen the roofs of a few houses in a subdivision. The Carlsbad-Vista area is growing and people who want to live "out in the country" are buying the houses from which the great Pacific Ocean can be seen off to the west.

From the high points of my ranch I also can see the Pacific stretching there in its illimitable distances and giving me a comforting feeling of being near the sea which I loved so much as a boy in my Santa Monica home.

There is not much time in the morning for sentimental musing. Many things have to be done: the feeding of the horses, the checking of the cattle during this calving season, the feeding of the chickens, putting out of grain for the peacocks, all the little things which mount up on a ranch.

Outside the kitchen door is a metal triangle with another piece of metal hanging nearby so the ringing notes can be struck at mealtime to bring in guests from their wanderings on the ranch. Up on the hillside is the little structure we call the "Indian House" where my wife Deedie loved to spend her time amid the paintings, the Indian artifacts, the drums, the pictures. From there she could gaze out all over the ranch, watching the horses and cattle, seeing the birds high in the sky, viewing the rising of the sun and its journey towards the Pacific in the evening.

She had learned some of the Indian arts, how to weave baskets and to make jewelry and these gave her hours of pleasure as she tried to bring back the ideals of beauty embodied in many of the works of the early red men.

As the morning progresses the foreman makes his rounds checking on the cow to see that she is going to calve naturally and will not need help from the ranch hands doubling as midwives.

Down the winding little road from the big gate comes a car. It is the tree expert, Nelson E. Westrie, who advises me on plantings. I now want to put in some avocados which do so well here, and some of the sub-tropicals which are being imported from South America and grown successfully in this mild clime.

Westrie is the man who helped me with a sentimental project. Just outside my bedroom window stands a gnarled and weather-beaten old orange tree about one hundred years old. Half of the trunk is gone but it looks healthy and still bears oranges. When I came here it was nothing but a dead looking stick. I watered it and saw that there was some life left and called in the expert. Soon new shoots were putting out and from these he was able to obtain buds to put on other orange trees. We even successfully planted some of the seeds for root stock for later budding. So now we have this magnificent old early California orange with the distinctive and delightful flavor growing on the limbs of new trees.

I like to think that this typifies the kind of thing that we are carrying on here—the new aiding the old, the present conjuring up splendid images out of the past and continuing traditions so that we can enjoy them today.

I love the sight of the peacocks. We started out with six and now there are nearly two dozen roaming the place, the males spreading their tremendous feathered tails with the springtime urge and strutting for the benefit of the females who sometimes don't pay much attention. The peacocks fancy they are glamor boys, and are stuck on themselves. I have even put out mirrors in the springtime so they could admire their own images, and this seemed to help satisfy their vanity. Peacocks at some seasons of the year make a good deal of noise but the rest of the time they are so beautiful and ornamental and relatively quiet that we are willing to put up with the cries for a little while just to have the benefit of their beauty the rest of the year.

Always we have banty chickens around the place because they are great gatherers of bothersome insects and also because, to me, a banty chicken is one of the liveliest and bravest of God's creatures. They are friendly and unworried by larger animal life and go their way all day long industriously carrying out their missions as if personifying the idea of private enterprise and the glorious nature of work on this earth.

Of course the horses are my particular favorites. I like to breed them in the hope that one day I may get another splendid Palomino—never to equal Conquistador, but at least to keep alive the memory of that great horse of mine by having one of similar color and conformation around the place.

Sentimentally, I have succeeded. Conquistador II, son of my great stallion, is here and he seems to sense the pride I feel in him. He carries the blood of three great breeds—the Arabian for conformation, the Quarterhorse for compactness, the Morgan for the neck.

In Conquistador II are the color and beauty which made his sire so famous throughout the world.

I never tire of seeing this reincarnation of the image of the horse I loved most. . . .

When the triangle sounds for the noon meal we are all hungry and Antoinette guides us to the table where we have our food to sustain us during the afternoon. Of course I will admit there is time here for a siesta and sometimes we indulge ourselves in this fine old custom, too.

Then along about the middle of the afternoon when the sun is shining hot and the morning mists have all been dissipated and the dew dried up we have to check again to see how the Hereford is coming along. Her time obviously is near. She has gone near a clump of chaparral in the midst of one of the meadows and we know that soon the calf will be born. We do not try to go too close because this is her moment for silence and privacy and we do not want to intrude.

In this hot part of the day I sometimes sit on the veranda and contemplate the grand procession along El Camino Real.

The whole sweep of California history passes there before me. I can see Father Junipero Serra with his painful injured leg dragging himself along and permitting no treatment except the same ointment which was used on the galled backs of the mules. Beside him is the mighty Captain Gaspar de Portola, the military head of the expedition entrusted with protecting the priests in their mission of salvation. Alongside him are the leather-jacket soldiers including my own great-great-grandfather José Raimundo Carrillo, with his shield of bullhide ready for any encounter.

The Cross marches triumphantly there.

Along this same route later I can visualize the incoming forces of the United States in their conquest of California. These include trusty old General Stephen Watts Kearny, Commodore Robert Stockton, Kit Carson the scout, and Midshipman Edward Fitzgerald Beale, later the Civil War General.

Also I see Governor Pío Pico, Don Andrés Pico, the great cavalry leader, carretas with groups of singing merrymakers headed for fiestas; caballeros and vaqueros driving cattle or on their way for romance or hunting; the children, the multi-colored cattle, the horses, all the parade of the almost two centuries since California was founded.

I can picture battles, roundups, horsemanship contests, fandangos, all the life of early California. I can see the hides being carried down towards Dana Point for dropping over the cliffs so they could be delivered to clipper ships off shore. I can see the Sepulvedas, the Bandinis, the de Pedrorenas, the Lingos, the de la Guerras, the Estudillos. I can imagine the naked feet of the Indians at the missions treading in the adobe to make the bricks for the chapels and the barracks and all the other buildings necessary to the great establishments where civilization flourished for the first time and the pinched bellies of the Indians were filled with the grain and the meat brought to them by the Spaniards.

Then my reverie is interrupted by a call from Antoinette, "The calf has been born."

We all go out to see the new little wet bundle of hide and bone, hardly capable of standing on its feet yet, with the proud mother standing over it chewing her cud and contemplating the miracle of reproduction with a placidity and contentment almost human. The birth of the calf is the big event of the day. It means the springtime has really arrived and the calving season has begun. In a couple of months it will be time for the roundup and the branding, with the "Flying LC," my brand, when the fires will gleam and the irons will be heated red hot and there will be the smell of singed hair in the air as the imprint is placed upon these additions to the herd. Life in these moments seems very good. It is embodying the fruitfulness of the earth, the spirit of youth, the satisfaction of accomplishment.

As we descend the hillside, we pass the native plants, many blooming now, which played so great a part in the primitive "folk medicine" of California. Even the bark of our oaks—the encinos—after being boiled six hours in salt to remove the tannic acid is used to treat poison ivy.

Here is Yerba Buena, the remedy for coughs. There is Yerba del Golpe, the healer of wounds after it has been passed through seven sands, and the roots of the woodwardia fern from which comes the remedy for internal bruises.

Over yonder are Las Tunas, the plain old cactus, from which the juice was extracted to be used as a kind of "filler" or glue when mixed with slack lime, to protect the adobes from rain and wind.

The te-mal-hepe is for skin eruptions, the Ting-gi-wit—which we call wild fuchsia—used for poultices on ulcers, the Pa-co-se-cheeh credited with curing the seven-year-itch. The Hul-vall was looked upon with favor by women for their particular ills. And the alto-cal should cure any case of stomach cramps.

I recognize them all from long association.

As we near the bottom of the hill, the first breeze of evening gently moves the tops of the trees. A breath of coolness is felt. The sun is taking on a red tinge as it nears the rim of the western hills in its downward path.

Quail call from the underbrush. A festive rabbit skips from behind some chaparral.

Odors of tortillas and oak coals for the broiling of steaks are wafted to us. Soon it will be time to sound the triangle again for supper.

In the patio, the peacocks are gathering to be fed.

Old Pancho, my big dog who loves to carry Antoinette's purse while he proudly looks at you soliciting admiration, comes to greet us from his own siesta spot.

We hear the creaking of the windmill nearest the house as the blades turn and the pump rod goes up and down, up and down. I love windmills and have them all over the ranch.

Don Quixote again? Perhaps. But they bring us precious water from the generous earth.

Logs are being laid in the fireplaces. Soon they will glow as the evening chill comes on, with that faint and tantalizing odor of the sea brought to us by the breeze.

So, in the twilight, the images of my loved ones cluster comfortingly around me. The earth itself speaks to me in the language of nature, as it has done all my life.

Out there, along El Camino Real, the grand procession still goes by on silent feet—Father Serra, Don Gaspar de Portola, my lusty forbear José Raimundo in his leather jacket, the beautiful Josefa and doughty Captain Fitch, the buccaneers of Hippolyte Bouchard, Governor Carlos Antonio Carrillo, the mighty Andrés Pico, all the host of California's immortal roster.

The fire of encina logs is lighted on my hearth. In its leaping flames the past recreates itself.

Carried on the evening breeze through the pepper trees and the palm fronds I hear the almost inaudible strains of my mother's cradle song *La Golondrina* once again. Up on the hillside, in the little house my wife loved, I can fancy a gay laugh and the flutter of a silken scarf.

Spiritually, a man can never be lonely. Always the living presence of tender souls, now departed, tend him in his receptive hours when the world presses in not too heavily.

These adobe walls nurture me as they did in that hour of my birth, when the good doctor asked my mother my name and she pronounced it for the first time so proudly:

"Leopoldo Antonio Carrillo."

I have ridden in many parades. I have trod many a stage. Applause has been mine. I have seen the far places of the earth. Many dreams have come true.

Now, here on the Rancho of the Spanish Daggers, the past, the present and the future flash their many-prismed mirrors before my eyes. The everlasting hills are my proscenium. The vaulted sky is my roof. The stars lean down to pronounce their benediction.

I have spoken my lines.

"País, agua, sol."

These are the simple things, the true things, the good things.

Let them, when the time comes, signify my exit.

Now, amigos, perhaps you understand why the adobe is my birthstone. . . .

LOVE

Familiar acts are
beautiful
through love.

—Percy Bysshe Shelley

As I continue
My talks with her,
I become aware
That, in my heart,
A window is opening.

—Akihito, Crown Prince of Japan

Love
is
best!

—Robert Browning

Love is the *mortar* that holds the human structure together.

—Karen Casey

Selflessness is...

the basic ingredient
of true love...mix well with
affection and respect and,
without a dime in your
pocket, you're rich.

—Pierre Berton

The woman who anxiously scans the face of her lover and reaches out with soothing hand to comfort him...is obeying the same kind of impulse that directs the heart to pump more blood to a wounded limb.

—Dr. Smiley Blanton

Love is that which
exists to *do good,*
not merely to
get good.

—Anonymous

One of the best
things about love—
the feeling of being
wrapped, like a gift,
in understanding.

—Anatole Broyard

Love is an
irresistible desire
to be
irresistibly

desired.

—Robert Frost

His love for me
was to let me
love him;

My love for him
was to let him
through me
love himself.

—Elisabeth Hermodsson

13

LOVE

I think we
have come out on
the other side...meaning
that we love each other
more than we ever did
when we loved each
other most.

—Archibald MacLeish

If love be timid
it is not true.

—Spanish proverb

Love is like a motor
that's going; you have
such vitality
to do things,
big things,
because
love is
goosing you
all the time.

—Fanny Brice

The important thing is not to think much but to love much; do, then, whatever most arouses you to love.

—Saint Teresa of Avila

And what do all
the great words
come to in the
end, but that?
I love you—
I am at rest with
you—I have
come home.

—Dorothy L. Sayers

When love
comes it comes
without effort,
like perfect
weather.

—Helen Yglesias

Love is a choice—
not simply, or necessarily,
a rational choice, but rather
a willingness to be present
to others without
pretense or guile.

—Carter Heyward

Habit,
of which passion must
be wary, may all the
same be the sweetest
part of love.

—Elizabeth Bowen

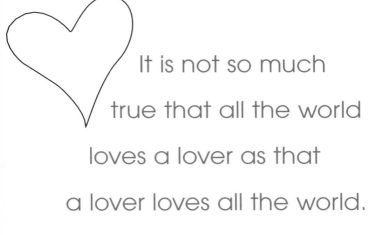

It is not so much
true that all the world
loves a lover as that
a lover loves all the world.

—Ruth Rendell

LOVE

Lovers
re-create
the world.

—Carter Heyward

A successful marriage requires falling in love many times, always with the same person.

—Mignon McLaughlin

Two persons love
in one another
the future good
which they aid
one another to
unfold.

—Margaret Fuller

In short I will part with
anything for you but you.

—Lady Mary Wortley Montagu

Each one of us
thinks our

experience of love

is different from
everybody else's.

—Vibhavari Shirurkar

To see coming toward
you the face that will
mean an end of
oneness is–far more
than birth itself–
the beginning of life.

—Holly Roth

31

There is *no question*
for which you are not
the answer.

—Bonnie Zucker Goldsmith

If I had never met him
I would have *dreamed
him into being.*

—Anzia Yezierska

Whatever our *souls* are
made of,
his and mine
are *the same.*

—Emily Brontë

We never leave
each other.
When does your
mouth say
goodbye to
your heart?

—Mary TallMountain

LOVE

When first we
fall in love, we feel
that we know all there is
to know about life, and
perhaps we are right.

—Mignon McLaughlin

It was a love like
a chord from Bach,
of such pure gravity.

—Nina Cassian

The world has little
to bestow
where two
fond
hearts in
equal love
are joined.

—Anna Laetitia Barbauld

There is a stage with people we love when we are no longer separate from them, but so close in sympathy that we live through them as directly as through ourselves...
We push back our hair because theirs is in their eyes.

—Nan Fairbrother

Him that

I love,

I wish to

be Free—

Even from me.

—Anne Morrow Lindbergh

Love needs
to be
proved by
action.

—Saint Thérese of Lisieux

A man falls in
love through his eyes,
a woman through her
imagination, and then
they both speak of it as
an affair of "the heart."

—Helen Rowland

Before we love
with our heart,
we already love with
our imagination.

—Louise Colet

Love is the white

light of emotion.

—Diane Ackerman

LOVE

Love is the extremely difficult *realization* that something other than oneself is *real.*

—Iris Murdoch

Love is a fruit

in season

at all times.

—Mother Teresa

We love
because it's
the only true
adventure.

—Nikki Giovanni

Love is the *wild care*
of existence.

—Rita Mae Brown

Love is the only thing that **keeps** me sane.

—Sue Townsend

The beginning of my history is—love. It is the beginning of every man and every woman's history, if they are only frank enough to admit it.

—Marie Corelli

I always want to be in love, always. It's like being a tuning fork.

—Edna O'Brien

Love
is repaid by
love alone.

—Saint Thérese of Lisieux

`Till I loved

I never lived—

Enough.

—Emily Dickinson

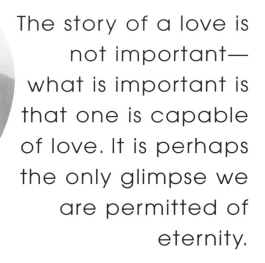

The story of a love is not important—what is important is that one is capable of love. It is perhaps the only glimpse we are permitted of eternity.

—Helen Hayes

LOVE

What we have once enjoyed we can never lose. All that we love deeply becomes a part of us.

—Helen Keller

It is impossible to
repent of love. The sin
of love does not exist.

—Muriel Spark

In the arithmetic of love, one plus one equals everything, and two minus one equals nothing.

—Mignon McLaughlin

We love as soon as we learn to distinguish a separate "you" and "me." Love is our attempt to assuage the terror and isolation of that separateness.

—Judith Viorst

Love is the same as like except you feel sexier.

—Judith Viorst

Whoso loves

Believes the

impossible.

—Elizabeth Barrett Browning

In love, everything
is two and everything
strives to be one.

—Octavio Paz

He came into my life as the warm wind of spring had awakened flowers, as the April showers awaken the earth. My love for him was an unchanging love, high and deep, free and faithful, strong as death. Each year I learned to love him more and more.

—Anna Chennault

There is something
that happens
between men and
women in the dark that
seems to make everything
else unimportant.

—Tennessee Williams

LOVE

The happy man is he who lives *the life of love*, not for the honors it may bring, but for the *life itself.*

—R.J. Baughan

When love is real love, when people's souls go out to their beloved, when they lose their hearts to them, when they act in the unselfish way in which these exquisite Old English phrases denote, a miracle is produced.

—Abbe Ernest Dimnet

Love

knows

hidden

paths.

—Anonymous

Love is a mutual *self-giving*
which ends in *self-recovery*.

—Bishop Fulton J. Sheen

Nobody has ever
measured, not even
poets, how much the
heart can hold.

—Zelda Fitzgerald

There is no surprise
more magical than
the surprise of being
loved. It is the
finger of God on
a man's shoulder.

—Charles Morgan

How it *improves*
people for us when we
begin to love them.

—David Grayson

Love for *one person*
implies *love* for man
as such.

—Erich Fromm

The entire sum of
existence is the

magic

of being
needed by just
one person.

—Vi Putnam

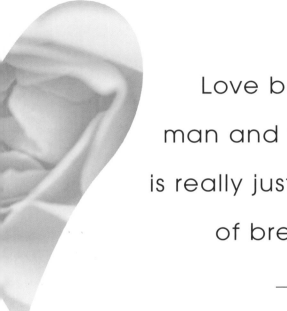

Love between
man and woman
is really just a kind
of breathing.

—D.H. Lawrence

LOVE

Respect is love

in plain clothes.

—Frankie Byrne

I will be the pattern of
all patience.

—William Shakespeare

To love means to
communicate to the
other that
you are all
for him,
that you will
never fail him
or let him down
when he needs

84

you, but that you will
always be standing by
with all the necessary
encouragements.
It is something one
can communicate
to another only
if one has it.

—Ashley Montagu

Never change
when love
has found its
home.

—Sextus Aurelius Propertius

Love knows
nothing of
order.

—Saint Jerome

Tomorrow let him love who has never loved and tomorrow let him who has loved love.

—Anonymous

Love kindled by virtue

always kindles another,

provided that its flame

appear outwardly.

—Dante Alighieri

But true love is
a durable fire,
In the mind ever
burning, Never sick,
never old, never dead,
From itself never turning.

—Sir Walter Raleigh

LOVE

Love comforteth
like *sunshine*
after rain.

—William Shakespeare

Love is swift, sincere, pious, pleasant, gentle, strong, patient, faithful, prudent, long-suffering, manly, and never seeking her own; for wheresoever a man seeketh his own, there he falleth from love.

—Thomas á Kempis

Love sought
is good, but giv'n
unsought
is better.

—William Shakespeare

If there is anything better
than *to be loved*, it is *loving*.

—Anonymous

Where *love is great,*
the littlest doubts
are fear;
When little fears
grow great, *great love*
grows there.

—William Shakespeare

Truly loving another means letting go of all expectations. It means full acceptance, even celebration of another's personhood.

—Karen Casey

The way to love
anything is to realize
that it *might be lost.*

—Gilbert K. Chesterton

I never knew how to worship until I knew how to love.

—Henry Ward Beecher

Love and you
shall be loved.
All love is
mathematically
just, as much
as the two sides
of an *algebraic*
equation.

—Ralph Waldo Emerson

To forgive is the highest, most beautiful form of love. In return, you will receive untold peace and happiness.

—Robert Muller

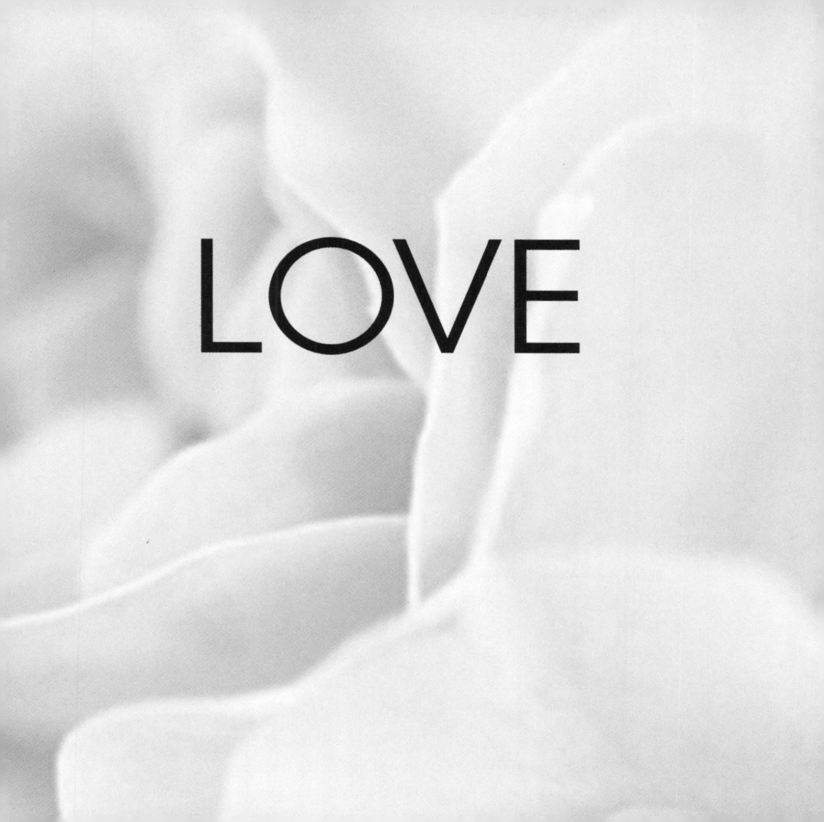
LOVE

Love,
and a cough,
cannot be hid.

—George Herbert

Love is saying
yes to belonging.

—David Steindl-Rast

Once our hearts are open, all existence appears naturally beautiful and harmonious.

—Tarthang Tulku

Love is, in fact, an intensification of life, a completeness, a fullness, a wholeness of life... Love is our true destiny.

—Thomas Merton

Pains of love
be sweeter far
Than all other
pleasures are.

—John Dryden

Be joyful
because it
is humanly
possible.

—Wendell Berry

What is a kiss?
Why this, as some
approve:
The sure, sweet cement,
glue, and lime of love.

—Robert Herrick

One opens the inner doors of one's heart to the infinite silences of the Spirit, out of whose abysses love wells up without fail and gives itself to all.

—Thomas Merton

Love makes those
young whom age
doth chill,
And whom he finds young,
keeps young still.

—William Cartwright

LOVE

It is a wonderful
*seasoning of all
enjoyments* to think
of those we love.

—Moliere

What permeates
the entire being
Like an
inexhaustible stream
Alone can be called love.

—Kabir

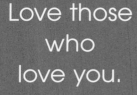

Love those
who
love you.

—Voltaire

Love is friendship
set to music.

—Edward Pollock

Absence is to love what wind is to fire; it extinguishes the small, it enkindles the great.

—Comte de Bussy

Happy he who
dares courageously
to defend what
he loves.

—Ovid

Love is the
enchanted dawn
of every heart.

—Alphonse de Lamartine

Love is a faith,
and one faith
leads to another.

—Henri-Frederic Amiel

Let your task be to render yourself *worthy of love* and this even more for your own happiness than for that of another.

—Maurice Maeterlinck

Home is the place where character is built, where sacrifices to contribute to the happiness of others are made, and where love has taken up its abode.

—Elijah Kellogg

LOVE

The joy of
life is variety;
the tenderest love
requires to be renewed
by intervals of
absence.

—Samuel Johnson

Where there is love,
there is no imposition.

—Albert Einstein

Love brings much
happiness,
much more
so than
pining for
someone
brings pain.

—Albert Einstein

Even in the common
affairs of life, in love,
friendship, and marriage,
how little security have
we when we trust our
happiness in the hands
of others!

—William Hazlitt

Love has always
been the most
important
business in
my life,
I should say
the only one.

—Stendhal

To love for the sake of being loved is human, but to love for the sake of loving is angelic.

—Alphonse de Lamartine

The love of liberty
is the love of others;
the love of power is the
love of ourselves.

—William Hazlitt

One day at a meeting...I told the people, "Husbands, smile at your wives; wives, smile at your husbands." They could not understand how I was able to tell them this sort of thing. One of them asked me, "Are you married?" I said, "Yes, and sometimes I find it very difficult to smile at Jesus because he can be so demanding."

—Mother Teresa

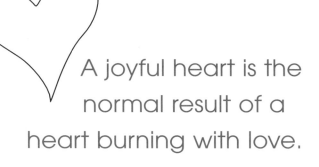

A joyful heart is the normal result of a heart burning with love.

—Mother Teresa

LOVE

It is better to have *loved* and *lost* than never to have *loved* at all.

—Samuel Butler

Falling in love is not
at all the most stupid
thing that people do—
but gravitation cannot be
held responsible for that.

—Albert Einstein

Intense love
does not
measure...
it just
gives.

—Mother Teresa

Love: softening of
the heartery.

—Anonymous

Why is it that the most unoriginal thing we can say to one another is still the thing we long to hear? *"I love you"* is always a quotation.

—Jeanette Winterson

Loving must be as
normal to us as
living and breathing,
day after day until
our death.

—Mother Teresa

In dreams and
in love there are
no impossibilities.

—Janos Arany

We learn only
from
those we love.

—Johann Wolfgang von Eckermann

The ultimate lesson all of us have to learn is *unconditional love*, which includes not only others, but *ourselves* as well.

—Anonymous

Love reckons
hours for
months, and
days for years;
And every little
absence is an age.

—John Dryden

LOVE

We are
all born for love.
It is the principle of
existence, and its
only end.

—Benjamin Disraeli

To love is to make of one's heart a swinging door.

—Howard Thurman

Try to remember to
forget anger, worry,
and regret.
Live while
you have
life to live.
Love while
you have
love to give.

—Anonymous

Love is something

that you can leave

behind when you die.

It's that powerful.

—John Lame Deer

Try saying "please" and "thank you" and "do you mind"—this is the language of love.

—Jill Briscoe

If you love
somebody
enough, you
can still hear
the laughter
after they're
gone.

—Al Baker

Perhaps the chief business of life is simply to learn how to love.

—Marsha Sinetar

Love stretches

your heart and makes

you big inside.

—Margaret Walker

The truth (is) that there is only one terminal dignity—love. And the story of a love is not important—what is important is that one is capable of love.

—Helen Hayes

LOVE

The *reduction* of the universe to a single being, the *expansion* of a single being even to God, ~~this is love.~~

—Victor Hugo

Serene will be our

days and bright,

And happy will our nature be,

When love is unerring light,

And joy its own security.

—William Wordsworth

It's
impossible
to love
and
be wise.

—Francis Bacon

Love is a *credulous* thing.

—Ovid

Of all forms of caution,
caution in love
is perhaps the most
fatal to true
happiness.

—Bertrand Russell

O powerful love! That
in some respects,
makes a beast a
man, in some others,
a man a beast.

—William Shakespeare

Love like ours
can
never die.

—Rudyard Kipling

Love is the *greatest*
pleasure open
to man.

—Seder de Rabbi Eliyahu Rabbah

He who truly loves
another can

read his
thoughts.

—The Koretser Rabbi

Love cannot endure indifference. It needs to be wanted. Like a lamp, it needs to be fed out of the oil of another's heart, or its flame burns low.

—Henry Ward Beecher

LOVE

Love turns
one person into two;
and two into one.

—Isaac Abravanel

Love renders one blind and deaf.

—Ibn Gabirol

The pleasure of love
is in loving.
We are
happier in
the passion
we feel
than in that
we inspire.

—François de La Rochefoucauld

If I truly love one person
I love all persons, I love the
world, I love life. If I can say
to somebody else, "I love
you," I must be able to say,
"I love in you everybody, I love
through you the world, I love
in you also myself."

—Erich Fromm

173

A cheerful
face makes
for love.

—Orhot Tsadikim

We love
the things we
love for what
they are.

—Robert Frost

Earth's the
right place for love:
I don't know where it's
likely to go better.

—Robert Frost

Love is a medicine for the

sickness of the world;

a prescription often given,

too rarely taken.

—Karl Menninger

My bounty is as
boundless as the sea,
My love as deep;
the more I give to thee
The more I have,
for both are infinite.

—William Shakespeare

LOVE

One does not
fall into love;
one *grows* into love,
and love grows in him.

—Karl Menninger

Will you love me in December as you do in May? Will you love me in the good old fashioned way? When my hair has all turned gray, Will you kiss me then and say, That you love me in December as you do in May?

—James J. Walker

All love is sweet,
Given or
returned.
Common as
light is love,
And its familiar
voice wearies
not ever.

—Percy Bysshe Shelley

And *all for love,*
and nothing for reward.

—Edmund Spenser

Love has no other desire but to fulfill itself. To *melt* and be like a running brook that *sings its melody* to the night. To wake at dawn with a *winged heart* and give thanks for another day of loving.

—Kahlil Gibran

There is music even in
the beauty, and the
silent note which Cupid
strikes, far sweeter
than the sound of an
instrument.

—Sir Thomas Browne

Till it has loved, no
man or woman can
become itself.

—Emily Dickinson

I'm glad it cannot happen twice, the *fever* of *first love.*

—Daphne du Maurier

It is not a matter
of *thinking* a
great deal
but of *loving* a
great deal.

—Saint Teresa of Avila

Lovers who
love truly do not
write down their
happiness.

—Anatole France

LOVE

Let no one
who loves be called
altogether unhappy.
Even love unreturned
has its rainbow.

—James Matthew Barrie

All mankind love
a lover.

—Ralph Waldo Emerson

I love the idea of
there being
two sexes,
don't you?

—James Thurber

For this is wisdom:

to love, to live,

To take what Fate,

or the Gods, may give.

—Laurence Hope

Such
ever was
love's way;
to rise,
it stoops.

—Robert Browning

Love
begets love.
This torment
is my joy.

—Theodore Roethke

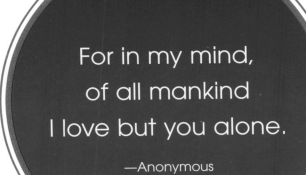

For in my mind,
of all mankind
I love but you alone.

—Anonymous

Even memory is not
necessary for love. There
is a land of the living and
a land of the dead and the
bridge is love, the only
survival, the only meaning.

—Thornton Niven Wilder

Little deeds of
kindness,
Little words of love,
Help to make
earth happy
Like the heaven above.

—Julia A. Fletcher Carney

LOVE

When *Silence* speaks
for *Love* she has
much to say.

—Richard Garnett

Ask nothing more of me, sweet, All I can give you I give; Heart of my heart, were it more, More would be laid at your feet: Love that should help you to live, Song that should spur you to soar.

—Algernon Charles Swinburne

There is

no love which

does not

become help.

—Paul Tillich

Love is the *reward* of love.

—Johann von Schiller

Mature love says:
"I need you because
I love you."

—Erich Fromm

Faith has to do with
the basis, the ground
on which we stand.
Hope is reaching out for
something to come.
Love is just being
there and acting.

—Emil Brunner

Love knows not its depth until the hour of separation.

—Kahlil Gibran

Where love is concerned, *too much is not even enough.*

—Pierre-Augustin de Beaumarchais

Love is
all we have
the only way
that each
can help
the other.

—Euripides

Delicacy
is to love
what grace
is to beauty.

—Madame de Maintenon

211

LOVE

It is love,
not reason,
that is stronger
than death.

—Thomas Mann

What is life without the radiance of love?

—Johann von Schiller

Love consists in
this, that two
solitudes
protect
and border
and salute
each other.

—Rainer Maria Rilke

One word frees us
of all the weight
and pain of life:
that word is love.

—Sophocles

O,
tell her,
brief is life
but love
is long.

—Alfred, Lord Tennyson

Love
conquers all:
and let us
too surrender
to love.

—Virgil

Love is the expansion of two natures in such fashion that each includes the other, each is enriched by the other.

—Felix Adler

Love at its highest point—Love,
sublime, unique, invincible—
leads us straight to the brink
of the great abyss, for it
speaks to us directly of the
infinite and of eternity.

—Henri-Frederic Amiel

The happy man
is he who lives the
life of love, not for
the honors it may bring,
but for the life itself.

—R.J. Baughan

LOVE

is the most *freely willed* of any *activity* of which we are able to think.

—Emil Brunner

The attraction of one creature for another, even when condemned by reason for its passionate origin, is always worthy of respect, because it reveals to us something of the order of creation.

—A. Carré

Let the
burden be
never so heavy,
love makes
it light.

—Robert Burton

Nothing *cures* like *time* and *love*.

—Laura Nyro

When a man
is in love he *endures*
more than at other
times; he *submits*
to everything.

—Friedrich Wilhelm Nietzsche

Experience shows us that love is not looking into one another's eyes but looking together in the same direction.

—Antoine de Saint-Exupéry

Oh, what a dear
ravishing thing is
the beginning of
an amour!

—Aphra Behn

All, everything that
I understand,
I understand only
because I love.

—Leo Tolstoy

231

Beware you be not
swallowed up
in books!
An *ounce of
love* is worth
a *pound of
knowledge.*

—John Wesley

Love is a desire of the whole being to be united to some thing, or some being, felt necessary to its completeness, by the most perfect means that nature permits, and reason dictates.

—Samuel Taylor Coleridge

LOVE

Sometimes

you know in your heart

you love someone, but you

have to go away before your

head can figure it out.

—Sharon Creech

We love being in love,
that's the truth on't.

—William Makepeace Thackeray

Where you love
somebody a whole lot,
and you know
that person
loves you,
that's the
most beautiful
place in the
world.

—Ann Cameron

Perhaps, after all, romance did not come into one's life with pop and blare, like a gay knight riding down; perhaps it crept to one's side like an old friend through quiet ways.

—L.M. Montgomery

I do love
nothing in
the world so
well as you.

—William Shakespeare

Love is,
above all
else, the gift
of oneself.

—Jean Anouilh

Marriage is popular because it combines the maximum of temptation with the maximum of opportunity.

—George Bernard Shaw

Then come the wild weather,

Come sleet or come snow,

We will stand by each other,

However it blow.

—Simon Dach

My heart was
wandering in the
sands, restless thing,
a scorn apart;
Love set his fire in my
hands, I clasped the
flame into my heart.

—Christopher Brennan

LOVE

Who can give
a law to lovers?
Love is a greater law
unto itself.

—Boethius

No cord, nor cable can
so forcibly draw, or hold
so fast, as love can do
with a twined thread.

—Robert Burton

How do I
love thee?
Let me count
the ways.

—Elizabeth Barrett Browning

Love is *friendship* plus sex.

—Havelock Ellis

In our life there is a single color, as on an *artist's palette,* which provides the meaning of life and art. It is the *color of love.*

—Marc Chagall

They say that love takes wit away from those who have it, and gives it to those who have none.

—Denis Diderot

Come live with me,
and be my love,
And we will all the
pleasures prove.

—Christopher Marlowe

252

No, there's nothing
half so *sweet* in life
As love's young
dream.

—Thomas Moore

Only connect the prose and the passion, and both will be exalted, and human love will be seen at its highest.

—E.M. Forster

Love one
another, but
make not a
bond of love:
let it be rather
a moving sea
between the shores
of your souls.

—Kahlil Gibran

LOVE

Love is

more than gold

or great riches.

—John Lydgate

What will survive
of us is love.

—Philip Larkin

There is always
some madness
in love.
But there
is also
always
some reason
in madness.

—Friedrich Wilhelm Nietzsche

Human love and the
delights of friendship,
out of which are built
the memories that endure,
are also to be treasured
up as hints of what
shall be hereafter.

—Bede Jarrett

Love means
that the
attributes of
the lover are
changed into
those of the
Beloved.

—Junayd of Baghdad

In love we find a joy which is ultimate because it is the ultimate truth.

—Rabindranath Tagore

Love is a force…
It is not a result; it is a
cause. It is not a product.
It is a power, like money or
steam or electricity. It is
valueless unless you can
give something else
by means of it.

—Anne Morrow Lindbergh

The greatest tragedy
of life is not that
men perish, but that
they cease to love.

—W. Somerset Maugham

For, you see,
each day I love
you more,
Today more than
yesterday and less
than tomorrow.

—Rosemonde Gerard

LOVE

One swallow may not make a summer, but a pair of *baby-blue eyes* can cause a fall.

—Wesleyan Wasp

Riches take wings,

comforts vanish, hope

withers away, but love

stays with us.

—Lew Wallace

Escape me?

Never—

Beloved

—Robert Browning

You must always be
a-waggle with LOVE.

—D.H. Lawrence

To love someone
deeply gives you
strength.
Being loved by
someone deeply
gives you
courage.

—Lao Tzu

Now join
your hands, and
with your hands
your hearts.

—William Shakespeare

What the heart knows today, the head will understand tomorrow.

—James Stephens

Love is not only
something you *feel*.
It is something
you *do*.

—David Wilkerson

Love is the magician,
the enchanter,
that changes
worthless
things to joy,
and makes right
royal kings and
queens of common
clay. It is the perfume

of that wondrous
flower, the heart,
and without that
sacred passion,
that divine
swoon, we are less
than beasts; but with
it, earth is heaven, and
we are gods.

—Robert G. Ingersoll

LOVE

There as

my heart is set,

there will I wive.

—Geoffrey Chaucer

All true love is
grounded on esteem.

—George Villiers

As your wedding
ring wears,
You'll wear
off your
cares.

—Thomas Fuller

Knit your hearts

With an unslipping

knot.

—William Shakespeare

Their hearts
are in the
right place.

—Benjamin Disraeli

Love
must be
reinvented.

—Arthur Rimbaud

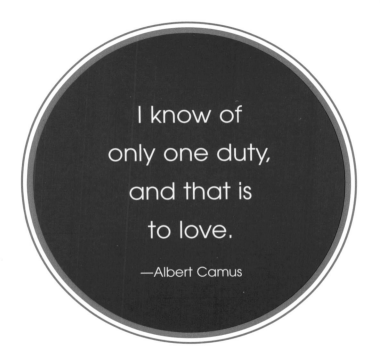

I know of
only one duty,
and that is
to love.

—Albert Camus

Something...

moves me to love,

and I do know I love, but

know not how or why.

—Alexander Brome

In love,

there is always

one who kisses and

one who offers

the cheek.

—French proverb

LOVE

Love has but *one word* and it never repeats itself.

—Henri Lacordaire

Truth and love are two of the most powerful things in the world; and when they both go together they cannot easily be withstood.

—Ralph Cudworth

Love

wakes men,

once a lifetime

each.

—Coventry Patmore

The heart that loves is *always young.*

—Greek proverb

At the
touch of love
everyone becomes
a poet.

—Plato

By the accident of fortune a man may rule the world for a time, but by virtue of love he may rule the world forever.

—Lao-Tse

Lovers are always
in a hurry...
like a racing river.

—Ben Ames Williams

Love is shown in your *deeds*, not in your words.

—Fr. Jerome Cummings

Knowledge, love,

power—

there is the

complete

life.

—Henri-Frederic Amiel

Love is little,
Love is low,
Love will make
our spirit grow.
Grow in peace,
Grow in light,
Love will do the
thing that's right.

—Shaker song c. 1800

LOVE

The joy
of the good,
the wonder of the wise,
the amazement of
the gods.

—Plato on love

Love, a gracious and
beautiful erotic art.

—Havelock Ellis

The wealth of man is
the number of things
which he
loves and
blesses,
which he is
loved and
blessed by.

—Thomas Carlyle

Treasure each other in the recognition that we do not know how long we shall have each other.

—Joshua Loth Liebman

Sex-appeal
is the
keynote
of our
civilization.

—Henri Bergson

Love is as
necessary to
human beings
as food and
shelter.

—Aldous Huxley

We are surrounded by eternity and by the uniting of love. There is but one center from which all species issue, as rays from a sun, and to which all species return.

—Giordano Bruno

Real love is only possible
in the freedom of
society; and freedom is
only possible when love
is a reality.

—Edward Carpenter

Love is not getting,
but giving; not a wild
dream of pleasure, and
a madness of desire—oh,
no, love is not that—it is
goodness, and honor, and
peace, and pure living.

—Henry Van Dyke

LOVE

What love does is
to arm. It arms the
worth of life
in spite of life.

—Archibald MacLeish

To love is to believe,

to hope, to know;

'Tis an essay, a taste

of Heaven below!

—Edmund Waller

Work and

love—

these are

the basics.

—Theodor Reik

Love is the *salt* of life.

—John Sheffield

Love
spends his all,
and still hath
store.

—P.J. Bailey

Love in
its essence
is spiritual
fire.

—Emanuel Swedenborg

Now I know
what love is.

—Virgil

Where love is,
there's *no lack*.

—Richard Brome

Love

teaches

letters to a

man

unlearn'd.

—Euripides

Love is
so very
timid when
'tis new.

—Henry James Byron

LOVE

Value each

lover according to the

gifts he brings.

—Ovid

Until I truly loved,
I was alone.

—Caroline Norton

The man that loves
and laughs
must
sure do
well.

—Alexander Pope

Love is always
in the mood
of believing
in miracles.

—J.C. Powys

Love's too
precious to
be lost.

—Alfred, Lord Tennyson

You must
get your living
by loving.

—Henry David Thoreau

We always
believe our first love
is our last, and our
last love, our first.

—Anonymous

A loving heart is
the beginning of all
knowledge.

—Thomas Carlyle

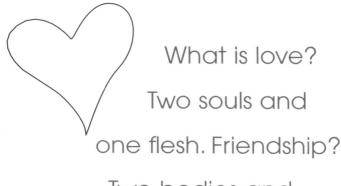

What is love?
Two souls and
one flesh. Friendship?
Two bodies and
one soul.

—Joseph Roux

LOVE

We were *two* and
had but *one heart.*

—François Villon

Those who love deeply
never grow old;
they may die of old age,
but they die young.

—Arthur Wing Pinero

Love stoops
as fondly as
he soars.

—Henry Wadsworth
Longfellow

Love is
a beautiful dream.

—William Sharp

What is love?
'Tis nature's treasure,
'Tis the storehouse
of her joys;
'Tis the highest *heaven*
of pleasure, 'Tis a bliss
which never
cloys.

—Thomas Chatterton

Love consists in desiring to give what is our own to another and feeling his delight as our own.

—Emanuel Swedenborg

To love is to know
the sacrifices which
eternity exacts
from life.

—John Oliver Hobbes

Love and desire
are the *spirit's wings*
to great deeds.

—Johann Wolfgang von Goethe

Love is a *lock* that
linketh noble
minds,
Faith is the
key that shuts
the spring
of love.

—Robert Greene

It is the special
quality of love
not to be able
to remain
stationary,
to be obliged to
increase under pain
of diminishing.

—Andre Gide

LOVE

Love keeps the cold out better than a cloak. It serves for food and raiment.

—Henry Wadsworth Longfellow

It adds a *precious seeing* to the eye.

—William Shakespeare

Take love away
from life
and you
take
away its
pleasures.

—Moliere

Love is the strange
bewilderment which
overtakes one person
on account of
another person.

—James Thurber

Whoever lives
true life,
will love
true love.

—Elizabeth Barrett Browning

Love, which
cannot be
paid but
with love.

—Edward Fenton

O, there is nothing holier, in this life of ours, than the first consciousness of love— the first fluttering of its silken wings.

—Henry Wadsworth Longfellow

If there's delight in love,

'tis when I see

That heart which others

bleed for, bleed for me.

—William Congreve

Tradition wears

a snowy beard.

Romance is always

young.

—John Greenleaf Whittier

LOVE

The only
present love
demands is
Love.

—John Gay

Love is kindest, and hath most length, The kisses are most sweet, When it's enjoyed in heat of strength, Where like affections meet.

—Patrick Hannay

Love prays
devoutly
when
it prays
for love.

—Thomas Hood

To be *beloved*, love.

—Decimus Magnus Ausonius

There is no heaven like

mutual love.

—George Granville

There is no pleasure
like the pain
of being loved,
and loving.

—W.M. Praed

Love rules his kingdom without a sword.

—George Herbert

Talking of love
is making it.

—W.G. Benham

The sight of
Lovers
feedeth
those
in love.

—William Shakespeare

There is
no remedy
for love but
to love more.

—Henry David Thoreau

LOVE

Love has
a thousand varied
notes to move the
human heart.

—George Crabbe

Habit causes love.

—Titus Lucretius Carus

To love and be
beloved, this
is the good,
which
for most
sovereign
all the world
will prove.

—William Alexander

Love will find its way

through paths where

wolves would fear

to prey.

—Henry James Byron

One can't
choose when
one is going
to love.

—Henrik Ibsen

Love and
laughter hold
us together.

—Ingrid Trobisch

Chance cannot
change my love,
nor time impair.

—Robert Browning

He is not a lover
who does not
love forever.

—Euripides

Think of my loyal love, my last adieu; absence and love are naught if we are true.

—Alfred de Musset

LOVE

When love is at its best,
one *loves so much* that
he cannot forget.

—Helen Hunt Jackson

Love, that all gentle

hearts so quickly know.

—Dante Alighieri

True love

is the ripe fruit

of a lifetime.

—Alphonse de Lamartine

Love is love
for evermore.

—Alfred, Lord Tennyson

The final word is

Love.

—Dorothy Day

Among those whom
I like, I can find no
common denominator,
but among those whom I
love, I can; all of them
make me laugh.

—W.H. Auden

There is no remedy for

Love but to

love more.

—Henry David Thoreau

Published by Sourcebooks, Inc.
P.O. Box 4410, Naperville, Illinois 60567-4410
(630) 961-3900
FAX: (630) 961-2168
www.sourcebooks.com
ISBN 1-57071-996-9

Printed and bound in the United States of America
IN   10 9 8 7 6 5 4 3 2 1

the promise of *Love*

Kathy Wagoner

SOURCEBOOKS CASABLANCA™
AN IMPRINT OF SOURCEBOOKS, INC.®
NAPERVILLE, ILLINOIS